W9-CRZ-775

MANIKANETISH

ALSO BY NAOMI FONTAINE

(in translation)

Kuessipan

MANIKANETISH

NAOMI FONTAINE
TRANSLATED BY LUISE VON FLOTOW

ARACHNIDE

Original title: Manikanetish
© Copyright 2017 Mémoire d'encrier
English translation copyright © 2021 Luise von Flotow

First published as Manikanetish in 2017 by Mémoire d'encrier
First published in English in 2021 by House of Anansi Press Inc.
www.houseofanansi.com

All rights reserved. No part of this publication may be reproduced or transmitted in any form or by any means, electronic or mechanical, including photocopying, recording, or any information storage and retrieval system, without permission in writing from the publisher.

House of Anansi Press is committed to protecting our natural environment. This book is made of material from well-managed FSC®-certified forests, recycled materials, and other controlled sources.

House of Anansi Press is a Global Certified Accessible™ (GCA by Benetech) publisher. The ebook version of this book meets stringent accessibility standards and is available to students and readers with print disabilities.

25 24 23 22 21   1 2 3 4 5

Library and Archives Canada Cataloguing in Publication

Title: Manikanetish / Naomi Fontaine ; translated by Luise von Flotow.
Other titles: Manikanetish. English
Names: Fontaine, Naomi, 1987- author. | von Flotow, Luise, 1951- translator.
Description: Translation of: Manikanetish.
Identifiers: Canadiana (print) 20210220805 | Canadiana (ebook) 2021022083X | ISBN 9781487008147 (softcover) | ISBN 9781487008154 (EPUB)
Subjects: LCGFT: Novels.
Classification: LCC PS8611.O5712 M3613 2021 | DDC C843/.6—dc23

Cover design: Lucia Kim
Text design and typesetting: Laura Brady

House of Anansi Press respectfully acknowledges that the land on which we operate is the Traditional Territory of many Nations, including the Anishinabeg, the Wendat, and the Haudenosaunee. It is also the Treaty Lands of the Mississaugas of the Credit.

 Canada Council for the Arts Conseil des Arts du Canada ONTARIO ARTS COUNCIL / CONSEIL DES ARTS DE L'ONTARIO

With the participation of the Government of Canada
Avec la participation du gouvernement du Canada | Canadä

We acknowledge the financial support of the Government of Canada through the National Translation Program for Book Publishing, an initiative of the Action Plan for Official Languages—2018–2023: Investing in Our Future, for our translation activities.

Printed and bound in Canada

 MIX
Paper from responsible sources
FSC® C103567

I dedicate this book to my students,
with love and appreciation.
Tshinashkumitinau.

Katshi minumamitunenitaman kie tiapuetatishuian e innu-ishkueuian tshetshi mashinaitsheian, eukuan nitishinishtuteti: kassinu auen ka itenitak tshekuannu tshetshi tutak tshika takuannu tshetshi ut animiut muk eiapit apu nita tshikut ui patshitenimut. Uemut eiapit nanitam peikutau tshikaui ishimamitunenitam kie apu tshikut takuannit tshekuannu tshetshi ui nanikanikut. Kie nete tshek tshika peikussu, apu tshikut tant uitsheuakan. Eiapit namienu nenu tsheut patshitenimut. Uemut eiapit anu tshikaui tutam nenu tshekuannu ka itenitak tshetshi tutak.

After thinking it over for a long time and deciding, once and for all, to write, as an Indigenous woman, here's what I have come to realize: anyone who sets out to accomplish something will be challenged but this should never be discouraging. They just have to pursue their idea. Nothing should incite them to give it up, even if they find themself quite alone. They may no longer have friends but this should not discourage them either. More than ever, they must accomplish what they set out to do.

— An Antane Kapesh, 1975

The return is inevitable. To this tiny little village and the thorny, sandy landscape surrounding it that I've been contemplating ever since childhood, lasting memories.

On my street along the edge of the bay, I would melt into the group. I was a quiet little girl. As a baby I hardly cried, and my mother would disturb my sleep to make sure I was still breathing. As a child I hardly ever cried, and my mother once forgot me on the steps. Later, the strange justice of life made up for every one of my tears.

Leaving our beige house meant leaving everything. Even if the everything seems pretty insignificant because you hardly have anything. A white steel bed and a quilted blanket. A dolls' house, a playroom in the basement with a cement floor painted blue. All winter my cheeks red with the cold, and all summer my skin as brown as the kids' in the Caribbean. Maybe one day I'll come back to the shore of this bay, kiss my aunt, and play in my room.

Exile was an eight-hour drive away, and had pale

skin. It took my mother two days to complete the journey, a distance I was able to calculate only by the number of villages we drove through. I ended up learning their names by heart. And the stops, the different stages. Following the modulation of the curves and the line of the mountains of the north coast. Making headway at the speed limit.

I was seven. A little brown girl among all those white faces, their pale eyes, blue or green, their blond or curly hair. A stranger. A new arrival. Different. Noticing my skin was dark. Not feeling at home.

I'm not sure if elsewhere the world has changed. But I know about the straight road they finally drove through the deadly curve at Saint-Siméon. About the eternal absence of a bridge between Baie-Sainte-Catherine and Tadoussac, where the dip in the river is as deep as the sea. About the tiny parish church whose name I no longer remember, that will soon close its doors because Route 138 will pass it by.

They say returning is the path of the exile. I didn't choose to leave. Fifteen years later I'm back, and I can see things have changed.

WHAT I DIDN'T KNOW

Them

I'd imagined them. Hundreds of times. Without knowing their names, their families, their stories. Or what
they wanted. Twenty or so teenagers, no two of them
alike, boys, girls, some shy, others show-offs. Adults,
in the process of becoming. A generation of children
with the common experience of quiet streets without
traffic lights. Of walking on the beach hand in hand at
the end of the day.

Nostalgia.

I'd already envisaged the yellow, almost brown
walls of my classroom and the enormous old wooden
desk I would use as a support. The melamine shelves
where French dictionaries would be lined up beside
Bescherelle grammars and useless copies of a thesaurus
considered indispensable to French writing classes for
far too long.

I wanted the empty walls of my classroom to be
filled with all sorts of fragments of literary history.

5

Quotations, photos of poets. Poster reproductions of paintings. Images from other places, created in other people's heads, that help us construct who we are. I couldn't imagine that I'd settle for teaching only grammar, all its incongruous rules, the cedilla that softens one letter. I would teach them the world. How to look at it. How to love it. And how to do away with that static and obsolete enclosure that is the reserve, that we describe as a community only to appease the heart.

Ever since getting the job, I'd been rehearsing ad nauseum how to introduce myself to my students. How to tell them in a straightforward way about my years at university, and what led me into the education sector. And how I came back here, to Uashat. I wouldn't mention what I was giving up. Or how afraid I was that people at home wouldn't recognize me. I'd not reveal how frightened I was starting out in my chosen career, how uncertain, how unconfident. And I wouldn't speak to them in Innu. Because of my poor syntax, my white-girl accent.

I wanted to make a good impression, and even if I struck them as a stranger at first, except for the colour of my skin and my dark eyes, I would find a way to forge strong ties. Somewhere between their learning French and learning themselves.

This was before. Before Marc's absences. Myriam's hunched shoulders. Melina's raw, secret talent. Rodrigue's rebellion. Mikuan's timid laughter. Before

tumbling into the void. Suddenly. No chance of turning back.

This was before me.

Him

Nicolas watched me leave. From the moment I started packing my boxes, he observed me in silence. I didn't procrastinate. The thought of spending the summer at Uashat, by the sea, relieved me. But his gaze weighed me down. Heavy. As heavy as the boxes that would accompany me up the 138 in my white Civic, dented from an accident on slippery snow. The constraints of our small apartment had become those of a free spirit once it has confined itself to a routine and a perfectly sketched-out path.

He continued to watch and I said nothing, feeling guilty because I was leaving him. That said, it was still winter when I informed him that the principal of the high school at Uashat had offered me a contract. I'd earned my degree and was afraid I wouldn't find anything better in the city. I'd heard too many stories of recent graduates working as cashiers in shops too expensive for them to afford even a simple jacket. And there was the idea of going back to my village. Of working in my community. Giving back. The contract satisfied so many of my aspirations.

That winter I'd made a quick visit to Uashat to meet the principal, and he'd confirmed a full-time position from mid-August.

Then spring surprised us.

"You want me to come with you? How's that going to work? I can't follow you everywhere. And what would I do in Uashat?"

I'd fallen in love with his Bas-Saint-Laurent accent during one of his solo guitar concerts. That was three years before. I'd quickly discovered his broad lumberjack shoulders. The plaid shirts he wore every Saturday. His strong hands. On his guitar. On his brushcutter whose blade would wear out as quickly as the weekends we spent together in his narrow and messy loft apartment. Wasn't he exactly my type? An artist who loved words as much as he did being out in the woods in the dog days of July. A thick beard and bushy eyebrows were all he needed to pass for one of his *coureurs de bois* ancestors. But his eyes were blue, his expression tender, and, much as I would have preferred him not to be so open, in that moment his face concealed nothing. Not even his pain, his powerlessness.

"I'm sure you could find a decent job at one of the

mills. That's all there is there. Timber. Timber. Timber. Everywhere."

His anger, his reproaches and entreaties, forced me to run away sooner than I needed to. I kept answering back, always tossing out the same arguments. Unable to convince him, I filed away replies that would warm my heart later on, up north.

He'd constructed a completely different future for us. Downriver. Happy days next to a vegetable garden. A white house built on a lot measured in acres. The scent of fields in mid-July, the soft breeze of evening. The maple sap boiled down come spring, and our many excited children licking the syrup off wooden sticks. Of course, I'd enjoy reading old novels on our wooden porch, on my own and in peace. Of course, the spruce trees would make me feel at home, despite our being surrounded by fields pungent with freshly spread manure, a practice so alien to life in nature. Of course, we were lovers. And maybe our love would have carried us, one into the other, until we grew old and carefree. But this life wasn't mine. I thought he would understand.

Standing at the door in my T-shirt and leggings, the most comfortable clothes for the eight-hour drive ahead, I looked at him looking at me. I was too proud to cry. I was choosing myself. Even if the act of choosing is, by definition, a renunciation. I had no wish to keep

talking, to repeat myself yet again, to burrow deeper.
I wanted to get out the door and breathe.

I left.

And what he said hit me. Hard.

"Okay. I'll wait for you."

Manikanetish

Twenty years ago they built a school on the main street of the reserve. On the empty lot beside the skating rink and the baseball diamond. The first brick building. And they named it Manikanetish, Little Marguerite, in memory of a woman who had died a few years before the work started. Little Marguerite never had children of her own, but that didn't stop her from raising dozens. Children who'd lost their parents. Children who'd been given away because there were already too many in the home. Difficult children. Children who, rather than being taken into care by the state, found refuge in her nest. A tiny woman, with the body of a child. But formidable. The Creator sometimes plays at contradicting what's been created.

Management decided to plant a lawn in front of the school. But the maintenance men didn't have one third of a green thumb among the five of them, and they couldn't tell the grass from the weeds. In summer, it was a mowed space, green for the one month of the year when the dandelions came up.

The school was intended for elementary and high school students. Until there were too many and the classrooms reached their capacity. Two more schools were built. And then they filled up too. Every year, the teachers, a few Innu but mostly white women, took in six new grade one classes. More than a hundred tiny pupils. Infants wanting to read, do arithmetic, and play sports. The majority spoke French. A very small number could speak only Innu. Some had learned the two languages. They used their mother tongue to say hello, name the seasons, and announce when they needed to go pee.

I decided to teach at the high school. Didn't have the patience or the discipline to tell stories about frogs, teach phonetics, or get the kids to sing little ditties while they clapped their hands. I wasn't prepared to deal with "Miss, he made a face at me." I knew I was incapable of handling miniature humans.

What I loved was discussion, the story writing, broad cultural issues, errors to be corrected, novels to be interpreted, PowerPoints, and questions like, "Madame, have you read Senécal's *Aliss*?"

I'd heard all kinds of stories about the school, which I'd never attended. Not always funny. Disturbing. Hard to understand. True? It was hard to know. A friend told me he used to roll joints with both hands under the desk during class. Somebody else described how the older boys would continually and insistently come on to the younger women teachers. Apparently there were lots of fights. Girls and boys, and usually over broken hearts and easy lays. And students would come and go as they liked to do a few lines of speed in the washroom. These were the stories that circulated. Embellished by teenage imaginations.

I'd also heard that things changed when the new principal arrived. A staunch, older man from Montreal. White hair, carefully combed. Solemn handshake. A science teacher by training, he seemed to be liked, feared, and respected. During my interview, I could immediately see why. Despite his diminutive stature, he made you listen. Ten years of service to the community had taught him what was necessary to work with the Innu. Self-deprecation, rigour, and a certain lack of pity are the weapons you need if you're dealing with people who've had their share of racial prejudice and taken easy shortcuts in their way of life. I'd soon find out if the teachers also benefited from the aura he projected.

The class

"Madame, what are we doing today?"
  "French."
  "Arrgh! I hate French!"

They called me Madame from the very first class. At the time, they didn't know my name. But even later, when we were more informal with each other and they played tricks on me, they'd still call me Madame. A rule established years earlier. Rigorously applied. At first, this *Madame* hurt my ears—I was straight out of university, not altogether an adult, not quite ready for such a mark of respect. Very quickly, it was a necessary one. Especially when the big boys with their deep voices would ask to leave class early. Especially when, one summer evening, I crossed paths with a few of my students in the pool hall and tried in vain to hide behind my glass of wine. Especially when laughter overwhelmed the class and I was on the verge of losing control. They called me Madame and I managed to reset the tone and calm things down.

Not much older than they were, I'd spend whole classes evaluating my performance. I wasn't at all happy with it. My hands talking too fast and not taking a break. These fluttery, nervous hands. These hands that ended up on my hips, childlike. A little girl scolding her dolls. Hands tired of persistently trying to attract attention. The sporadic attention of my students who calmly kept their own hands on the desks in front of them.

Perched on high heels and almost always wearing jeans, I was playing the role of the idealistic young teacher. Who looks for a little too much affirmation from her students, who apologizes every time she's talked herself into a corner. Sounded fake. I tried to remember what my professors taught me about motivation, discipline, and success, but couldn't. I was improvising. The whole time.

The pictures

Old black-and-white photos hang in the corridor between the administrative office and the staff room. An old, very wrinkled woman wearing the traditional Innu red-and-black felt bonnet. Not bothering to look directly at the camera. I was told later on that the missionaries were the ones who made Innu women wear the bonnets and keep their hair in braids rolled up on the sides of their heads and pinned at their temples. Because, with their long hair caressing their backs *au naturel*, they were beautiful. Attractive. Savage. Too beautiful for men of God and their oath of celibacy. They made them ugly.

Another portrait is of an Indigenous man with an axe in his hand and a pipe in his mouth. No smile. A prospector's tent behind him. He's staring at the photographer with the look men typically have when they're grasping a tool and heading out to work. He's in no rush to cut wood. He's smoking. Has no idea that he'll serve as an archetypal image of the Indian for generations to come.

Then there's the little girl. It's a close-up. She must be two, maybe younger. Dark skin, round cheeks, black eyes. She's wearing a peaked hat that conceals everything but the roundness of her face. A sort of hood to protect her from the voracious June flies. Except that this particular hood is made of a printed fabric decorated with ribbons. This is the photograph I like best. She's pointing her little finger at something that can only be imagined. She's not laughing. Her mouth is heart-shaped. She's speaking.

The earrings

The girls wore impressive, colourful earrings. Beaded pieces of hide, or long symmetrical strings of beads. They wore them with ripped jeans and T-shirts that said *Get more NYC*. Flashes of traditional Indigenous art in their long, straight, dark hair.

"Did you make these?"

"No, I bought them last summer at the powwow in Obedjiwan."

"They're really lovely."

"Thanks, Madame. I also make some myself, but not this style."

"Show me sometime. I'd love to buy some."

She pushed her thick hair behind her ear. Looked at me proudly.

There was this history class in middle school. I was fourteen. The textbook had pictures of teepees, longhouses, clothing made from animal skins, drums, small fruit. The word *indigenous* alone was enough to make me blush. Feeling anxious in my seat near the teacher's desk, I hoped desperately that he wouldn't ask me any questions about my culture. Or, worse, make me say *hello* in my language in front of the whole class.

Sometimes people I met for the first time would think I was Latina. I liked that. Because my skin is brown, my hair black and long, and my eyes less slanted than my mother's. Because my accent is hard to place. And because I never wore earrings like that as a teenager. I never even wanted to.

Had I already been humiliated because I was Innu? Maybe once or twice. Not enough for the shame to stick. But still, the shame was there, in my inability to identify with them. With this *them* that should have been *us*. This *us* that slipped down my throat whenever I was expected to explain where I belonged.

The essay

It was a work of art. Almost the last paper in a stack I was forcing myself to grade, all alone one evening, without even a cat to purr its affection my way. Small letters, lined up and leaning perfectly to the right. Not a single error of syntax. Exactly the kind of essay I would have liked to write at sixteen. And not only was the grammar entirely correct, but there was a clarity to the narrative, a way of naming things unambiguously, without repetition. It took me in. Completely. Who had taught her to write like this?

The essay argued against clear-cutting in the North, with always a pivotal sentence to steer me through it. I read it in one go, not thinking at all about the assignment they'd been given. I read it with pleasure, forgetting I needed to grade it, that my time was precious and the stack of essays had to decrease. I reread it, and because students should always try to improve their work I singled out a small problem in the first paragraph, a slight structural fault in the second. Without much conviction.

The next day, there was Melina, my precious writer. I'd never taken the time to look at her as an individual, outside the group. For the duration of the class, I studied her. She'd made up her eyes and was wearing lipstick. It only partly camouflaged her fatigue. That said, it didn't diminish her beauty. Brown skin and black hair. Slender. Maybe a little too slender. She said little and never responded to any of the questions on the day's lesson or more general knowledge that I would put to the class. She barely raised her head when I explained the homework I was assigning. She was so far from the rest of us.

At the end of the class I asked her to stay so we could talk. Her expression, which had been so weary, revealed to me that she was anxious.

"Melina, I marked your essay yesterday." I gave her a contented smile. "It's excellent. I wanted to let you know."

She responded with a smile of her own, slight, her mouth closed.

"Thank you, Madame."

"I've hardly ever read anything as well-written. Not many people can write like you. And at sixteen."

"I'm fifteen."

"It's a gift, you know."

"I don't know. Maybe."

"Fine. See you tomorrow."

Weekend

Friday at four, my bags are packed. Chips and pop, comfortable warm clothes, no makeup and no perfume, hair elastics and a toothbrush. My uncle is loading the pickup. I go into the house to talk to my aunt. There's a difficult student who is driving me insane. It feels like I am totally losing control of him. My aunt tells me who the father is. She knows the story of the mother taking off with a lover from Schefferville. And how angry the betrayed father was. Family cohesion reduced to zero because of a girlish infatuation. It's obvious that my aunt disapproves.

Two hours on the road. Old country tunes by an Innu band. The cigarettes my aunt and I smoke like two chimneys. A coffee at Port-Cartier. The gravel road you have to keep your eyes on for the inevitable porcupine. The trees growing into each other and the streams separating them. The fall isn't red and orange as it is in the south. It's dark green with yellow patches.

I keep thinking about how much the student enrages me. I understand his anger a little better. Two dead pheasants on the side of the road. One hit on the head, the other on the breast.

Fir and spruce trees surround the cabin. A few birches, short with yellow leaves. The lake near which Grandpa built his cabin stretches the length of the horizon. You can reach other families, other hunters, by canoe. My aunts, one after another, built cabins of their own near Grandpa's. There are five of them in all. It's a little village.

Grey tree trunks drown on a bit of headland close to the shore. At first glance it looks like a moose taking a swim. You need to scrutinize it a little more closely, and the temptation to alert a hunter to the gigantic animal out there passes. But it's not impossible, and you need to be aware.

The big window of the cabin looks out over the lake. The coffee tastes better when it's made in a metal pot. My uncle built his cabin five years ago. A single big room. Three beds with thick covers my aunt sewed. The wood stove by the kitchen serves as a heater and a toaster. There's something about this modest, unpretentious place that adds to the peace of the lake and the spruce trees.

That evening, it is cold. I put on a heavy sweater and my uncle feeds a log into the stove. He asks if I'm cold. I say yes, a little. He keeps on about it all weekend. He makes fun of me as he throws on a few logs before nightfall. I laugh with him.

Dissatisfaction is displaced by simplicity. No looking at yourself in a mirror. You gaze at a limpid lake and search for the circular ripples that rise from the trout in the depths. You drink the water from the stream and discard nothing near the cabin, because of the bears and the way they gobble up everything. You don't want to attract them with your garbage.

In the morning, the smell of the bacon and eggs my aunt is preparing. One of my uncles joins us for a coffee. He mentions moose tracks on the dirt road just behind our cabin. Asks about the hikes we're planning for later in the day. He heads out. He's said everything he had to say.

We'll go to check the rabbit traps before we leave Sunday, around eleven. They say that when a rabbit is caught, it shrieks like a baby. But we rarely hear that. It's during the night, two or three miles from our slumber, that they're strangled and undergo their last fight. Better not to be a witness. They say it can kill your taste for the hunt.

Two days in this forest are not enough. Not enough for me to re-appropriate what I abandoned as a child. Trout fishing and marshmallows roasted over a fire. I had no idea I missed the forest so much. All those years.

And so I return the next weekend. And the one after that. I learn to set traps and not be afraid of the dark. Then another weekend. Until the first snow makes the road impassable.

The class

"Madame?"

　"Yes?"

　"Do you know Patrice?"

　"Patrice who?"

　"Patrice Jourdain."

　"Yes, he's my uncle."

　"Ah, okay. He's my father."

　"Seriously? So we're cousins, then!"

　"Yeah."

I smiled at her, affectionately. Looked at her differently. Only a few years separated us. For the time being, there was a chasm of untold family stories between us. She returned my smile. The other students behind her cast astonished looks in our direction, eyes wide open, whispering. No question, it's strange not to recognize your family, your uncles' children.

Every day I discovered some new relative. I wished I knew their names. It was apparent to me just how troubling my ignorance was. Genealogy stretching out, enlarging. Ties to everyone, through everyone.

Sometimes I'd pretend to know who they were discussing, pretend to recollect anecdotes I was hearing for the first time. During family suppers, or on bingo nights, I preferred having no opinion to being a stranger. I wanted to be part of it, to lose myself in the crowd. Again.

Mikuan

On Monday mornings Mikuan always arrived ten minutes late. Tuesdays too, and Wednesdays, right to Friday, when instinctively I didn't really expect her. Ever since the first weeks of class I was surprised whenever I took attendance and realized all my grade eleven students were actually there, sitting in front of me and ready to learn something about French syntax or reading strategies. And I would tell them. I would tell them somewhat frantically, *it's a beautiful day*. There was no point dwelling on students who were absent. I welcomed those who were there, carried on teaching, and proceeded in a way that would make the absentees feel sorry when I marked their assignments and exercises, an attempt at coercion that failed. To mark my dissatisfaction, I'd note the absent student when I took attendance with ironic comments of a sometimes inappropriate nature that would be greeted with an *ummm* or *that's how it is.*

Mikuan, though, struck me as a serious student. At twenty, she already had the air of a mature woman, her adolescence done. Round face, hair the length of her back when she didn't tie it up, and an accent that didn't lie, the lilting accent of the North. In class, she would sit alone, at a safe remove from the whispering. She'd watch me, her eyes questioning, her mind open. She worked when I asked her to. She listened when I gave instructions, and even provided answers to questions that required an awareness of very recent material. The only problem, and it was minor, was her lack of attention to the timetable. She was living, I believe, in another time.

Mikuan had left her community with her boyfriend, seventeen and pregnant. In her village, which was accessible only by sea, school stopped at grade nine. After that, students had to make a choice: quit or move. She'd decided to stay in school, but Uashat was not her home. I understood. Despite my efforts to integrate since returning to Uashat, I mostly felt the same. Excluded.

Maybe that's why she was the first one I talked to after class, the other students fleeing as soon as the bell rang. We would talk about everything and nothing. About the two-year-old son she'd had to take to the hospital the night before, and how she'd left without seeing a doctor because the long hours of waiting had been so exasperating. She told me she'd be going back if the fever didn't abate. I tried to be supportive in the face of the burden weighing on her back. I often wondered how she would ever manage to get her diploma. Because, despite her extraordinary determination, she kept failing at reading and writing. It was hard for me to assign her extra work because of her needing to take care of her boy every night. I listened. Nodding, empathizing. I said, *See you tomorrow.*

The class

"Madame, what are we doing today?"
　"French."
　"Yeah, but what in French?"
　"A dictation."
　"*Arrgh*, I hate dictation!"
The student nonchalantly sauntered over to the bookshelf to retrieve his schoolbag, locating it among the thirty or so multicoloured and disorganized others. He turned, made his way to his desk, and took out his dictation book. Wrote the date in the top right-hand corner. Then, sighing, he tossed his pencil on the desk.

My students were not talkative. They weren't shy, either. Just reserved. On their guard. If I approached, interested in how they were doing, they would go rigid. Expecting something from me. And I would wait as well. For a question, or a comment. But nothing would come. I'd move on, wandering around the classroom with a smile on my lips that said nothing. I learned that the most accommodating spot for me was my own desk. That I could stop waiting there. The trips I was making back and forth from my desk to the back of the room served no purpose. I sat back down. Pitiful.

In one morning class, I caught two of the girls in conversation. They were bantering and giggling about their weekend. The nighttime escapades still fresh in their laughter. Their eyes bright. Two carefree teenagers. I felt a sudden longing to join them, to burst out laughing, ask indiscreet questions. But I held back. I called them to order, to correct their texts. The stern looks I got. Was I so transparent?

Marc's mother

He was absent that morning. It didn't worry anyone because he was so often not in class, and for no valid reason. His absences contributed to the tension he gave off anytime he was required to read, write, or conjugate a verb. I couldn't get used to his negative attitude and told him so constantly. We'd come to the end of a term and I permitted myself to tell the class how his truancy annoyed me, repeating for the zillionth time just how critical it was to show up at school. That this was the most important factor for success.

One of the students interrupted me and, in a voice filled with outrage — another tone I wasn't used to — she said, "Come on, Madame, I don't think you know but he's in Quebec City. His mom's sick and may die."

I had no idea. I went to my source — not the girl with outrage in her voice but the one who circulated all the news about the community, true or not — and asked her what she'd heard.

She said it seemed his mother had suffered a heart attack and they weren't sure she'd survive. "They flew her to Quebec City so she could see specialists, because everybody knows the ones we have at the hospital here are no good. The others, Marc and his brother, drove down this morning. They don't know if they'll be able to see her before . . . It's really sad for Marc, Madame. I don't understand how it is you haven't heard."

I didn't understand either. And I spent the rest of the class thinking about Marc, his fears, his uncertainties. My heart came to a slight stop each time I silently repeated the student's words. *They don't know if they'll be able to see her before . . .*

That day, I went to have supper with my mother.

News

Two days went by without any real information about Marc's mother's condition. We were unable to say if her situation was better, worse, stable, or deteriorating. In the staff room, we exchanged the same information at every break. We couldn't stop thinking about the two teenagers, Marc and his younger brother. The anxiety this generated. Worse, we could feel life revealing how precarious it is. Illnesses: those of our immediate families, those of the past, those that haunted us, those we had to fight; Marc's mother's.

I learned the news from the principal's weekly report. The note let it be known that either social workers or psychologists would take charge of the two boys, if they so desired. The time and date of the funeral. An invitation to attend if we had the boys in class. A sentence of condolence. I felt a lump rising in my throat that I didn't let escape. Fragmentary thoughts swirled in my head. Marc falling asleep in class. Me making him feel guilty for homework not handed in. Marc asserting how much he hates French because he doesn't understand a bit of it. Marc on his way to Quebec City without knowing if . . . Marc who isn't in class today. His breaking voice and his child's cheeks. Marc, who'll have to trade his customary jogging pants for a black suit. Carry his mother's coffin on his adolescent shoulders. Marc, whom I'd like to hug close, telling him everything will be okay, even though I don't know that. Marc, far too young not to have a mother anymore.

I knew I wouldn't be able to attend the funeral, or even visit the house of the grieving family in the three days of vigil preceding it. Death paralyzed me. Left me without words, gestures. Death has always had this grip on me. My only escape is to avoid it. Deny it.

The staff room

I felt powerless before death. I asked a colleague about how to behave with the students, and in particular toward Marc. What words should I use to mitigate the pain? At university, we'd been taught to avoid physical contact with students, especially those of the opposite sex, in order to maintain an ethical and professional distance. Did the rule apply in this situation? A child had lost his mother.

The teacher I asked had been at the school for twenty years. She taught math. At first glance, she'd seemed stiff and harsh. Tall, always dressed sombrely, hardly ever smiling. She'd groan as she corrected student exams. Mutter her dissatisfaction at answers that were either incomplete, incorrect, or simply not there. At first, I'd not held her in any esteem. I saw her as one of those civil servants who've become embittered and indifferent, who go to school as though they are going to prison. But the detail she applied to preparing her classes, the advice she provided for supply teachers, the attention she paid her students, the way she worried about those who were absent, all this revealed the attachment she felt for them. Which was evidently mutual.

"Yammie," she said, "it's not really your job to get involved. The principal and Marc's counsellor will talk to him. Your job is to keep teaching. You can always tell him how sorry you are, so that he knows. We're not yet sure when he'll be back, but he'll want to keep his routine, like before."

"Like before . . . is that possible?"

"You'll see. It'll be all right. They're stronger than you think."

The class

"Madame, how does it make you feel that Marc's mom died?"

"It makes me feel sad."

"When's he coming back?"

"I don't know. When he's ready, I suppose."

"Will he have to take the exams?"

"Yes, if he wants. Maybe they'll help him think about something else. But listen, when he comes back, be nice to him. He'll need your support and your friendship. Think of something positive to tell him."

"And you? What will you tell him?"

"I don't know."

Alone

My apartment is in town, five minutes from the reserve. It is very dark. Few windows. My mother gave me an impressive wooden bookcase when I got my diploma. It takes up nearly all the space in the kitchen. Dozens and dozens of books are piled up there. Those I've read for pleasure. Those I received as gifts. The ones I had to read for courses. The ones about prayer. Those I devoured as a teenager. The ones I've reread in the summers, out on the balcony with a cigarette burning away in the ashtray. I haven't read a new book in a long time.

I rarely have visitors. My phone only rings for surveys. I had a plan to start running again as soon I was established, but I spend so much time planning my lessons, correcting assignments, fulfilling requirements. I'm exhausted. I've gained weight because I have meals delivered every evening. And the plonk from the convenience store doesn't help either.

In the beginning, I'd hoped to make friends with my colleagues, but it seems they already have full, well-organized lives, and what little time they have left to socialize is for a brief get-together every third Friday of the month from five to seven. This solitude is not like me. I used to love organizing big dinner parties. Inviting friends, and friends of friends. I've turned into a bear. Nobody comes near a bear.

It's crazy how much I miss him. Nicolas hasn't called in two weeks. He hardly responds to my emails. A few quick words that don't say much. I'd like to know what he's up to, and who with. How naive I was to think the distance wouldn't affect us. But I know it's there. And it's growing every day.

Winter arrived in mid-November. Yesterday it was minus fifteen. I haven't even bought a warm coat yet. Every time I went out for a smoke break I shivered with cold. My colleagues laughed, said, *Welcome to Sept-Îles*.

Then, in the middle of two nights of insomnia wracked with weariness and thoughts too profound for my tired mind, an idea took root. Maybe I made a mistake. Maybe this is not my path. Too ambitious given my lack of experience. These kids are impossible to fathom. A barrier between us. Nicolas would have the words to console me. Encourage me. He'd take me into his woodsman's arms. His presence would be enough to reassure me. And we'd drink wine to the point of forgetting. Words of love and utopian promises would be sufficient, like before.

I emptied my glass of red in silence.

Why doesn't he call?

Cottage

At the big cottage table, while peeling potatoes and plucking pheasants, their hands stained with blood, my aunts were talking. I listened, interjecting a few exclamations here and there. Until, at thirty-three, she became a grandmother, everyone called my youngest aunt Baby. She was telling the story of my grandmother's — their mother's — last days. She told us she'd been there when they took my grandmother to the hospital. The whole family knew it was the end. My grandmother had been having a hard time for months. Finding it more and more difficult to breathe, and her body covered in open sores from the diabetes. In those days, older people only went to hospital to die. Bed baths, incapacitating pain, insomnia were family affairs kept at home. On the night she died, when the rest of us — children, grandchildren, great-grandchildren — trailed through the tiny grey hospital room to say a last goodbye to the woman who had given us life, my grandfather refused to be present. He told his youngest daughter that he'd watched his wife suffer enough, he couldn't watch her die. Didn't have the strength. And no one forced him. We listened as she recounted this moment of weakness with a lot of tenderness. Like a prayer.

That evening, tucked up in a warm single bed, engulfed by the noises of my aunt and uncle snoring and the crackling of the fire, I thought about my grandfather some more. How he must have loved his wife. United for a lifetime, sharing all the miseries of the world. The poverty they ate for breakfast, the stillborn babies. How great their love must have been for a man as strong as he was, who'd faced all sorts of adversity head-on, to feel incapable of seeing the woman of his life meet her end. Such intense love was hard for me to grasp. But I knew it was part of my heritage.

The silence

Marc returned to class one week after the funeral. His slow walk, his pragmatic demeanour. He who'd never stopped complaining about my classes suddenly didn't react at all when I asked him to open his notebook. Wouldn't speak, except to say that he didn't want to miss the final exams, didn't want to fail the year. The looks we gave him filled with what we couldn't say. I smiled at him. Not a full, toothy smile, more like the forced smile of a helpless old woman watching a child make a mess eating. The student with the outraged voice surprised me. Looked after him. Chose the desk immediately in front of his. She told him what we still had to cover before the exams. She even managed to make him laugh. Not raucously, more like the laugh of someone able to breathe again after being underwater a few seconds too long. I watched her in action. Envious of her ability to approach Marc. Full of gratitude, too, because that day I was busy teaching a lesson on how to locate markers of time and place in a narrative text. Didn't know how else to behave.

Mikuan

"Madame, can I make a call on your cell, please? I missed the bus."

She laughs, unbothered. Despite the official notice strongly discouraging this. And also because the girl is twenty, and over the past few weeks we've developed the habit of chatting after class. And because the wind is icy cold.

"Where do you live?"

"Behind the cinema."

"I can give you a ride if you like. I'm going that way."

"Okay."

The cold made it hard to start my car. Mikuan watched me light a cigarette. She lit one too.

"You should buy a new car. You're a teacher." She laughs.

"You're right. I've thought about it, especially one with

a remote starter. I can't believe how cold it gets here."

She smiles at me.

"And what about you?" I ask as we stop at a red light. "Do you like living in Uashat?"

"Yes, I like it here. But it's not always easy. Like when I get back to the apartment and see my boyfriend hasn't done a thing. None of the housework, the cooking, the dishes. And then I have to make supper and look after my boy. Sometimes I just want to go back to Pakua Shipi."

"Oh, I understand. It can't be easy having to do everything."

"Yeah. If my boyfriend helped, it would be easier."

"Have you tried to talk to him?"

"About what?"

"About wanting him to help more."

"Yes, and we always end up fighting. And what about you, Madame, have you got a boyfriend?"

"I did have a boyfriend. Maybe I still have one, I don't really know anymore. He stayed in Quebec City."

"Yeah, I get it. My boyfriend didn't want to come here with me either. But then he changed his mind. Maybe yours will change his mind, too."

"Perhaps."

I brought the car to a halt near the address she'd given me. Said good night. Mikuan thanked me. And in spite of her daily troubles, she left happily, off to join the people she loved.

Marc

He'd not missed a single day of school since his return. He'd stopped complaining, and was taking my assignments seriously. Paradoxically, I was afraid he might be suffering from a serious depression. Even if everything about his comportment contradicted this hypothesis. The change in his behaviour concerned me more and more.

After class, I took him aside. Stopped worrying about putting my foot in it and reviving pain that had only recently subsided.

"Marc, I want you to know that I can see all the effort you're making in class. If you keep it up you'll be heading for a very nice finish."

"Oh, that's cool, Madame."

"But I want to ask you a question. How are things outside school? How are things at home? And with your friends?"

"Well . . ." He took a deep breath.

"Yes?" I encouraged him.

"I'm leaving here. As soon as I'm done grade eleven I'm moving to Quebec City. I want to go to college down there. I'm kind of fed up with here, Madame. I need to get out of Uashat."

It was affecting. His determination, the decision he'd made, moved me.

"So that's why you've noticed me working harder, Madame."

"Yes, I see. And believe me, we'll both be working hard to make sure that you succeed."

The math teacher was right. Marc's resilience was so much greater than I'd imagined.

Christmas bingo

I organized a fondue lunch with my older students for the last day of class before the holidays. Everybody contributed. Bread, potatoes, packets of bouillon, cheese, salads. One girl managed to convince her father to provide a plate of sliced caribou meat, and I had the school principal order more meat for the fondue. The class, which normally sat in rows, was arranged in small groups. I put white plastic tablecloths and red plates on the desks. Christmas-themed music was on when they arrived. I smiled. At last, I was able to play the perfect hostess again.

They entered one by one, placed their bags of food on my desk, and hung their jackets over the backs of the chairs, with comments like, *wow, not bad, this is cool,* that were not particularly upbeat. But they were sincere.

I'd learned the pleasures of group activity from my mother. I chose three simple games that would allow us to laugh and talk and compete. Forget the roles of teacher and student for an hour or two. Build bridges.

The first was a game of charades. The aim was to help your team guess the name of the celebrity whose name was written on your scrap of paper. Simple enough, but not necessarily easy. My students asked me to provide an example. To mime the Hulk in the process of transforming. I had to set my vanity aside. I sauntered casually from the door toward the window and, in the middle of the room, I launched into action. Uttered a grunt and twisted my face into a monster's. Everybody burst out laughing. Me too. And they asked for more. I had to repeat my act twice before I was able to convince them to join in. Then they took to it like fish to water. One after another.

"No way! I'm not doing that."

True to form, Melina objected to anything that might open her to ridicule.

"Come on, Melina, it's your turn. You don't have to act, just say a few words," I encouraged her.

"No, Madame. I hate this kind of game."

"Come on . . . she said all you need to do is say a few words. Don't be shy," said Mikuan, trying to coax her.

"Yeah, it really isn't hard," another student said.

"All right then . . . hmmm. I don't know what to say."

"She's being a real pain, Madame. Let her miss her turn."

"I'm sure she can do it."

We watched her for a few seconds as she visibly struggled between abandoning her pride and trying to make her fellow students laugh.

"Okay . . . here goes . . . uh . . . *my precious* . . ."

"*Lord of the Rings!*"

The whole class erupted with laughter. Melina too. I was astonished by it. Recorded it in my head. And the half-moon eyes, the big smiles animating the students' faces, their heads tipped back as though laughing was as much a question of posture as humour. For the first time since the start of the school year they were making room for me in their world.

Our lunch was followed by organized activities. Street hockey outside, karaoke, crafts, movies. Cross-country skiing for the whole school. I'd signed up for hockey. Hadn't played in years. The students kept passing me the puck but I couldn't intercept it. I kept running out of breath and was replaced every five minutes by another player. The boys were strong, and they were fast. Many of them played on hockey teams. People said they dominated in tournaments. They continued to pass me the puck. Passes that were neither too powerful nor too frequent and came directly to my stick. The air was cold and dry. Some of the students had prepared hot chocolate with marshmallows.

———

At the end of the afternoon, tables were lined up in the gym. Some two hundred students, each with a marker in hand, were ready for the last activity of the day: bingo. I chose to sit with a couple of students I didn't teach. They'd been on my team and I'd learned their names: Mathias and André. They were both in the individual education section, for those who fall too far behind in the basics. A kind of adult learning program, with workbooks to be completed but very little teaching. I was hard put to imagine the students achieving much in such a framework. I wondered about teenagers having the motivation needed to stick to this kind of independent learning.

They were two jokers. Matthias had long hair that fell forward across part of his face, and André had a short buzz cut. They were constantly making fun of themselves. Always piling on each other's jokes. I laughed. And maybe it was the fatigue of the long day, the cold of the hockey game, the lunch I'd enjoyed so much, and the impending holidays promising a chance to catch my breath . . . or perhaps it was merely because of this pair reminding me of my own not-so-distant adolescence that I laughed. I laughed out loud, holding my belly, wiping my eyes. I laughed and laughed.

Nicolas

It had been a joyous day and I wanted to share it with him. His phone rang twice. Then he answered.

"Hi, it's me," I said.

"Yammie, how are you?"

"Super!" I laughed. "And you?"

"I've been wanting to call for ages but haven't had the time. I'm staying at my parents'."

"Yes, I can hear them talking. Say hi for me."

"Yammie . . . I'm sorry I haven't called. I brought someone with me to my parents'."

"I don't understand . . . You brought who? What are you trying to say?"

"I've met someone."

"Oh. I see."

"Yes . . ."

"And so? You took her to your parents'?"

"Yeah."

"That's how you're telling me we're not together anymore?"

"Sorry."

"What's your damn problem? Can't you just say you're done with me and you've already hooked up with somebody else?"

"We're not hooked up."

"Yes, but you've introduced her to your parents . . ."

"It's just that she's never been downriver and she didn't have anything to do this weekend. She's kind of a friend."

"A friend . . ."

"Yeah, a friend."

"A friend, my ass!"

"Yeah."

"You know what?"

"What?"

"Fuck you!"

I slammed down the phone, unaware of the huge tears rolling down my cheeks. I pictured him there with his girlfriend, relieved that he'd finally told me the truth. And his parents happy to see him with a girl from nearby, ready to seriously engage. A white girl, I was sure of it. With Nicolas's blue eyes, and hair not as straight as mine. This was his way of dumping me. Like a pair of worn-out shoes tossed in the garbage.

That night, I was in pieces and poured my pain into the Cabernet. Later, I wrote him a furious email. Fell asleep on the couch, my face swollen and streaks of mascara under my eyes.

LIFE IS A STRUGGLE

The new term

I hoped to ease back into classes. The holidays had been a combination of dinners and compulsive shopping. I'd stayed with my family. And just the idea of being in the same town as Nicolas, even for a weekend of shopping in Quebec City, was devastating. My mother began right away asking questions about my long-distance relationship. I figured she knew even before I answered that we'd decided to break up. And that's what she said when she took me in her arms, as I swallowed my tears.

"Go ahead, cry, my sweet. The choices we make are often hard to explain. And when people don't understand our choices, they push us away because they're afraid we'll leave them first."

I knew she wasn't talking about me. She was talking about herself twenty years earlier. About her escape to the big city. About how her parents and her sisters didn't understand and rejected her. Her rebelling against the unwritten law that you stay on the reserve. Raise your kids there. Build your house there. I knew her memories meant she could feel my pain.

And because she knew Nicolas, and he'd been charming with her, because she was attached to him, I think she had a few grey days, too.

Several times during the long holiday I had the intense urge to phone him. Hear his voice begging me to forgive him for the mistake he'd made. Especially when I was alone in my two-room apartment. Especially when my anger let up and I could see how my absence had pushed him toward another girl. Especially because I felt guilty for not staying with him, abandoning our love and putting my career first. But I never succumbed to the urge, because a part of me demanded that I be loved with no limitations on distance, or phone calls cut short by accumulated exhaustion. And so I held back. Persuading myself the pain would fade away. That this, too, would pass.

Back at school, the principal called me to his office. That was unusual. He tended not to get mixed up in teachers' work, their results, or the difficulties they might have in class. He didn't make surprise visits right in the middle of a lesson, the way some do, first spending a few minutes outside the classroom peering through the window. He seemed to trust us. I learned later that he kept a journal in which the names of all the employees working under him were listed. And that he had a notebook in which he wrote down whatever rumours he heard about them, whether disputed or confirmed. So calling a teacher to his office was never a random attempt to acquire information. It was for a very specific, and often unpleasant, reason.

"Yammie, I have a project for you," he said. "The Arts Council is offering new funding for Indigenous schools to put on a play. My art teacher no longer knows what to do with her students for extracurricular activities. There are about thirty, and I thought you might be interested in doing a little theatre with some of them. It goes well with French. Diction, orality, that kind of thing. And you're young. You're full of energy. You could do it after school, twice a week. I'd give you fifteen students, grades nine to eleven. What do you think?"

I listened, nodding.

"It sounds like a good project. Can I think it over for a few days? Some of the kids are pretty far behind in French, and I'd like to make sure the grade elevens are ready for the Ministry exams. I'm not sure I'll have the time."

"Yes, I understand." He spoke with the same tone of voice he used for a student testing the limits of respect. "I'll let you think it over. But I want you to know I'm offering you this because I've heard good things about your classes, and I believe you're capable of running such a project."

"I've never done theatre. I really don't know if I'm qualified," I said in my defence.

"Fine, yes. The students have never done any theatre either. You'll all be learning at the same time. It can't be that complicated to learn texts by heart and recite them in costume. I know these young people and, you know, theatre might well help them improve their competency in French. Listen, I could offer the project to someone else, but from experience I can tell you this kind of course provides the opportunity to connect with students. Because you're new, I thought that might please you."

That was enough to convince me. I didn't need to think it over anymore. I accepted.

"Perfect," he said, clearing his throat. "We'll start next week. Tomorrow, we'll register the names of students who are interested. We'll provide you with the list and you'll be ready to start" — he looked over his schedule — "on Wednesday."

That's how my first visit to the principal's office ended. In all honesty, I told myself that it wasn't all that bad.

Theatre

I'd had to read Shakespeare's *Romeo and Juliet* and *Hamlet*, Ionesco's *Rhinocéros*, Voltaire's *Le malade imaginaire*, and similar plays at college for the sake of a general education in the humanities. And they'd been assigned at university to shock us into realizing just how little we knew. I rummaged through my bookshelves: *La face cachée de la lune* by Robert Lepage, Marie Laberge's *C'était avant la guerre à l'Anse-à-Gilles*, Wajdi Mouawad's *Rêves*, Molière's *Tartuffe*, and Corneille's *Le Cid*. As I browsed *Le Cid*, its story of vengeance, love, and honour came back to me and I imagined medieval costumes, the set of a chateau, and its pointed dialogue emanating from the students' mouths. I reread the whole of Corneille's play. The edition I had was one I'd bought for a course on children's literature, and it was designed for adolescents. We'd read *The Catcher in the Rye* in that course, too. That book was fresh in my mind, and I'd promised myself that I'd read it with my students, until it became apparent that the school had neither the budget nor the desire to invest in novels deemed rebellious.

The edition of *Le Cid* I had in hand was illustrated, and the typography made the alexandrine verses easy to read. But I could see the vocabulary was difficult, and the play was too long to handle with just a couple of rehearsals a week. A challenge. Which was exactly what I needed. A project impossible to achieve. I fell asleep, satisfied with the choice I'd made.

Rodrigue

Once again, the last period of the day, he was driving me crazy. At first he refused to work. Rested his head on his desk, let his arms hang down toward the floor so that all I could see was his unkempt hair in the back row. I'd purposely assigned him the seat so I wouldn't have him near me in every class.

"C'mon, Rodrigue," I said, a touch of impatience in my voice, "raise your head. And open your book."

No answer, just an unpleasant growl travelling through the sleeves of his padded cotton jacket. Barely suppressed laughter around him. This class was already short on discipline. Even though, over the months, I'd managed to establish enough calm for me to be able to teach and for them to work on their own, I never, ever let them work in groups. And they didn't shy away from telling me how I was *not cool* and was *really boring* compared to the other teachers.

Their laughter left me even more determined, and my tone became more severe.

"Rodrigue, raise your head and get to work. I'm not going to tell you a hundred times."

Reluctantly, he lifted his head, pushed the textbook away, and folded his arms across his chest. Now I was the one growling—a tic I've had for years. If I don't like a situation, I growl like a cat whose tail's been stepped on. I confronted him openly, which made the whole class anxious. My authority was on the line, and I couldn't let it crumble.

"Rodrigue, if you don't change your attitude then you'll have to see Monsieur Boulanger. I'm fed up with always having to push you to do your work."

"Well, if you're fed up, leave me alone."

He put his head back down on the desk and shut his eyes.

I blew up.

"Rodrigue, if all you're going to do is sleep and not work, then I don't understand why you're here. I don't know what gets you out of bed in the morning if you're not here to learn. Explain yourself." I was almost shouting.

"Leave me alone," said Rodrigue, pushing back on his chair. "I don't care what you say. And I'm not sleeping. Just leave me alone."

I felt my heart beating hard.

"Okay, okay, I'll leave you alone. But get out of my

class. I don't want to see you back until I decide to meet with you."

He got up. Fifteen, but built like a man of twenty. Taller than average. And solid. He knew the effect he had on others, and especially on a woman teacher who was barely five feet tall. He wasn't angry. Didn't have to be angry to be threatening.

I returned to my desk and sat down while he collected his bag and pens. I noticed a little smirk on his lips. Tried to keep my eyes riveted to the corrections I was doing. Talked to myself in order to keep my cool. But his last remark did me in.

"Finally, no more French," he said, giving us all the finger. Me and the whole class.

"Get out of here!"

I couldn't stop my eyes from filling with tears. It took all my concentration and energy to stop them running down my cheeks. I didn't hear the bell ring a few minutes later, just noticed the students rush out of class, and how they were far too agitated for a Monday afternoon. As I put away the textbooks, I made the decision to ban Rodrigue from class until the end of the year. No discussion.

The ensemble

Tuesday afternoon I received the list of students who would make up the drama group, a list that wasn't final, said the secretary. I hesitated to describe this new group—essentially made up of students of varying degrees of seriousness who were tired of pottery or art projects and looking for something new—as an ensemble. But that was what we needed to become. And I was the director. No one could have anticipated such a thing. My sisters would have made fun of me. Reminded me how useless I am at mimicking voices or telling a joke in public.

I was already teaching most of the students who signed up. Sixteen names on the list. Among them were a number of mischievous students, excitable and categorized as ADHD by certain teachers, though they'd never been properly diagnosed. That didn't surprise me. They probably figured they'd found a crevasse to slip into and let loose all that energy reined in during hours spent sitting at a desk. A recipe for success? I hoped so. I also saw Mikuan, Marc, and Rodrigue had registered. That last name gave me a shock. I'd told the principal his coming back to my French class was out of the question. Even though he'd shown up at the door at the beginning of class every day since our altercation. Each time, I'd waved my hand to let him know he wasn't welcome. I'd decided to establish martial law in the face of such disrespect. No discussion, no compromise. His name on the list was a blow to my pride. Was the school not taking me seriously? I felt my anger mount. Rodrigue would be barred from theatre as well as French until I was ready to meet. I resolved to make him wait as long as I wanted. My decision wasn't fair. I knew. I owned it.

A party

My cousin decided to get married that winter. The maids of honour and their friends turned the community centre, with its pale-yellow walls, into a banquet hall for the night. Translucent fabrics veiled the ceiling, silvered ribbons dangled from red and white helium-filled balloons, and pine trees were lit up with Christmas lights. It was a triumph. Guests started to arrive for the evening dance after bingo. The soft candlelight made for a warm ambiance. With the tables set up on both sides of the stage, where the musicians were tuning their instruments, there was plenty of room to dance. I took a seat at a round table with my aunts, my mother's older sisters, who were waiting for the first chords to start dancing. As if they were still in their twenties. The newlyweds arrived to applause and camera flashes. They served their guests champagne.

Sitting in a corner of the room, I see him coming over to talk to me. I can still hear his voice in my head. Smoky. Confident. Our shoulders touching. Completely drunk on laughter and wine. Again, I hear him tell me I'm the prettiest thing he's seen all evening. Sweet words whispered close to my ear, my fragile soul. It's not my fault if, after he finishes his set, after the dance, at last call, I throw my arms around his neck to hear him murmur once more that I'm beautiful. The scent of aftershave mixed with sweat.

He leaves with his guitar in one hand, a cigarette in the other. He's tall, slender, his dark hair is in a long ponytail. A three-day beard. Bright, animated eyes. He says we'll see each other again. I'm helpless, like chocolate melting in the sun. I slip my phone number into his pocket.

Theatre

We had no time to lose. It was January, and the play was supposed to be ready for mid-June. I was assailed by all kinds of emotions. Fear, stress, excitement. What did I know? I made hundreds of photocopies for the first class. We would stage *Le Cid*, nothing else. Learning the text would monopolize our time. Creating sets and costumes. I imagined blocking the movements on stage, the duels. Chaos in my head, incapacity in my hands. I was jittery with impatience.

I should have expected as much. When I described the play and read them a few particularly eloquent excerpts, I received howls of protest.

"Honestly, Madame, the text is too hard!"

"It's super old. Nobody's going to understand what we're saying."

"No way! I'm not playing some Spaniard."

"Why didn't you pick a play that deals with the Innu? Or is set in Quebec, at least?"

It took me a good ten minutes to explain, through their protestations, that playing characters so far removed from their own reality would plunge them more readily into theatre. They'd be less afraid to let themselves go. And then on top of it there'd be costumes, props, and sets, and time to rehearse. Even if, in the moment, it seemed too much, we had to take a chance.

Disappointed by their reactions, I couldn't muster the arguments to convince them. Mikuan came to the rescue.

"Me, I think it's a good play. We can do this, and imagine the ball gowns and the sets. It's like *Romeo and Juliet*. Isn't that right, Madame?"

"Yes. Exactly. I'll bet you've already dreamed of performing in a play like this! *Le Cid* is the one. We'll do something amazing. Agreed?"

Bit by bit, the mutterings subsided. I sighed with relief. I could see the enterprise was only just beginning.

Luckily, casting the roles was easier. After a meticulous description of the characters, we decided jointly how to assign the parts, who should play which character. I figured it was better to have them all involved. Marc would play the lead, Don Rodrigue. Three boys wanted the role, but I could sense the goodwill of my ensemble toward the boy who had recently lost a large part of himself. I concurred. Then, Myriam said she'd like to play Chimène, a lovestruck woman. Behind her short hair and timid eyes was the courage to take on the play's principal female character, and this took me altogether by surprise. Still, I kept her in the role. And Mikuan would play Elvira, Chimène's governess. The fact that she already had a mother's attributes pleased me. All the parts were cast by the end of the first meeting. We agreed that those with lesser roles would take on more responsibility for other tasks. The students left in good humour, some of them reciting an alexandrine or two, *à la française.* Joking around as though they were learning a new language.

> *Il verra comme il faut dompter des nations*
> *Attaquer une place, ordonner une armée*
> *Et sur de grands exploits bâtir sa renommée.*[*]

---

[*] *He shall see how we must tame the nations / Attack a place and organize an army / Build his reputation through great exploits.*

School trip

It was open house at the college in Sept-Îles. The students at the high school were invited to explore future careers. At least, those that were possible in such a modest town. The kids were excited and happy not to be in class that afternoon.

I moved from kiosk to kiosk wondering why I hadn't decided to become a journalist or reporter. Writing had always been part of my life, and I could easily see myself producing a daily column for page five of a local paper, expounding a position on some topic of national interest according to my relatively conservative views, assiduously analyzing current affairs and writing passionate editorials on hot topics. I was sure that a certain contentment resided in the columnist's pen. They didn't have to endure a gang of teenagers heckling them for choosing a play they felt was antiquated.

Two girls, both grade ten students, were sitting on a

bench near the door, watching people and whispering. I went up to them.

"They're really mean, the way they're racist with us."

"Yeah, they should be fined."

"Yeah! Like five hundred dollars each."

The girls giggled.

"We'd be rich."

There was purpose in being a columnist. Still, you'd have to be able to draw a lucid picture of society. Like these two girls, who rarely set foot outside the reserve.

When night falls

The cold had been intense since January. From forty below at night to thirty below by midday. I especially hated the wind from the north. Blasts that blew out the cigarette I'd only just lit up nine metres away from the main door. I would run from my car to the school, pulling my hood in tight around my head.

The principal's voice came on the PA system as I arrived in the staff room, asking all personnel to assemble there immediately. Some of the teachers were taking off their coats, their enormous scarves, and slipping into woollen jackets. Others, disrupted in their last-minute tasks, arrived with a Thermos in one hand, a wad of photocopies in the other. Steadily, the noise grew. Monsieur Boulanger checked to see if we were all there, calling out the names of those he figured would be late. Which made us laugh, though he simply nodded in disdain. Quiet spread through the room. He closed the door behind him.

"What I have to tell you this morning is very difficult, so I won't beat around the bush. Marithée killed
herself last night."

Breathing stopped. Total silence. All of us in its grip.
Marithée had left school at the beginning of the year.
She felt she was too old, and I'd gathered she wasn't
managing to pass the basic courses. She'd shown up a
few times since to visit with her teachers, her two-year-
old son in a new stroller. A strikingly beautiful girl. Tall
and pale-skinned.

From where I was sitting I could see that our
typically unflappable principal's face was distant and
misty-eyed. He took some time before he went on.

"Most of the students must already know. Her family
and friends found out in the night. You know how news
travels in this community. It's possible some students
haven't heard yet. It is our job to be tactful."

He paused, and the teachers looked down at the
floor, nodding. One of us couldn't hold back her tears.
Kept wiping her eyes between sobs. She taught in the
individual education program. I gathered that Marithée
had been her student, probably for several years.

My mind quickly turned to Myriam. Her younger
sister, my sweet Chimène. Where was she right now?
With her family? Her boyfriend? Close, very close to
the people she loved? I imagined her pain. Her heart
breaking. The nightmare of someone waking her up
in the middle of the night to tell her . . . tell her what,

80

exactly? My eyes welled up as I thought of her. And of mortality. Of the suffering that prompts death. And the fear. The irrepressible yearning to be somewhere else.

"What I'm asking is for you to be steadfast. Do what you would normally do. I expect I'll be managing crises all day today. Please do your part, do what you can to keep the students in class."

He cleared his throat noisily.

"We'll try to see this day through the best we can. The best way possible."

He had no right to walk away. He needed to be strong. Unfamiliar emotion was palpable in him. He seemed to want to grasp hold of the table he was leaning on and send it flying. And the sighs he let out didn't placate his feelings at all. He summarily stepped out of the room, assuring us that social services would be on hand imminently. A tactical squad the council had established for just such a moment: a suicide.

I started the day with my grade elevens. I'd planned to go over argumentative writing with them again — God knows they needed the review — using a Pierre Foglia column about nurses working in long-term-care centres. I wanted to do a first reading collectively, which was how we'd been working, and then, individually, they'd extrapolate the columnist's principal thesis and list the arguments he used. I'd be in my element. I had an unfettered admiration for this particular columnist and found the text both sensitive and informative.

I watched as the students came into class, a greater number than I'd expected on such a tragic day. Some of them looking down in silence, others trying to hold back their tears. Facing me were trembling girls and tall, motionless boys. I had no idea what to do. This time around, I'd not had the opportunity to ask my colleague how to cope. The principal had told us to carry on as usual. And yet something was urging me to do things differently.

"I don't know about you, but I don't feel like teaching today," I said.

A tear rolled down my cheek and I crushed it with my hand. Standing there, immediately in front of them, vulnerable, was so affecting that I felt justified in the approach I was about to take.

"I'd like to propose something. Let's take the time to talk. If you're okay with that, we'll push the desks aside and move the chairs into a circle."

No answer. Except that they got up and did what I suggested. With reserve. With ceremony.

Circle

Seated between two students, I quickly come to understand there's no improvising this kind of group therapy. I'm also in shock, completely shaken. Over the last several years I've lost two cousins to suicide myself. Living in Quebec City at the time and not on the reserve, I didn't feel the grief, the anger, or the drama as intensely.

I look at the students one by one. Their posture, the way they're staring at the floor with their backs more hunched than usual. Confronted by the silence—the uncomfortable and awkward silence of the circle—I decide to speak up.

"I believe we should take the time to say what we feel. There's nothing worse than keeping these things to ourselves. Simply the fact of your talking, even if it's painful, will help you to better . . . to breathe afterward. I'll start and then, if you want, I'll let you talk."

Everyone takes a breath. What can they be thinking?

Where are their thoughts going? Why does this day have to be so dark? And what do we do when the pain reminds us so savagely that life is a struggle?

"I don't understand and I won't pretend to understand why this happened," I say, looking at them one by one.

I'm not able to actually say the word *death*.

"I feel so sad for Myriam, and for Marithée's boyfriend and her little boy. I can't stop thinking about them, and I'm so afraid."

At that point I'm in tears and I don't care. If they have the courage to show up in class on such a day, then I should also be courageous and show them how sad I feel.

"I don't want you to take this the wrong way, but I have to admit I'm angry, too. This shouldn't happen. She wasn't meant to leave us. She should still be here with us, and we should be able to see her taking her little boy for a walk."

The memory of a course I took on adolescent psychology comes to me. The professor presented various theories about suicide. He said that of all the types of violence that exist, suicide is the worst. The most violent act a human being can commit is against themself. The thought turns my blood cold.

And in that instant, Maya pushes open the classroom door. She sees us seated in the circle, our expressions solemn. She sobs, briefly, then hides her face in her hands. I quickly rise and put my arms around her, stroking her long black hair. I'd forgotten about Maya, Marithée's best friend. There'd been rumours about her recently. She'd apparently tried to take her life herself and had been confined to the psychiatric ward of the hospital for a few days. That's how things were done. Her failed suicide attempt led to a week in the company of some who'd lost their minds inhaling cheap and powerful drugs, others who no longer felt anything thanks to the antidepressants the doctors prescribed, and more who, much like Maya, were living bottomless dark days, lost in the shadows with no hope of seeing the light again.

Maya is collapsing in my arms. I sit her down next to me. Cry with her. Maya's a mother too. Two small children.

"Love, honey, it's love that will save us," I whisper in her ear. "Tonight, you'll take your little ones in your arms and, even if it hurts, you're going to tell them you love them. More than anything."

The students don't say much for the rest of the class. I encourage them, but without undue pressure. I learn her family didn't expect this. Nothing in her behaviour suggested the distress she was experiencing. A despair that was invisible. Insurmountable. Driving her to hang herself from a branch at the edge of the forest. I also discover that she's from a big family. That her youngest brother is the same age as her son. When Marithée's mother gathered her children to tell them what had happened, her little brother kept on playing with his yellow truck. And his mother watched him wistfully. What she'd have given for an unconscious moment.

"Madame, I think we should do something for her family. Letters, words. Don't know exactly."

"Yes, we should do that."

"And Madame?"

"Yes."

"Can we pray?"

I nod.

She starts her prayer very softly. The others, in unison, recite the Lord's Prayer. They know it by heart.

Nutauinan, Tshin uashkut ka tain
Tshima tshitimauenitakanit tshitishinikashun,
Tshima papanit tshitipaitsheun eshpish pishitshikuin nete
uashkut Tshima it ute assit.
Ashaminan anutshish kashikat pakueshikan
peikutshishikua tshe ishpaniat, ek^u,
shueniminan ka ishpish tshishuaitat,
Miam ka ishpish shuenimatshiht anat ka tshishuaimit.
Eka uin patshiteniminan netshishkakuiat,
tiekut pikuinan ka takuak ka matshikaut.
Tshima it.

My students leave the room, a procession of puffy eyes and sad, sighing faces gazing down at the floor.

Had the circle done them any good? I never heard. Even if there'd been no closure, even though it would take time for the pain to abate, and even though I hadn't necessarily said everything I should have said, or used the right crisis-management words, I wanted to believe — I needed to believe — that something was born that morning. Between them and me. Something fragile, no doubt. But, at least, something real. Something like the beginning of trust.

The radio

Saturday, early afternoon, at home alone. I remembered it was time. I switched off the TV and turned on the radio. I heard a woman with a clear voice singing an Innu hymn. The song was an entreaty to God for His love and welcome. A funeral song. Then the priest started to speak. Despite the mimicry of his intonation and the lilting sound he gave the Innu texts he was reciting, I immediately pictured a white priest dressed in long ceremonial robes with a magisterial cross at his neck.

I'd decided not to attend the funeral, not to have to kiss the wet cheeks of the grieving family, not to take a seat in the farthest corner of the chapel, not to have to ask the many students of mine in attendance how they were feeling.

How sad it was. As only funeral rites for a young mother can be. Ecclesiastical readings whispered by the family. The noise of crying babies and weeping women in the background. The battered hopes of the priest arranging, for the umpteenth time in his tenure, the final rest of a member of the congregation far younger than him. It's impossible to be inured to tragedy. Even in the advent of eternal life. Even if, in his last prayer, the priest vows that Marithée is now an angel.

The mass concluded, it was my turn to pray. First of all for my students saying goodbye to one of their own. Then for my family, that God might spare us from such misfortune.

Stanley

"I can come over tonight if you're bored."

"It's not so much that I'm bored. I'm sad."

"Yeah, what a crazy awful time. You have to try and forget. Think about something else. I'll come and distract you. You'll see."

"Okay, I'll be here."

I hung up. It was easy with Stanley. No backstory, no expectations. Ever since my cousin's wedding, when I'd innocently touched his lips with mine, we'd been seeing each other occasionally. He'd come to my apartment. I'd spend hours listening to him tell me about his life, his exploits, and why he was at the top of his game with his music and with women. He amused me. His deep voice, the way he talked non-stop with his guitar on his lap, his throat on fire, or his confidence when he called in the middle of the night, completely wrecked, as though everything were normal—it was all entertaining. He was five years older than me.

The three years I'd spent with Nicolas, a very proper guy—nice, responsible, polite and all—had completely twisted my perception of men. I'd thought they were all gentlemen. But Stanley was not responsible. He smoked in my apartment even though I asked him not to, drank too much, and used more swear words in one sentence than I did in a month. He was arrogant, would go on about his various young girlfriends to make me jealous, and I'd listen and ask for details, just to piss him off. I told him straight up that I would never fall in love with him. And he answered that love was for weaklings.

But on this particular evening, he was calmer than usual. He arrived early. Dug a beer out of his backpack and handed it to me. I took it, whispering a thank-you. I was like a cat that's been hurt and made wary. I was already in my pyjamas, my makeup removed. I'd curled up in a blanket and the television was on. He sat down beside me and opened his beer. Looked at me.

"You're beautiful tonight. I'm happy to see you."

Theatre

"Madame?"

"Yes, Caro."

"I thought about something yesterday. My mom's really good at sewing dresses and stuff like that."

"Oh, yes?"

"Yes, and I think if I ask her, and then if we buy the material, she can make the costumes, sort of to measure."

"Oh! That would be super!"

"Yeah."

"Have you asked her yet?"

"No."

"Okay. So why don't you have a chat with her and see if she's interested. If she is, I could call and discuss it. What a great idea, Caro."

"I think I could help her a little. I'm not super good," she said with a shrug, "but I can do some of it."

"Really, that's a good idea."

And before she left my room.

"Caro, I appreciate you thinking of this."

As I returned to my marking, I told myself that this sort of spontaneous participation was worth all the booing in the world.

Rodrigue

I knocked on the door of the English class. The teacher opened it and asked if everything was okay. I told her I wanted to meet with Rodrigue.

She called him. He came out, head bowed, and followed me to my homeroom. The lights were turned off and the morning sun was blazing in over the desks. I'd woken up in a good mood and had decided to include him again.

He took a chair off the top of the desk facing mine and sat down, hands on his knees.

"Right, are you ready for us to talk?"

"Yeah."

"Do you understand why I kicked you out?"

"Yeah."

"So, tell me why you think I did."

"Well . . . because I didn't want to work."

"That's right. And are you ready to work now?"

"Yeah."

"But you know it wasn't just for that?"

"Yeah . . ." His smile was one of embarrassment. "Because I gave you the finger. *Fuck you*."

I looked him straight in the eyes.

"You disrespected me, and you disrespected the whole class. That I can't accept."

He stared at the floor.

"I know, Madame. I won't do it again."

"I'd also like you to apologize."

"Yes, sure . . . I apologize."

I continued, but with a softer tone.

"Fine. You can come back to class."

"Right on."

"Go join the English class now, though," I told him, with a smile.

"Okay."

He put the chair back on the desk and headed to the door. Before he left he turned around and said from the threshold, "And what about the play?"

"Sure, you can come to that, too."

He smiled, saying nothing. I watched him exit the classroom, carrying his head higher and more easily, it seemed.

The class

"What're we doing today, Madame?" she asked.

"French, my sweet. This is the last period you have to finish your written work. But weren't you already writing your last draft?"

"Yes, I'm almost done."

And before the bell sounded the start of the class, my young student was back to work. She opened the exam document entitled *Indigenous Stories and Arts,* took her blue pen, and started writing. Her title: *Letter to My Son.*

Theatre

The question I kept asking myself was touchy but essential. Which of my students would now play Chimène? Two weeks had gone by and Myriam still wasn't back. I understood why she was absent and would never in the world have allowed myself to judge her for it. To lose your sister at that age is like losing an arm. You're not sure how to move anymore, or play, or keep your balance. You no longer want to dance, make others laugh, or rock your little boy — because Myriam was also a mother, of a baby barely a year old.

When school started, she'd made a deal with her mother-in-law in order to attend. After class, her day would end only once the house was clean and the baby asleep and the dozens of tiny clothes washed and dried and folded. She was seventeen. And despite all this, from the beginning of the school year, she had never balked at the long writing assignments or the novels she needed to read for homework. Of course, there were times when she'd use the sick baby as an excuse, as the other mothers in my classes also did, but she always asked after the work she'd missed. Which was why, even though it was a big part with a lot of lines to learn, when she'd asked me if she could play Chimène, I'd agreed. She was trustworthy.

Except that her life had been thrown out of whack. She'd graduated from being the second oldest to the oldest in the family. She was now the one her mother counted on to help with her brothers and sisters. It must have been a burden, comforting each of them. Telling them, no, Marithée isn't here anymore, but where she is now, up in the blue sky, there's no more anger, no more pain, no more tears. Imagining my student and the drama weighing on her shoulders tore at my heart a little more. And then the rest. The company. Marc, Mikuan, Caro, Steeve, Shikuan, and Rodrigue, too. I had to take their work into consideration. Their perseverance during the readings. How they concentrated on not mucking up the difficult words. I couldn't allow the staging of the play to be jeopardized.

We'd been rehearsing for more than a month. One by one, the students would enter the classroom that I'd arranged differently each time, depending on what we were doing: rehearsing the text, or doing vocal exercises, or brainstorming ideas for the costumes and set.

This time, as soon as the bell rang, the students hurried in. They saw the classroom was set up for a reading.

Marc walked up to me and asked, "We'll be rehearsing again without Myriam?"

"That's what I wanted to discuss with all of you today."

"Discuss what, exactly?"

"Her role. Look, I'll take attendance and then we'll talk about it as a group."

I took a breath. How had they guessed what I was thinking about? Maybe they were worrying, as I was. What choice was there but to replace Myriam? I didn't think she'd have the energy to engage as intensively as before. The students stopped talking as soon as I joined them in the circle of chairs.

"Right, I've thought about this a lot, and I think together we should decide who is to replace Myriam."

You could have heard a fly's wings beating. I wanted to learn their opinions because it was their decision to make as much as it was mine. They were investing themselves in the play during as well as after class. I knew that. It was evident in our rehearsals that they already knew passages from the text that we had not yet practised. And they were no longer asking questions about challenging words they didn't understand. On the contrary, they were figuring them out among themselves. I found listening to them very moving.

"I know that what's happened is really terrible. And, believe me, the last thing I want is to do wrong by Myriam."

"So why do it then?" my co-director, Patrick, asked angrily.

"Is that how you see it, that we'd be hurting Myriam?"

"Yep."

He scowled at me. He, who had derived so much pleasure these last few weeks from imagining the battle scenes and the play's notorious slap, was now making me feel quite small.

"So, tell me, how do you see things?"

"I think she'll be back soon," Mikuan said calmly.

"Me too," said Marc.

"Yeah," added Caro. "Let's wait for her to come back and keep working on the other scenes we've started. The sets. The costumes."

"We could do that," I said, without much conviction.

They nodded their approval.

"But I have to tell you, I'm still worried. The lines are really hard to learn, and I'm afraid we'll run out of time."

"Not a problem, Madame. We'll get there."

"Yeah. Meanwhile we can rehearse the scenes in which Chimène doesn't appear," Patrick decided.

"That could work. We can do that," I agreed.

Before ending the session, I made a last attempt.

"And if she doesn't appear for the rest of the year?"

"She'll come back. We just have to give her time. There's no way she'll miss the whole year."

I cleared my throat.

"Fine. We'll wait for her."

That day, it was their tenacity more than their solidarity toward Myriam that impressed me. One of the group was going through a terrible time, perhaps the most tragic moment she'd have to endure in her entire life, and they were maintaining the faith. They knew she'd overcome this test and return to finish what she'd started. And this wasn't innocence. They were far from naive, these youths conscious of life and death, of suffering and happy moments. Where did they find this resilience? I felt a strangely painful emotion in my stomach. I'd made a mistake, and knew the time would come when I would need to atone for it and convey my admiration. But not yet.

Stanley

One evening he arrived with a bottle of Châteauneuf-du-Pape. He wanted to impress me. We emptied that bottle and a second one he was happy to open.

I was keeping the relationship a secret. Out of vanity. I couldn't imagine the two of us, him and me, sitting in my mother's living room discussing the rather cool summer weather. Or introducing him to my Quebec City friends. Because, on the reserve, he had the reputation of a good-for-nothing. Didn't have a diploma, or a job, or even a driver's licence. He played guitar and was the father of three kids he practically never saw. On top of which I added his problems with alcohol, drugs, and related dependencies. But I found him seductive and couldn't defend myself. He had the biting humour of a guy who doesn't care what others think. The arrogance of a man who almost always has his way. The way he held my face in both hands when he kissed me.

"I've got a gig two weeks from now. Want to come with me?"

"Where is it?"

"In Natashquan."

"Ah . . ."

He was having a cigarette by the open window, blowing the smoke out. Which didn't stop it from coming back in. I indicated that I'd like a drag. I was on my fifth glass. The wine was good.

"I don't know. I don't want to be a bother."

"You won't be a bother. I'll treat you like a queen. You'll see."

I laughed. "Who're you going to be with?"

"My drummer and my bass player."

"Ah . . ."

I took a few seconds. I thought of myself backstage in a village where I didn't know anyone. A lone groupie in the middle of a noisy, excited crowd. Like Rosie in the song by Cabrel.

"I'm not sure . . ."

"What're you scared of?"

"I didn't say I was scared. I just don't feel like being with all your friends in Natashquan." I pinched my lips.

"Hmmm." He looked honestly dismayed.

"It would be too weird for people to see us together, as though we were a couple or something," I said, leaning my head toward him.

"Yeah, I know."

I finished my glass in one gulp. A little disappointed as I did so. Because maybe he wasn't too keen on finding himself and me in his own parents' living room, either.

The empty bottles and the generic music on TV irritated me. I laid my feet on his knees.

"Are we going to bed?"

"Okay, after you."

THE THINGS I CAN'T CHANGE

A Call

On the eve of the winter break, I was correcting papers and compiling students' grades for the end of the second term. Some of them had surprised me with the quality of their writing, far exceeding my expectations. Others had very specific difficulties, not with the content or coherence of their texts—in fact, most of them distinguished themselves in their choice of vocabulary—but with the damn rules of French grammar and its thousands of exceptions. Syntax was complicated, too. All in all, they'd improved, but the last challenge would be the most demanding.

The principal burst into the staff room, quiet on this Professional Development day. He was in a hurry, asked me to come to his office, and turned on his heels as soon as I got up. I sat down in front of him and he muttered a vague greeting as he dug around in his files.

"Yammie, would you object if I had you accompany the students on a field trip to the woods?"

It didn't really sound like a question. And I didn't see how I could answer that I didn't have only one objection, I had several. That I had to keep the intensive rehearsals with the students going, and every moment was precious, especially as they hadn't yet mastered declaiming in alexandrines. That the set was taking up an enormous amount of time, and for expediency's sake I'd divided the group into actors and stagehands, but this was actually making the creative work harder because it was impossible to tear myself in half, and I had to find a way to be present in both places. That the students and I, we all lacked experience, and they wanted my approval for every set-building decision they made in order to continue working. And besides, we were approaching the end-of-year exams and I still hadn't found a way to help the graduating students progress quickly enough to meet the challenge of writing a five-hundred-word text with fewer than twenty mistakes. Of course, I loved being on the land, and the idea of taking a train for the first time delighted me, but going away for a whole week was not something I could envisage.

Confronted by my silence and perplexed air, he added, "I know this is rather last minute — in fact, the trip was planned for after the winter break — but the teacher who was supposed to go with them now cannot, and I know you have a good relationship with the students."

"Yes, I'd very much like to go, but —"

Interrupting, he said, "I really need someone to go with them, Yammie. I know you're really busy with the play but, you understand, I can't send just anybody."

He was flattering me. And the trick worked. I smiled, raising my eyes to the sky.

"All right, I'll go."

"Perfect."

He handed me a sheet of paper with the train timetable and all the information I needed for the departure.

I left his office. I had one day to prepare the supply teacher for an entire week's work, and to finish my marking and enter their grades in the report cards. I had the distinct impression I'd been conned.

Train

I arrived at the station at a quarter after seven. Some of the students were already waiting at the door with their bags. They were wearing heavy coats, tall moccasins, and worn snow pants, and they were clutching colourful hand-knitted toques. I could see that they knew exactly where we were headed. To a cold place where, even in early March, it was wise to have warm clothes.

"Madame, we've been waiting half an hour for you already. You need to be here early to get the best seats."

"Yes, yes, let's go."

I regretted the time I'd spent making up my eyes and matching my sports T-shirt and wool sweater so that I might look casual and relaxed.

Before boarding, on the other side of the barrier that separates those who are travelling from those who are staying, I smoked one cigarette after another. Smoking on the train had been prohibited a few years earlier.

"Go, go, go, Madame, keep smoking," said Marc, making fun of me.

I laughed, even though he was disapproving of my bad habit. We'd not reach the camp before mid-afternoon, so I needed to get my fill of nicotine for the trip.

We'd be hiking in the woods for six days. My only worry was that the students would be bored. These kids, constantly connected to their cellphones, to their computers, the television series they watched, would have to do without, because there was neither electricity nor reception in the depths of the forest. I'd often heard people talk about Nutshimit, and had often imagined it. Untouched countryside, as far as you can see, in all four directions. The wind. The cold. The expanse, and the silence. This would be the first time I set foot on the land of my ancestors.

Our destination was a little more than five hundred miles from Sept-Îles, the train travelling north along a sinuous railroad track that crossed mountains and rivers, never going more than thirty miles an hour. From my seat by the window, I admired the snow lying on the branches of the tall pines, the size of the lakes, and the shapes of the mountains. The train came to a halt many times, and I learned that each stop was for a different hunting ground or cottage, a family getting off the train for a stay of a week or two. Places that weren't on any map. But each one had a name, and a genealogy.

We arrived at Mile 163 around three in the afternoon.

The snow was gleaming in the sun. Everywhere. An old man, lean and toothless, was waiting for us on a snowmobile with a sled attached. We could see a cabin in the distance. He said there were three of them and he'd be making a few trips back and forth. The most impatient kids left on the first load. I was enjoying a cigarette. And watching them happily load their bags, big and small. The way they moved about in the cold, laughing awkwardly, sunglasses on their faces, I realized we'd entered another space.

Nutshimit

Our hosts were Anne-Marie and Jean-Guy. A kind couple with a simple and open way of being. Melded. So much so that they hardly spoke at all, each anticipating the other's actions with no need for anything to be said.

Jean-Guy was fascinating. From spring to late fall he worked as a caretaker in an iron ore mine in Fermont, and in winter he spent his weeks of unemployment in a cabin at Dolliver. He was an Innu who lived the life of an Innu. When he put on his heavy coat of embroidered hide, made to measure for his shoulders. When he tore around on his snowmobile, his rifle strapped across his back, following trails covered in ice and snow. When, trusting, he set his trapline a few miles from the cabin. I had a hard time figuring out what it was I liked about this man. Was it the physical strength he displayed in spite of his apparent fragility? Was it the calm he exuded as we crossed frozen lakes, and the skis of the snowmobile dug deep into worrisome slush? Was it the tone of his voice when he asked his wife to make tea? And his gentleness toward her when she served it, with sugar? Or maybe it was his woodsman's language, Innu-aimun, in which he told us stories of long ago. A language even more unfamiliar than this place, where we were listening to him teach us about the world.

In truth, though, some of the students were also used to life on the land. They'd been in the region with their families. They showed me how to hold a rifle and aim at the head of a partridge, how to dress so that my feet wouldn't freeze, and, as we lay in our beds in the girls' cabin, the pleasures of storytelling by candlelight.

My students had stopped calling me Madame, and I didn't notice. They said, *Yammie, you'll never guess what happened to us!* Or, *Yammie, you have to come see what the boys are doing outside, it's too funny!* Or, *Yammie, how come you don't have a boyfriend?*

We were in another country, far from our books and desks. Far, far from social media and the gossip of the reserve. And far from the pain and dramas of family life. Farther away than anywhere I had ever set foot. And yet we were so close. So close to ourselves.

Jean-Guy

One evening, at dinner in the main chalet where we gathered to eat and spend the evenings, we were talking about what had happened that morning. After a long outing, two of the girls and I had been stuck under an overturned snowmobile. We talked about how scared we'd been, about the extreme cold, and our exhaustion during those few minutes that seemed an eternity. Then, about how we'd managed to right the heavy machine, set it back on its skis, and find our way back to the cabins. We were still laughing about this mishap when Jean-Guy started speaking in Innu and telling this story.

"A few years ago," he said, "when I was still a young man, I worked as a guide for the Whites. One time a White hired me to hunt caribou. Early one morning we flew out of Sept-Îles. He was piloting his own plane and just the two of us were on board. We were headed north of Schefferville.

"We were still quite a ways away from where we were headed. I never understood how or why, though my companion tried to explain it several times afterward, but the plane developed a mechanical problem and we had to make an emergency landing in the forest. I quickly realized we were going to crash, and I closed my eyes and prayed and held on tight to the seat in front of me. I thought my last hour had come.

"But despite the forced landing, we weren't hurt, and we managed to extract ourselves from the plane. Instinct told me the first thing I needed to do was build a fire. Then, I'd have to set up a shelter for the night. The crash hadn't killed us, and now the freezing cold was our worst enemy. The pilot, who seemed desperate, stayed inside the plane and tried to repair the radio. It was obvious to me that he didn't know how, but I left him to it. I spread out a carpet of pine and cedar branches, thick enough to light a fire. And I made tea. We still had enough provisions to last us several days. Some biscuits, water, a few cans of beans and pea soup. And we had warm covers and rifles.

"Night fell quickly. It was February, and we'd crashed near the edge of a lake. I'd set up our shelter among trees protecting us from Tshiuetin, the north wind. We could see the lake from where we were, and I listened one more time to my hunting partner repeat his sincere apologies before he fell into a deep sleep.

"The next day I rose early. I'd already been up a few

times in the night, afraid the fire might go out and the cold kill us. In the first rays of sunlight, the sky still a dark blue-ish, I saw a mother caribou and her calf maybe thirty or forty metres from our shelter. I took the rifle and shot the little one. The mother ran off, and the pilot woke up, startled. We went to fetch the caribou and I started to butcher it, thanking Tshishe-Manitou for assuring our survival for two more weeks.

"Six days passed without any sign of help. Every day, I insulated our shelter a little more. Every day, I cut wood, and went hunting for small game. Every day, I took a different path, hoping to find a hunting cabin or the railroad track. Every day, the waiting was harder and our hopes for survival slimmer.

"Then, one morning, we heard a helicopter over-head. The pilot went straight to his radio. He'd told me he could pick up shortwave frequencies, and we received a message from the rescue team. They asked if we were hurt. The White said no. They asked if we were hungry or thirsty, the White said no. Then they asked us how much longer we could hold on in the forest, and the White said, one more day. Which is when I threw myself at him in a black rage and told him we needed to be rescued immediately! If I hadn't controlled myself I would have strangled him with my own two hands!"

Jean-Guy burst into laughter, slapping his thighs.

"Wait till the next day! What a crazy idea."

And all of us at the table laughed with him.

"Jean-Guy?" I asked.

"Yes," he said, wiping his eyes.

"If you'd let me, I'd love to write your story. A book, maybe."

"Sure, sure, do what you think is right."

Shaputuan

The night before our last day we assembled in the big tent near the girls' cabin. During the afternoon, some of the students had collected pine branches, and Jean-Guy had kept a fire going in the iron stove in the middle of the tent. Two students had set up their mattresses at one end, intending to sleep there that night. The heat from the *shaputuan* warmed us up after a day of almost minus thirty. We were fifteen, nestled together and eating chips and chocolate, treats I'd saved for the last evening. I was thinking about Nicolas. I knew it was exactly the kind of trip he would have loved. For its uncomplicated nature, its grandeur, the peacefulness of it all. My students breathed in the tranquility.

"You know what I'm thinking?" I said. "It's our last night here, and I'm wondering what you're most impatient to get back to. What do you miss the most right now?"

"My kids!" said Maya, bright and happy.

"My bed," said Patrick.

"My son," Mikuan sighed.

"Poutine!"

We all laughed.

"What about you, Yammie?"

"If I tell you, do you promise not to tell anybody else?"

"Well, yes . . ."

"My ex. His name is Nicolas. I would have loved to show him how beautiful it is here."

"Ohhh, poor you," my students commiserated. I smiled, to hide how sad I felt.

"And you, Marc?" He'd not said anything yet.

"I don't know. Depends. Do you want to hear something funny or something sad?"

"We want to hear something true," I told him.

He let a few seconds pass.

"I miss my mom," he said, and lowered his head.

Silence came over us. The truth of it was that we'd be returning home to a sad reality. And that we'd have to keep living with it. The solitude, survival, the stress, and serenity. *The serenity to accept the things we cannot change.* A whole week spent in isolation had made us believe we were invincible. We were enveloped in a lightness of being and didn't want to leave. One student had even joked that she wouldn't be going back to Uashat, she'd have her children sent up by train. That her ex-boyfriend would join them. That they'd become the family in the forest. And we'd encouraged her fantasy, describing their days of walking and the food we'd send them on the train. We'd shared everything these past days. Our crazy ideas and our waking with the dawn. And now we were sad to have to go.

When we stepped out of the tent to go to sleep in our cabins, a bright sky lit the way. The full moon and thousands of stars our nightlights.

Theatre

Myriam returned on the Monday after our trip. The students had predicted it. Less joyful, definitely, her shoulders more hunched, her gaze often reflective and absent. She didn't talk much. And we didn't ask questions. As though to explain why she was back for rehearsals, she said simply that in the evenings, once her son was asleep, she'd continued to practise her lines, with her boyfriend reading the responses. She said, in a matter-of-fact way, that it was one of the few things that had helped her feel better these last weeks. And thanks to her presence, the group manifested a renewed enthusiasm for rehearsals, and I was able to breathe a little easier.

Rodrigue still had no clear responsibility. He helped out here and there but had no specific task. As the day of the performance approached, I took him aside.

"I've thought of something for you to do."

"What's that?"

"All the roles are taken, so you could be our prompter."

"What's a prompter?"

"The person who helps the actors remember their lines. He's hidden close to the stage and whispers out the words when he sees an actor is having trouble remembering."

"Okay . . ."

"We really do need a prompter. The text isn't easy, and without a prompter they'll never remember it all."

"Okay . . ."

"Would you have preferred to be on stage?"

"Not sure."

I could hear his disappointment.

"Well, just tell yourself that if we succeed with this play, then there's a good chance we'll do more theatre next year."

"Yeah."

"That's all I have for you right now."

"Okay. I'll be the prompter."

Theatre

The day for costume-fitting was eagerly anticipated. Caro's mother had sewn most of the dresses. They were simple and in good taste. Lace at the neckline and the wrists. Crinolines puffing out the skirts. Royal colours. Burgundy red, gold, white. Long pearl necklaces, white gloves, and slightly exaggerated makeup. The girls would resemble bourgeois ladies perfectly.

We visited a professional costume shop for the boys because the truth of the matter was we had no idea how young seventeenth-century Spaniards would have dressed, and we'd agreed in countless discussions that we wanted the play to be as authentic as possible. The shop was small and narrow, but the boys found a selection of costumes in chivalresque medieval styles. I'd insisted that they wear long, curly-haired wigs but was unable to convince them. But they promised to smooth out their long straight hair with gel and draw moustaches on their faces.

Ultimately, the disguises contributed to their role-playing. Practically all of them were now deploying aristocratic accents from I had no idea which part of European history. It worked out wonderfully. We just needed to emphasize the comic aspects of the tragedy a little more.

Body

Disappointed, I realized that I'd gained weight. I'd never been particularly svelte or athletic but had always maintained an acceptable figure. Anne-Marie's rich meals had accumulated on my belly and my hips. I'd blamed my excessive appetite on the fresh air and my hikes in the woods, and gorged on the delicious food our hostess provided.

I considered various ways of losing the extra pounds. Get some exercise. Stop snacking in the evenings. Or maybe both, to a degree.

And then, suddenly, I started to count. My heart raced. We'd been gone a week, then before that had been the week of winter break, the ten days of exams at the end of term, Rodrigue's reintegration, Myriam's return — and then Stanley. I felt faint. Zipped on my coat and headed to the pharmacy. Not the one on the reserve, better the one farther away, where I wasn't likely to meet anyone.

Slap

It was almost noon. A Saturday. For the first time in months there was only a light breeze and the temperature was mild. The sun was shining bright in a completely blue sky. A blue I'd rarely ever seen back in Quebec City. A cloudless, smokeless blue. And here I was, naked in the bathtub, enclosed within four walls, crying my eyes out.

How could I have been so stupid, so irresponsible, so thoughtless? What had I done to God to deserve this? And why Stanley? Why not Nicolas? Why hadn't this happened before I ended up here in Uashat, all alone? Why hadn't it happened when Nicolas promised me he would buy a house in the suburbs, down by the river? Why now, when my career was just beginning? Why had this thing lodged in my belly? Why couldn't it simply go away again?

And no one to talk to. I submerged my head in the water and closed my eyes. Held my breath.

Inside me, something heavy and bulky hurting me. My heart that wouldn't stop beating at a crazy pace, a taste of tears in my mouth, and the pain. Stubborn. Penetrating.

This moment when my thoughts implode. A slap. Right across the face. At noon. I fall apart.

Class

The week that followed was one of torment and misery. Lost between the obligations of my life and my wish to abandon them all. I often felt nauseous, which reminded me of my pregnancy and my fear of my pregnancy. Determined not to tell anyone, I walked around with a huge lump in my throat. And to make matters worse, I couldn't resort to a couple of glasses of wine to dissociate myself from my reality. I didn't answer Stanley's text messages. My anger turned on him. It was his fault. I was bearing the fruit of our careless, future-less relations. I was furious with him. He was even more irresponsible than me. Mediocre. No attachments.

The hours in class seemed to grow longer. The students were baffled by my listlessness, my indifferent comments, my silences. They were behaving the same way. They asked no questions. I noticed how quiet they were. Were they aware that a storm had invaded my being? Did they realize the least little mistake might make it blow up? My eyes filled with tears every time they whispered among themselves, apologized for nothing, and refused to make fun of whatever was distracting me.

I decided that I'd not mention my predicament until things were clear in my own mind. And only God knew when that would be. At first, I contemplated calling Nicolas. Perhaps some compassion remained from our three years of love. The cruel taste of someone else's sympathy. And of having no solid, trustworthy shoulder to lean on. In the evenings I lay in my bath for hours. Cursing my life. Then I'd fall asleep between my cold, dry sheets, my head too exhausted to dream.

Melina

I ran into her in the corridor between classes. Her schoolbag, laden with notebooks, was hanging on one shoulder. Because she was so petite, she appeared to be off balance. She had that defeated look on her face that I'd learned to recognize in my students. Somewhere between guilt and disappointment.

"Melina?"

"Hi, Madame."

"How are you?"

"Ugh, not so good. I'm going home."

"How's that?"

"I just met with Monsieur Boulanger. He says I've missed too many classes. So he sent me home."

"Oh, no . . ."

"Yeah."

"For how long?"

"Till the end of the year, I think . . ."

"Oh, come on, that's too much."

"Yeah."

"Want me to talk to him?"

"Not sure."

"I can talk to him. It doesn't make sense, not to let you finish the year."

"You think so?"

"I'll go see him. I think maybe I can convince him. I just need to be sure that's what you want."

"Well, yeah, Madame. I'm in a bad spot right now . . . but I still want to finish my year."

"Agreed. Hang in there. If you want to talk, I'm around."

I convinced the principal to let her return to class the next day. Explained to him that she was one of the few who would obtain her diploma. Still, she had to promise that for the rest of the year she would not miss a single class. Which she did, a few days later. And then, I never really found out why, she decided to completely abandon her high school education. Melina, my precious writer.

A few days after she left, I wrote to tell her that few people could write the way she did. So naturally. And that I knew what I was talking about. I bragged about my good taste in literature. And that no matter what job she chose she should make sure to keep writing.

She answered, curtly, *Thanks, Madame.* Which I took, egotistically, as a personal failure.

Stanley

"C'mon, tell me what's up. You don't want to see me anymore?"

I'd finally decided to answer one of his nocturnal calls. After all the nights of insomnia, I'd developed the illusion that we existed. Him and me. I felt, again, an urgent need to snuggle up to him. To hear him say it would all work out. Maybe he wasn't so bad. Maybe he loved me and I loved him. Maybe, how did I know, he'd be there to hold my hand.

"I'm so sad."

"Why?"

"I don't want to tell you."

"Did I do something?"

"Yes, you did."

"What exactly?"

A long, very long, sigh.

"If you want me to come over, you just have to say. I'll find a lift and be there."

"No. I don't want you to come over."

"Fine."

A pause.

"I don't get it."

"I'm pregnant."

Silence.

"And I'm the . . . ?"

"Yes . . ."

"Okay . . ."

A very long silence.

"So, what will you do?"

"What would you have me do?" I said imploringly.

"I'm not sure," he said quietly.

"Neither am I."

I started to cry.

"I'll come see you, just give me some time. I'll . . . I'll do what I can and be there."

I waited. One hour, two. Till the early hours of the morning. He never came. I couldn't prevent myself screaming out my pain from the depths of my bed, my pillow barely muffling the cries. Again and again. Until my voice broke. Something in me was beyond repair.

Class

At the end of the period, Julie took her time organizing her papers and putting her folder back on the shelf. We were alone.

"Yammie," she said, "I wanted to have a word."

"Absolutely. What's going on?"

In order to be discreet, I closed the door to the classroom and went back to my desk. She struck me as more agitated than usual.

"Everybody's going to know pretty soon, and you'll hear about it. So I wanted to tell you myself."

She smiled.

"I'm pregnant."

I felt an enormous punch to my belly. Couldn't help my eyes filling with tears.

"Oh, Madame . . . it's not that sad."

She seemed a little shaken. She wiped a tear off her cheek with the back of her hand. And yet she was still smiling.

"Yes, you're right. I'm not sad. I'm moved."

I regained my self-control, cleared my throat, and asked, "When did you find out?"

"When we came back from the bush. You remember, at Dolliver I was waiting for my period and it didn't come. I was even wearing a Kotex, just in case . . ."

She laughed.

"Now I just think how dumb I was!"

I vaguely remembered being in the girls' cabin during the trip and her alluding to her late period, but nobody had reacted because there was nothing all that strange about a period being late. I laughed along with her.

"So, then, it's good news?"

"Yes, I think so. My boyfriend is happy. He's finishing his carpentry course next year. And me, well, I can still start college, though I'll have to take it slower. My dad's the only one who's not pleased. He's so protective. But it'll sort itself out."

"Well, that's good. I'm happy for the two of you. Don't mind my tears. I was surprised, that's all. But I can see you're in good shape and I'm proud of you. And, on top of everything, you'll be getting your diploma this year."

All this time, I'd not stopped looking her straight in the eyes. She was six years younger than me and still had a few years of school ahead of her if she was to get the nursing degree she'd confided she wanted. She was barely old enough to vote, and already she needed to think about how best to raise a child. Except that the girl I was talking to wasn't a teenager anymore. And in the life she was preparing for, she would turn into a woman. She wasn't the first to go through this, and, just like all the girls who'd preceded her, she would figure out how to manage visits to the doctor amid her June exams. I knew she had the will to do so. And though she couldn't have known it, I felt her transferring some of that will to me.

That evening, I called Emma, a childhood friend. Shared everything. My fear, my doubts, my shame, my powerlessness, my wanting to run away, my nighttime panicking. Everything. My silence, my loneliness, Stanley, his guitar, his kisses, his rejection. Right down to the last tear.

Choice

The more I focused on my condition, the more irrational my thinking became. In the end, I accepted my truth. A being not much bigger than an appleseed was growing in my belly.

I would have liked to have had a choice. Like most women of my generation. I would have liked to be able to weigh the pros and cons. Make lists. Analyze those lists. Then make my decision. But there was this promise. Naive. Intimate. That I'd made to the Creator. When I was fifteen. A promise I'd formulated and uttered out loud. A teacher of ethics had incited us to make immediate decisions about our futures. Because, he said, when the moment did come, we'd be in crisis mode and unable to see clearly. Not long afterwards, I'd sworn never to have an abortion. The promise had been made a long time before, and didn't take my current life into account, my career, my loneliness, my fear. It was a promise I'd made in whispered prayers. An agonizing promise. One that hemmed me in. I no longer saw the future — not even a window where daylight might shine in. My body was the witness, my tears the confirmation. I knew the promise was one I'd keep.

Theatre

A month before the performance, Olivier announced he was moving to Schefferville. Olivier was playing Don Sancho, Chimène's rather timid lover. And he was doing a good job. I asked him a thousand questions until finally I found out things were no longer working out with his mother, who'd more or less kicked him out, so his only option was to go live with his father. He repeated several times that he was extremely sorry to have to drop out of the ensemble.

At first I was disappointed to lose such a good actor for the part. Then, realizing how torn he felt made me sad. I'd made the same decision not so long ago. To leave everything behind. And I understood his affectingly emotive expression. Like that of a child. I said, *Good luck*, and gave him a hug.

———

Still, we were only a few weeks from the date of the show, and I was disappointed. For a short while. Until, that afternoon, I saw my lifeline at the end of the hallway.

"Rodrigue!" I called out.

"Yes?"

"Rodrigue, listen, my darling Rodrigue. I need you—no, the ensemble needs you."

"What do you mean?" Intrigued, he approached.

"Did you know Olivier is moving to Schefferville?"

"No. When?"

"Soon, I think . . . We need you to play Don Sancho."

"What?" He took a step back. "I can't. I don't know the part."

"Yes, you do. I'm sure you can learn it."

"But Madame, who's going to be the prompter?"

"I don't know yet. I'll find someone. Please tell me you'll do it."

"Of course, Madame."

He flashed an enormous smile.

"Yes," he said. "I'll do it."

Olivier's departure had opened up unexpected doors. Very quickly, Rodrigue's innate talent came to the fore. He played the role so well, so precisely, and so naturally that his mere presence on the stage made the other actors more confident.

Exams

The grade eleven final exam in French essay writing was set for mid-May. The topic was freedom of expression. The preparatory material included texts on human rights, on the dictatorships of certain countries, hate speech, and basic definitions of freedom. Could teenagers in the full throes of their development have anything against freedom of expression? I didn't believe so. Still, I drew their attention to its limits and to the various paths a democracy can take. We thought about how our society was set up.

"You have to see democracy as a circle. That being said, democracy doesn't signify equality. It depends on the people brought into the circle. If everyone — women, men, the poor, the rich, right-wing or left, Innu and Quebeckers — have an equal place in the circle, then you can talk about a successful democracy. In your opinion, is this what we have in Canada? In Quebec? In Uashat? In Maliotenam?"

Some of the students gazed at the ceiling. Others peered at the windows, or my face. A sign that they were thinking. A hand went up.

"Yes, Patrick?"

"I think democracy is impossible."

"Why?"

"Well, just take the Innu and the Whites. You know they'll never be equal."

"I understand what you're trying to say, but can you give an example?"

"Well, my dad, for instance. When he says the territory has to be protected, and then Hydro-Québec builds a dam and cuts down the forests to make room for its poles. It's pretty obvious my dad is unable to fight back. Y'know, his words don't have the same impact."

We were slowly going off topic. I struggled to bring him back while holding on to his train of thought as he told his truths.

"So, for you, the equality of voices is fundamental to freedom of expression."

"Yeah. If we're in a free and egalitarian country, my dad should be heard when he talks about his hunting grounds. Even if that means the government or I don't know who else loses money."

"Of course. That's really interesting. Thanks, Patrick."

I looked around the classroom. "Anybody else?"

"Me, I think that even in Uashat there's injustice," said Maya.

"What do you mean?"

"Well, when you look at who the council is giving housing to, you see right away that it's the people who vote for them."

"That's one opinion. Can you explain?"

"My cousin, for instance. She's been waiting for a house for years. She has to rent a super expensive apartment in town, and she's got four kids."

"Yes, I see."

"Other people make one request and get a house right off the bat. It's so transparent."

There were mutterings in the class. Of both dissatisfaction and approbation. I could feel that we were getting into sensitive territory. Every social sphere in the community was affected by politics. Best to leave it there.

"So, if I'm hearing you right, all societies—whether ours here in Uashat, or in the province as a whole—have their inequalities. I find your ideas really pertinent. Now, the most important thing is to express those ideas in ways that convince your readers. With arguments and examples."

The students spent the rest of the period studying the texts in front of them. Meticulously, they highlighted parts, took notes, and underlined the passages that seemed most telling. There were nineteen graduating students, and every one of them was intent on doing the best they could to pass the test. I was sure of it.

The performance

From behind the curtain I could hear murmurs in the audience and children mewling. We'd set the date for the Friday between the prom and final exams. The troupe had sold tickets for ten dollars each to their families and friends. Two hundred and fifty in total. Which surprised me. A full house for the first play ever put on at the school. The gymnasium had been set up as a theatre, with dimmed lighting. A raised stage with black curtains. The actors were already in costume, made-up, serious, scripts in hand.

"Yammie," Patrick called. He was dressed all in black with his hat perched on one side of his head. "You have to come see what's happened to the set. A piece just fell over."

"Oh, no!"

I followed him on stage. One of the panels, painted with grey bricks that represented the royal palace, didn't want to stay in place.

"What do we do, Madame? Real sorry, Madame."

"Shit . . . we'll have to remove it . . . but then the set won't look like the court anymore."

"No worries," said Marcel, who'd designed most of it. "I'll hold it up."

"For the whole play?"

"Yes. No choice."

"Fine, that's what we'll do, then."

Marcel wanted everything to be just right.

I rejoined the students in the locker room that was serving as our green room. Clothes piled up everywhere. Tall mirrors. Shoes. A stimulating mess.

"All right. The time has come. I have something I want to tell you. The room is packed. All these people have come to watch you perform. So, go for it! Give it your best. Don't be afraid of making mistakes or of people laughing at you."

"Heh, Madame," Mikuan interjected. "You're scaring us, like we're going to be super awful."

"Not at all, Mikuan, not at all. If you only knew how proud I am of all of you." I looked at each one of them in turn. Tried to look reassuring. I could see they were looking to me for the power to launch themselves on stage. And, despite my trembling voice, I finished with an emphatic, "Right, off we go!" directing them toward the gymnasium with open arms.

Standing behind the curtain, stage left, I watched as the play unfolded. Partly moved, partly scared. The audience laughed when Caro, who'd replaced Rodrigue as prompter, spoke a line so loudly it could be heard in the entire hall. She adjusted her volume. I observed, astonished, as they confidently recited the lines they'd learned by heart. Astonished by their gestures and movements, conceived hundreds of years after the play was written and thousands of miles from where it was first performed. What sense was there in these alexandrines, declaimed by young Innu students dressed up as Spaniards? The ancient tragedy had come to join ours.

A woman's love, spurned.

Finally, I realized what I had demanded of them a few months earlier.

Dressed up as the governess, Mikuan moved downstage to comfort Chimène. Their dialogue was a short one evoking a mother's attachments. She was perfect.

Mikuan, my sweet friend. Thanks for being there from the very beginning, when I was full of doubt. You were my first confidante. You showed me kindness when I thought this place was hostile. We both know you won't be getting your diploma this year, despite your trying, despite your mother's courage. I want to tell you that sometimes life's like that. It's a struggle. And, when you fail, you have to struggle even harder. You hope to be a doctor. It's almost unimaginable at present. But walls were built to be broken down. And I know you know that.

The silence following Marc's tirade was striking. People holding their breath. A magical moment. A surge of love washed over me.

Dear Marc. You lost your mom, and though I don't understand everything, I do know you're suffering terribly. And yet, I'm convinced that you'll get over this suffering. That you'll continue to grow. Forgive me for not giving you a hug when you needed one. Believe me, it's not because I didn't want to, but because I was afraid—of everything that makes us unhappy. I thought I was strong. But I was fragile. And you're the one who showed me how not to flounder. You, and the bravery you've shown. The others, too. Go, Marc, go away as far and for as long a time as you want. And come back to see us now and then.

Myriam muffed a few of her lines, despite Caro's efforts to communicate them to her. Don Diego had already come on stage and started to declaim.

Myriam, did I tell you how wonderful you were today? Every day, actually. It's hard for me to come to terms with even half of what you've had to live through since your sister's suicide. But I want you to know what I've seen. Your head rise up again, your spirit, your power. I believe that a person who confronts challenges like yours so vigorously will overcome any further obstacles. I am loving your performance of Chimène tonight. Your cheeks red with happiness. You could be a television actress. And everyone would stand and applaud you. I have no idea what you want to do next. But I really do hope you'll do it. For your sake, for your son's.

For your sister's. Because a human is beautiful when she chooses life.

I saw Melina in the second row, sitting on the edge of her seat. Transfixed.

How it pleases me to see you here, Melina. So delicate, so beautiful. And you're not even aware. You have no idea how much talent is hidden in your hands. You push away the people who believe in you. Like a wounded bird. You were born to write. I've already told you. I'll tell you again next time our paths cross. Maybe one day you'll believe it. And on that day, I shall read every word, as I did the first time, passionately. And I will be proud, do you see, to have been your teacher. The world is waiting for you. Don't make it wait too long.

Rodrigue was more ardent than he'd ever been in any of the rehearsals. He was the one who literally transcended the audience. And it was he who allayed all my fears. He was the one who vindicated the importance of it all for me.

Dear Rodrigue. My rebel. Who would have thought it would end like this? You don't have that look anymore, the look of a guy who would yell at me. I can't prevent myself from believing that I contributed, in my own way, to this new person you're becoming. Steady, serious, committed. It's so gratifying. Maybe, at the end of the day, that's Manikanetish for you. What Little Marguerite wanted to pass on to us. She wanted to show us what teaching actually is. Raising other people's children. Extending a hand, loving them. And, most of all, wanting to see them grow. It took me time to understand that, Rodrigue, but now I do. Me too, I had some barriers to take down.

The ending won the audience's heart. They rose to their feet as soon as the curtain fell. They applauded and shouted bravos. I could hardly speak. Overcome with emotion. And happy. Three curtain calls. Full of smiles. The lights went up. Total joy.

Last class

"Madame, is it true you're not coming back next year?"

I'd not yet decided. Didn't have a clue. No. Though I was certain of one thing. That I'd be a mother in a few months. Of a little baby. And that my life would be changed forever. Would I come back in September and then abandon the students halfway through the term on maternity leave? Or would I go back to Quebec City and study literature? Or take a sabbatical year in my apartment in town and wait for my child to arrive?

"I don't know, Rodrigue. Truly."

"We were that bad?"

"No, quite the opposite, I've grown really attached to you. It's just that, in this instant, I have no idea what I'm going to do next year."

"Well, you'll have to stay, 'cause we want to do more theatre. But we would like to do a more modern play next time."

"Okay, I'll keep that in mind . . . and Rodrigue?"

"Yeah?"

"It was still fun to do *Le Cid*, wasn't it?"

"Sure, Madame."

He shrugged his shoulders, the way he always did when he couldn't find the words.

"Most of all, it was great that we had you for a teacher this year."

Then he turned on his heels and I watched him walk away. And told myself that I wanted the child I was soon to bring into the world, and raise, and love, to be a boy.

NAOMI FONTAINE is a member of the Innu Nation of Uashat and a graduate of the Université de Laval. Her first novel, *Kuessipan*, was made into a feature film that debuted at the Toronto International Film Festival in 2019. *Manikanetish* was a finalist for the Governor General's Literary Award and ICI-Radio Canada's Combat national des livres. Her third novel, *Shuni*, was also a finalist for the Governor General's Literary Award.

LUISE VON FLOTOW is a translator of French and German literature. Her novel translations include *La femme du stalinien, Une belle éducation,* and *L'hôtel aux quatre chemins* by France Théoret, and she also edited the essay collection *Translating Women: Different Voices and New Horizons.* She is a professor at the School of Translation and Interpretation at the University of Ottawa.

NEW
WEBSTER'S
DICTIONARY

edited by
R. F. PATTERSON, M.A., D.Litt.

1996 EDITION

Paradise
Press, Inc.

Plantation, Florida

W9-CTF-304

This book is not associated with, or published by, the original publishers of WEBSTER'S DICTIONARY or their successors.

Cover Design 1996 - Carol-Ann McDonald

Printed in U.S.A. All Rights Reserved.

Copyright © 1996
Paradise Press, Inc.

ISBN #1-884907-02-4
30464

A

a, the indefinite article, used before a consonant.

abbreviate, ab-brē'vi-āt, vt. To shorten.

abbreviation, ab-brē'vi-ā'shon, n. A shortening, contraction.

abdomen, ab-dō'men, n. The lower belly.

abduct, ab-dukt', vt. To entice or lead away wrongly.

aberrant, ab-e'rant, a. Wandering from; deviating from an established rule.

ability, a-bil'li-ti, n. Power to do anything; talent; skill; in pl. the powers of the mind.

abnegate, ab'nē-gāt, vt. To deny; to renounce.

aboard, a-bōrd', adv. or prep. On board, in a ship or vessel.

abode, a-bōd', n. Residence; habitation.

abolish, a-bol'ish, vt. To destroy; to abrogate.

abortion, a-bor'shon, n. A miscarriage.

abound, a-bound', vi. To be, or have in great plenty.

about, a-bout', prep. Around, near to; relating to; engaged in.—adv. Around; round; nearly; here and there.

above, a-buv', prep. To or in a higher place than; superior to more than; beyond, before.—adv. To or in a higher place; chiefly.

abrasion, ab-rā'zhon, n. A rubbing off; substance worn off by rubbing.

abreast, a-brest', adv. In a line side by side.

abridge, a-brij', vt. To shorten; to condense.

abroad, a-bröd', adv. At large; away from home; in a foreign country.

absent, ab'sent, a. Being away from; not present; wanting in attention.

absentee, ab-sen-tē', n. One who absents himself.

absolute, ab'sō-lūt, a. Unlimited; unconditional, certain, despotic.

absolve, ab-solv', vt. To free from as from guilt or punishment; acquit, pardon.

absorb, ab-sorb', vt. To drink in; to engross.

absorbent, ab-sorb'ent, a. Imbibing; swallowing.—n. That which absorbs.

absorption, ab-sorp'shon, n. Act or process of imbibing or swallowing up.

abstain, ab-stān', vi. To keep back from; to refrain; to forbear.

abundant, a-bun'dant, a. Abounding, plentiful, ample.

abuse, a-būz', vt. (abusing abused). To turn from the proper use; to ill-use; to deceive; to vilify; to violate.

abut, a-but', vi. (abutting, abutted). To border, to meet. (With upon.)

abyss, a-bis', n. A bottomless gulf; a deep pit or mass of waters, hell.

Acacia, a-kä'shi-a, n. A genus of ornamental plants, yielding catechu, gumarabic, etc.

academic, Academical, ak-a-dem'ik, ak-a-dem'ik-al, a. Belonging to an academy or university.

academy, a-kad'ē-mi, n. A seminary of arts or sciences; a society of persons for the cultivation of arts and sciences.

acaridan a-kar'i-dan, n. A mite tick, or allied animal.

accede, ak-sēd', vi. (acceding, acceded). To assent to; to comply with.

accelerate, ak-sel'le-rāt, vt. (accelerating, accelerated). To hasten; to quicken the speed of.

accent, ak 'sent, n. A tone or modulation of the voice; stress of the voice on a syllable or word; the mark which indicates this stress manner of speaking.

accent, ak-sent', vt. To express or note the accent of.

accept, ak-sept', vt. To receive, to admit; to promise to pay, by attaching one's signature.

acceptable, ak-sept'a-bl, a. That may be accepted; pleasing; gratifying.

access, ak'ses, n. Approach; admission; means of approach; increase.

accessible, ak-ses'i-bl, a. Easy of approach, affable.

accession, ak-se'shon, n. The act of acceding; augmentation; succession to a throne.

accessory, ak'ses-sō-ri, a. Additional, contributing to.—n. An accomplice, an adjunct.

acclamation, ak-kla-mā'shon, n. A shout of applause, assent, or approbation.

accolade, ak-kö-lād', n. A ceremony used in conferring knighthood, usually a blow on the shoulder with the flat of a sword.

accommodate, ak-kom'mō-dāt, vt. (accommodating, accommodated). To make suitable; to adjust, to furnish with.

accompaniment, ak-kum'pa-ni-ment, n. That which accompanies; the subordinate part or parts, in music.

accordion, ak-kord'i-on, n. A small melodious, keyed wind-instrument.

accost, ak-kost', *vt.* To speak to first; to address.

account, ak-kount ', *n.* A reckoning; a register of facts relating to money; narration; advantage end, importance.—*vt.* To reckon, to consider, to deem, to value.—*vi.* To give or render reasons; to explain (with *for*).

accountant, ak-kount'ant, *n.* One skilled or employed in accounts; one whose profession is to examine accounts.

accumulate, ak-ku'mū-lāt, *vt.* (accumulating, accumulated). To heap up; to amass.—*vi.* To increase.

accumulater ak-ku'mū-lāt-er, *n.* A kind of battery which stores electric energy.

accurate, ak'ku-rāt, *a.* Done with care; exact; without error.

accursed, ak-kērs'ed, *a.* Lying under a curse; doomed; wicked.

accusation, ak-kū-zā'shon, *n.* Act of accusing; impeachment, that of which one is accused.

accusative, ak-kūz'at-iv. *a.* or *n.* A case in grammar, in English the objective.

accuse ak-kūz', *vt.* (accusing, accused) To charge with a crime; to impeach, to censure.

accustom, ak-kus'tum, *vt.* To inure to a custom; to make familiar with by use.

ace, äs *n.* A unit, a single point on cards or dice; a distinguished airman, who has destroyed many enemy planes.

aching, āk'ing, *p.a.* Being in continued pain.—*n.* Pain.

achromatic, ak-rō-mat'ik, *a.* Free from color.

acoustic, a-kous'tik, *a.* Pertaining to the sense of hearing, or to the doctrine of sounds.

acoustics, a-kous'tiks, *n.* The science of sound.

acquaint, ak-kwānt', *vt.* To make to know; to make familiar; to inform.

acre, a'kèr, *n.* A quantity of land containing 4840 square yards.

acreage, a'kèr-āj, *n.* A number of acres in a piece of land.

acrid, ak'rid, *a.* Sharp; hot or biting to the taste, corroding, harsh.

acrimony, ak'ri-mo-ni, *n.* Sharpness; harshness; severity.

acrobat, ak'rō -bat, *n.* A rope-dancer; one who practices vaulting, tumbling, etc.

acrogen, ak'rōjen, *n.* A plant increasing by extension of the stem at the top.

Acropolis, a-krop'o-lis, *n.* The citadel of a Greek city, as of Athens.

across, a-kros', *prep.* or *adv.* From side to side; transversely; crosswise.

act, akt, *vi.* To be in action, to exert power; to conduct oneself.—*vt.* To do; to perform, as an assumed part; to counterfeit.—*n.* A deed power, or the effect of power, put forth; a state of reality; a part of a play; law, as an act of parliament.

actinia, ak-tin'i-a, *n.; pl.* **-iae.** A sea anemone.

actinism, ak'tin-izm, *n.* The chemical action of the sun's rays.

action, ak'shon, *n.* A deed; operation; a series of events; gesture; a suit or process; an engagement, battle.

active, ak'tiv, *a.* That acts or is in action; busy; quick; denoting action.

actor, aktèr *n.* One who acts; an active agent, a stage-player.

adapt, a-dapt', *vt.* To fit; to adjust; to suit.

add, ad, *vt.* To join to; to annex; to say further.

addendum, ad-den'dum, *n., pl.* **-da.** A thing to be added, an appendix.

additive, ad'it-iv, *a.* That is to be or may be added.

addle, ad'l, *a.* Rotten; barren.—*vt.* (addling, addled). To make corrupt or barren.

address, ad-dres', *vt.* To direct; to apply to by words or writing; to speak to; to apply (oneself) to write a name and destination on.—*n.* Verbal or written application; speech or discourse to a person; tact; courtship (generally in *plural);* direction of a letter.

adduce, ad-dūs', *vt.* (adducing, adduced). To bring forward; to cite.

adhibit, ad-hib'it, *vt.* To attach (one's signature).

adieu, a-dū', *interj.* Farewell.—*n.; pl.* **-us** or **-ux.** A farewell.

adit, ad'it, *n.* An approach; the horizontal opening into a mine.

adjacent, ad-jā'sent, *a.* Lying near adjoining; contiguous; neighboring.

adjective, ad'jek-tiv, *n.* A word used with a noun, to express some quality or circumstance.

adjoin, ad-join', *vt.* To join to.—*vi.* To lie or be next, to be contiguous.

adjourn. ad-jèrn', *vt.* To put off to a future day; to postpone.—*vi.* To leave off for a future meeting.

admeasure, ad-me'zhūr, *vt.* To ascertain the size or capacity of.

adminicle, ad-min'i-kl, *n.* Support; aid.

administer, ad-min'is-tèr, *vt.* To manage; to dispense; to distribute.

administration, ad-min'is-trā'shon, *n.* Management, executive part of a government.

admirable, ad'mi-ra-bl, *a.* Worthy of admiration; excellent.

admonish, ad-mon'ish, *vt.* To warn; to reprove solemnly or quietly; to exhort.

admonition, ad-mō-ni'shon, *n.* Gentle or solemn reproof, instruction; caution.

ado, a-dö', *n.* Stir; bustle; difficulty.

adobe, a-dö'be, *n.* A sun-dried brick.

adolescent, ad-ō -les'ent, *a.* Advancing to manhood.

adopt, a-dopt', *vt.* To take and treat as a child, giving a title to the rights of a child; to embrace.

Adorable, a-dō r'a-bl, *a.* Worthy to be adored.

Adoration, a-dōr'ā'shon, *n.* Worship paid to God; profound reverence.

adore, a-dō r', *vt.* (adoring, adored). To address in prayer; to worship with reverence and awe; to love intensely.

adorn, a-dōrn', *vt.* To deck with ornaments, to embellish, to beautify.

adrift, a-drift', *adv.* Floating at random; at the mercy of any impulse.

adroit, a-droit', *a.* Dexterous; skilful; ready.

adulation, ad-ū-lā'shon, *n.* Servile flattery; excessive praise.

adult, a-dult', *a.* Grown to maturity. —*n.* A person grown to manhood.

adultery, a-dul'tė-ri, *n.* Unfaithfulness to the marriage-bed.

Advent, ad'vent, *n.* Arrival, the coming of Christ; the four weeks before Christmas.

adventitious, ad-ven-ti'shi-us, *a.* Accidental; casual; accessory; foreign.

adventure, ad-ven'tūr, *n.* Hazardous enterprise; a bold undertaking—*vt.* To risk or hazard.—*vi.* To dare, to venture.

adventurous, ad-ven'tū r-us, *a.* Prone to incur hazard; daring; full of hazard.

adverb, ad'vėrb, *n.* A word which modifies a verb, adjective, or another adverb.

adversary, ad'vėr-sa-ri, *n.* An enemy; an antagonist.

adversative, ad-vėrs'at-iv, *a.* Noting or causing opposition.—*n.* A word denoting opposition.

adverse, ad'vėrs, *a.* Hostile; unprosperous.

adversity, ad-vėrs'i-ti, *n.* Misfortune, affliction, calamity, distress.

advise, ad-vīz', *vt.* (advising, advised). To counsel, to warn, to inform.—*vi.* To deliberate or consider.

advised, ad-vīzd', *p.a.* Cautious; done with advice.

advocate, ad'vō -kā t, *n.* One who pleads for another, an intercessor.—*vt.* (advocating, advocated). To plead in favor of; to vindicate.

adze, adz, *n.* A kind of axe, with the edge at right angles to the handle.

aegis, e'jis, *n.* A shield; protection.

Aeolian, e-o'li-an, *a.* Pertaining to Aeolus, the god of the winds; played upon by the wind.

aerate, a'er-at, *vt.* (aerating, aerated). To put air into; to combine
with carbonic acid.

aerie, e're, *n.* The nest of a bird of prey; a brood of such birds.

affair, af-far', *n.* That which is to do, or which is done; business.

affect, af-fekt', *vt.* To act upon; to move the feelings of; to aim at; to pretend.

affectedly, af-fekt'ed-li, *adv.* In an affected manner feignedly.

affecting, af-fekt'ing, *p.a.* Pathetic; tender; exciting.

affection, af fek'shon, *n.* The state of being affected; fondness, love.

affectionate, af-fek'shon-āt, *a.* Tender; loving; fond.

afferent, af'fė r-ent, *a.* Carrying to or inwards.

affiance, af-fī'ans, *n.* Faith pledged; marriage contract; reliance.—*vt.* (affiancing, affianced). To pledge one's faith to; to betroth.

affidavit, af-fi-dā'vit, *n.* A written declaration upon oath.

affiliate, af-fil'li-āt, *vt.* (affiliating, affiliated). To adopt, to assign to a father; to unite to a chief society or body.

affiliation, af-fil'li-ā'shon, *n.* Act of affiliating, association.

affinity, af-fin'i-ti, *n.* Relation by marriage; resemblance; chemical attraction.

affirm, af-fėrm', *vt.* To assert; to declare; to ratify.—*vi.* To declare solemnly.

affix, af-fiks', *vt.* To fasten to, to subjoin.—*n.* af'fiks. A syllable or letter added to a word.

afield a-fēld', *adv.* To or in the field.

afloat, a-flōt ', *adv.* or *a.* Floating; in circulation (as a rumor).

afoot, a-füt ', *adv.* On foot, in action.

after, äft'ėr, *a.* Later in time; subsequent.—*prep.* Later in time than; behind, according to; in imitation of.—*adv.* Later in time.

aftermath, äft'ė r-math, *n.* A second crop of grass in the same season, consequences, results.

afternoon, äft'ė r-nön, *n.* The part of the

day which follows noon.

age, āj, *n.* A period of time; an epoch; number of years during which a person has lived; decline of life; oldness; legal maturity.—*vi.* and *t.* (aging, aged). To grow or make old; to show signs of advancing age.

agency, ā-jen-si, *n.* Instrumentality; office or business of an agent.

agenda, a-jen'da, *n.pl.* Memoranda, business to be transacted at a meeting.

agent, ā'jent, *n.* One who acts; a deputy, an active cause or power.

Agglutinant, ag-glū'tin-ant, *n.* Any viscous or gluey substance.

aggrandize, ag'gran-dī z, *vt.* To make great; to magnify.

aggravate, ag'gra-vā t, *vt.* (aggravating, aggravated). To intensify: to exasperate.

aggression, ag-gre'shon, *n.* The first act of hostility, attack.

aggressor, ag gres'or, *n.* The person who commences hostilities.

aggrieve, ag-grēv', *vt.* To pain, oppress, or injure.

aghast, a-gast', *a.* or *adv.* Amazed; stupefied. Also *agast.*

agile, aj'il, *a.* Ready to act; nimble.

ago, a-go, *adv.* or *a.* Past; gone.

agony, ag'ō-ni, *n.* Extreme pain of body or mind; anguish; the pangs of death.

agrarian, a-grā'ri-an, *a.* Relating to lands.

agree, a-grē', *vi.* (agreeing, agreed). To be in concord, to correspond; to suit.

agreement, a-grē'ment, *n.* Harmony, conformity, stipulation.

agriculture, ag'ri-kul-tūr, *n.* The art or science of cultivating the ground.

AIDS, ā dz, *n.* Acquired Immune Deficiency Syndrome. A break down of the human body's immune system.

ail, āl, *vt.* To pain; to affect with uneasiness.—*vi.* To be in pain or trouble.

aim, ā m, *vi.* To point with a missive weapon; to intend; to endeavor.— *vt.* To level or direct as a firearm.— *n.* That which is aimed at, direction; purpose; drift.

air, ār, *n.* The fluid which we breathe; a light breeze, a tune; mien; *pl.* affected manner.—*vt.* To expose to the air; to ventilate; to dry.

airport, ār'pōrt, *n.* An area for landing airplanes, usually having customs houses, servicing facilities, etc.

air pump, ā r'pump, *n.* A machine for pumping the air out of a vessel.

air-shaft, ār'shaft, *n.* A passage for air into a mine

air-tight, ār'tīt, *a.* So tight or compact as not to let air pass.

airy, ā'ri, *a.* Open to the free air; high in air; light; thin; vain; gay.

aisle, īl, *n.* A wing or side of a church, a passage in a church.

ajar, a-jär', *adv.* Partly open, as a door.

akin, a-kin', *a.* Of kin; related to; partaking of the same properties.

alabaster, al'a-bas-tè r, *n.* A soft marblelike mineral.—*a.* Made of alabaster.

alacrity, a-lak'ri-ti, *n.* Liveliness; cheerful readiness, promptitude.

albumen, al-bū 'men, *n.* The white of an egg; a substance of the same kind found in animals and vegetables.

alburnum, al-bè r'num, *n.* Sapwood of a tree.

Alchemy, al'ke-mi, *n.* An obsolete science, aiming at changing metals into gold etc.

alcoholic, al-kō -hol'ik, *a.* Pertaining to alcohol.

alcoholism, al'kō -hol-izm, *n.* The condition of habitual drunkards.

alcove, al'kōv, *n.* A recess.

alga, al 'ga, *n.; pl.* **-gae,** A sea-weed.

Algebra, al'je-bra, *n.* The science of computing by symbols.

alias, ā 'li-as, *adv.* Otherwise. *n.; pl.* **–ses,** An assumed name.

alibi, ali-bī , *n.* The plea of a person who, charged with a crime, alleges that he was elsewhere when the crime was committed.

alien, ā l'yen, *a.* Foreign; estranged from.—*n.* A foreigner.

aliquot, al'i-kwot, *a.* A part of a number which divides the whole without remainder.

alive, a-līv', *a.* Living; lively; susceptible.

all, äl, *a.* Every part; every one.—*n.* The whole, everything.—*adv.* Wholly entirely.

Allah, ai'la, *n.* The Arabic name of God.

allay, al-lā, *vt.* To repress; to assuage.

allege, al-lej', *vt.* (alleging, alleged). To adduce; to assert; to plead in excuse.

alley, al 'i, *n.* A narrow walk or passage.

alliance, al-lī'ans, *n.* State of being allied; confederacy; league.

allied, al-līd', *p.a.* United by treaty.

allopathy, al-lop'a-thi, *n.* The ordinary mode of curing diseases, by using medicines which produce a condition contrary to that of the disease.

allot, al-lot' *vt.* (allotting, allotted). To give by lot; to apportion.

allotrophy, al-lot'ro-pi, *n.* The capability

of substances of existing in more than one form.

alloy, al-loi', *vt.* To mix with baser metals; to abate by mixture.—*n.* A baser metal mixed with a finer, a metallic compound.

allspice, äl-spīs, *n.* Pimento or Jamaica pepper, supposed to combine many different flavors.

allude, al-lūd', *vi.* (alluding, alluded). To refer to; to hint at.

allusion, al-lūzhon, *n.* The act of alluding, a hint, a reference.

almost, äl'most, *adv.* Nearly, well; nigh; for the greatest part.

alms, ämz, *n.pl.* A charitable gift.

aloft, a-loft', *adv.* In the sky; on high.

alone, a-lōn', *a.* Solitary.—*adv.* Separately.

along, a-long', *adv.* Lengthwise forward.—*prep.* By the side of, lengthwise.

aloof, a-löf', *adv.* At a distance; apart.

aloud, a-loud', *adv.* Loudly.

alpaca, al-pak'a, *n.* A Peruvian animal, with long, soft, and woolly hair; cloth made of its hair, or a similar cloth.

alpha, al'fa, *n.* The first letter in the Greek alphabet; the first or beginning.

alphabet, al'fa-bet, *n.* The letters of a language arranged in the customary order.

already, äl-red'i, *adv.* Before or by this time; even now.

also, äl'sō, *adv.* Likewise; in the same manner, further.

altar, äl'tèr, *n.* An elevated place on which sacrifices were offered, the communion table.

alternation al-tern-ā'shon *n.* Reciprocal succession, interchange.

alternative, al-té rn'at-iv, *n.* A choice of two things.

altitude, al'ti-tūd, *n.* Height; eminence; elevation.

alto, al'tō, *a.* High.—*n.* In *music,* contralto.

altruism, al'trö-izm, *n.* Devotion to others or to humanity, the opposite of selfishness.

alum, al'um, *n.* An astringent salt of great use in medicine and the arts.

aluminum, a-lu-mi-num, *n.* A very light metal of a silvery white color.

alumnus, a-lum'nus, *n.;* pl. **-ni.** A pupil, a graduate of a university.

amaranthine, am-a-ran'thin, *a.* Unfading.

amass, a-mas', *vt.* To form into a mass; to accumulate; to heap up.

amateur, am-a-tūr', *n.* A lover of any art or science, not a professor.

amatory, am'a-tō-ri, *a.* Relating to love;

causing love; amorous.

amaze, a-māz', *vt.* (amazing, amazed). To astonish; to bewilder.

Amazon, am'a-zon, *n.* A warlike or masculine woman; a virago.

ambassador, am-bas'sa-dor, *n.* A representative of a sovereign or state at a foreign court.

ambit, am'bit, *n.* Compass; scope.

ambition, am-bi'shon, *n.* Desire of preferment or power.

ambitious, am-bi'shus, *a.* Aspiring.

ambrosia, am-brōzhi-a, *n.* The imaginary food of the gods, which conferred immortality.

ambulance, am'bū-lans, *n.* An itinerant hospital; a wagon for the sick or wounded.

ambulatory, am'bū-lā-tō-ri *a.* Movable.— *n.* A part of a building to walk in.

amends, a-mendz', *n.pl.* Compensation; satisfaction; recompense.

amenity, a-men'i-ti, *n.* Pleasantness; agreeableness of situation.

American, a-me'ri-kan, *n.* A native of America.—*a.* Pertaining to America.

amiable, ämi-a-bl, *a.* Lovable; sweet-tempered.

amicable, am'ik-a-bl, *a.* Friendly; kind.

amnesty, am'nes-ti, *n.* A general pardon of offenses against a government.

amnion, am'ni-on, *n.* The innermost membrane surrounding the fetus of mammals, birds, and reptiles.

amoeba, a-mē'ba, *n.;* pl. **-bae.** A microscopic animal commonly found in fresh water.

among, amongst, a-mung', a-mungst', *prep.* Amidst; throughout; of the number.

amorous, am'or-us, *a.* Inclined to love; enamored; fond; relating to love.

amorphous, a-mor'fus, *a.* Without shape; of irregular shape.

amount, a-mount', *vi.* To mount up to, to result in.—*n.* The sum total effect or result.

ample, am'pl, *a.* Spacious; copious; rich.

amplification, am'pli-fī-kā'shon *n.* Act of amplifying; enlargement, discussion.

amplify, am'plif-ī, *vt.* (amplifying amplified). To enlarge; to treat copiously.— *vi.* To speak copiously; to be diffuse.

amplitude, am'pli-tūd, *n.* Ampleness, extent, abundance.

amply, am'pli, *adv.* Largely; liberally; fully; copiously.

amputate, am'pū-tāt, *vt.* (amputating, amputated). To cut off; as a limb.

amuck, a-muk', *n.* or *adv.* Only in phrase to *run amuck,* to rush about frantically, to attack all and sundry.

amulet, am'ū-let, *n.* A charm against evils or witchcraft.

amuse, a-mūz', *vt.* (amusing amused). To entertain; to beguile.

anagram, an'a-gram, *n.* A transposition of the letters of a name or sentence, by which a new word or sentence is formed.

anal, ā'nal, *a.* Pertaining to the anus.

analogous, an-al'og-us, *a.* Having analogy; corresponding.

analogy, an-al'o-ji, *n.* Likeness; similarity.

analyze, an'a-līz, *vt.* (analyzing, analyzed) To subject to analysis, to resolve into its elements.

ancestor, an'ses-tėr, *n.* A progenitor; forefather.

anchor, ang'kėr, *n.* An iron instrument for holding a ship at rest in water. *vt.* To hold fast by an anchor.—*vi.* To cast anchor.

anchorage, ang'kėr-āj, *n.* A place where a ship can anchor; duty on ships for anchoring.

anchorite, ang'kō-rīt, *n.* A hermit.

anchovy, an-chō'vi, *n.* A small fish of the herring kind, furnishing a fine sauce.

ancient, ān'shent, *a.* That happened in former times; old, antique.

ancillary, an'sil-la-ri, *a.* Pertaining to a maid-servant; subservient or subordinate.

aneroid, an'e-roid, *a.* Dispensing with fluid, said of a kind of barometer.

anesthetic, an-es-thet'ik, *a.* Producing insensibility.—*n.* A sub- stance, as chloroform, which produces insensibility.

aneurysm, an'ū-rizm, *n.* Dilatation of an artery.

angel, ān'jel, *n.* A divine messenger, a spirit, an old English gold coin worth ten shillings.

anger, ang'gėr, *n.* A violent passion, excited by real or supposed injury; resentment.—*vt.* To excite anger; to irritate.

angina, an-ji'na, *n.* Angina pectoris, a fatal disease characterized by paroxysms of intense pain and a feeling of constriction in the chest.

angle, ang'gl, *n.* The inclination of two lines which meet in a point but have different directions; a corner.

angle, ang'gl, *n.* A fishing-hook, or hook with line and rod.—*vi.* (angling, angled). To fish with an angle.

Anglican, ang'glik-an, *a.* Pertaining to England, or to the English Church.

angular, ang'gū-lē r, *a.* Having an angle, stiff.

anile, an'īl, *a.* Aged; imbecile.

aniline, an'i-lin, *n.* A substance obtained from coal-tar, used in dyeing.

animadvert, an'i-mad-vėr", *vi.* To criticize; to censure (with *upon*).

animal, an'i-mal, *n.* A living being having sensation and voluntary motion; a quadruped.—*a.* Belonging to animals; gross.

animus, an'i-mus, *n.* Intention; hostile spirit.

anise, an'is, *n.* An aromatic plant, the seeds of which are used in making cordials.

annals, an'nalz, *n.pl.* A record of events under the years in which they happened.

anneal, an'nēl', *vt.* To temper glass or metals by heat, to fix colors laid on glass.

annelid, an'ne-lid, *n.* An invertebrate animal whose body is formed of numerous small rings, as the worm, leech, etc.

annex, an-neks', *vt.* To unite at the end; to subjoin; to take possession of.

annihilate, an-nī'hil-āt, *vt.* (annihilating, annihilated). To reduce to nothing; to destroy the existence of

anniversary, an-ni-vė rs'a-rī, *n.* A day on which some event is annually celebrated.

annotate, an'nō-tāt, *vt.* (annotating, annotated). To write notes upon.

annular, an'nu-ler, *a.* Having the form of a ring; pertaining to a ring.

annulose, an'nū-lōs, *a.* Having a body composed of rings; applied to annelids.

annunciation, an-nun'si-ā "shon *n.* The angel's salutation to the Virgin Mary, and its anniversary the 25th of March.

anode, an'ō d, *n.* The positive pole of a voltaic current.

anoint, a-noint', *vt.* To rub over with oil, to consecrate by unction.

anomaly, a-nom'a-li, *n.* Irregularity; deviation from common rule.

anonymous, a-non'im-us, *a.* Name-less; without the real name of the author.

another, an-uTH 'ėr, *a.* Not the same different, any other.

answer, an'sėr, *vt.* To reply to; to satisfy; to suit—*vi.* To reply; to be accountable, to succeed.—*n.* A reply, a solution.

antecedent, an-tē-sē'dent, *a.* Going before, prior.—*n.* That which goes before, the noun to which a relative refers; *pl.* a man's previous history, etc.

antechamber, an'tē -chā m-bė r, *n.* An

apartment leading into a chief apartment.

antedate, an'tē-dā t, *n*. Prior date.—*vt*. To date before the true time.

anthem, an'them, n. A sacred song sung in alternate parts; a piece of Scripture set to music.

anthology, an-thol'o-ji, *n*. A collection of poems.

anthracite, an'thra-sīt, *n*. A hard compact coal which burns almost without flame.

anthropoid, an'thrō-poid, *a*. Resembling man applied to the higher apes.

Anthropology, an-thrō -pol'o-ji, *n*. The science of man and mankind the study of the physical and mental constitution of man.

antidote, an'ti-dōt, *n*. A remedy for poison or any evil.

antinomian, an-ti-nō 'mi-an, *n*. One who opposes the moral law.

antipathy, an-tip'a-thi, *n*. Instinctive aversion; dislike; opposition.

antiphrasis, an-tif'ra-sis, *n*. The use of words in a sense opposite to the proper one.

antipodes, an-tip'o-dē z, *n.pl*. Those who live on opposite sides of the globe; the opposite side of the globe.

antipyrin, an-ti-pī'rin, *n*. A drug used to reduce fever and relieve pain.

antitype, an'ti-tīp, *n*. That which is shadowed out by a type or emblem.

antler, ant'lėr, *n*. A branch of a stag's horn.

antonym, ant'ō-nim, *n*. A word of directly contrary signification to another the opposite of a synonym.

anus, ā'nus *n*. The opening of the body by which excrement is expelled.

anvil, an'vil, *n*. An iron block on which smiths hammer and shape their work.

apathy, ap 'a-thi, *n*. Want of feeling; insensibility, Indifference.

ape, ā p, *n*. A monkey; an imitator.— *vt*. (aping, aped). To imitate servilely, to mimic.

apex, ā 'peks, *n*.; pl. **-exes** and **-ices.** The summit of anything.

aphorism, af-or-izm, *n*. A precept expressed in few words; a maxim.

apiary, ā'pi-a-ri, *n*. A place where bees are kept.

apiece, a-pēs', *adv*. In a separate share; to each; noting the share of each.

Apocalypse, a-pok'a-lips, *n*. Revelation; the last book of the New Testament.

apology, a-pol'ō -ji, *n*. That which is said in defense; vindication; excuse.

apophthegm, apothegm, ap'o-them, *n*. A

terse pointed saying .

apoplexy, ap'ō-plek'si, *n*. A sudden privation of sense and voluntary motion.

apostasy, a-pos'ta-si, *n*. departure from one's faith; desertion of a party.

apostrophe, a-pos'tro-fē, *n*. An addressing of the absent or the dead as if present; a mark (') indicating contraction of a word, or the possessive case.

Apothecary, a-poth'e-ka-ri, *n*. One who prepares and sells drugs or medicines.

apotheosis, ap-o-thē'ō -sis or -thē-ō' sis, *n*. A deification; a placing among the gods.

appal, ap-päl', *vt*. (appalling, appalled). To depress with fear; to dismay.

apparel, ap-pa'rel, *n*. Equipment; clothing. *vt*. (apparelling, apparelled). To dress; to array.

apparent, ap-pa'rent, *a*. That may be seen; evident; seeming, not real.

apparition, ap-pa-ri'shon, *n*. An appearance; a specter; a ghost or phantom.

appear, ap-pē r', *vi*. To be or become visible; to seem.

appease, ap-pē z', *vt*. (appeasing, appeased). To pacify; to tranquilize.

appetite, ap'pē-tīt, *n*. A desire or relish for food or other sensual gratifications.

apple, ap'l, *n*. The fruit of the apple-tree; the pupil of the eye.

appliance, ap-plī'ans, *n*. Act of applying; thing applied; article of equipment.

applicable, ap'pli-ka-bl, *a*. That may be applied, suitable.

appraise, ap-prā z', *vt*. (appraising, appraised). To fix or set a price on; to estimate.

appreciate, ap-prēshi-āt, *vt*. (appreciating, appreciated). To value; to estimate justly.

apprehend, ap-prē-hend', *vt*. To take hold of; to arrest, to conceive; to fear.—*vi*. To think; to imagine.

appropriate, ap-prōpri-āt, *vt*. (appropriating, appropriated). To take to oneself as one s own; to set apart for.—*a*. Set apart for a particular use or person; suitable; adapted.

appropriateness, ap-prō'pri-āt-nes, *n*. Peculiar fitness.

approval, ap-prōv'al, *n*. Approbation.

approve, ap-prōv', *vt*. (approving approved). To deem good; to like, to sanction.—*vi*. To feel or express approbation (with *of*).

approximate, ap-prok'si-māt, *a*. Near, approaching.—*vt*. (approximating, approximated). To bring near.—*vi*. To come near; to approach.

aquarium, a-kwā'ri-um, *n.*; pl. **-iums or -la.** A vessel or tank for aquatic plants and animals; a collection of such vessels.

aquatic, a-kwat'ik, *a.* Living or growing in water.—*n.* A plant which grows in water; *pl.* sports or exercises in water.

aqueduct, ak 'wē-dukt, *n.* A conduit made for conveying water.

aqueous a'kwē-us, *a.* Watery.

aquiline, ak'wil-ī n, *a.* Belonging to the eagle; hooked like the beak of an eagle.

Arab, a'rab, *n.* A native of Arabia; street urchin, an Arabian horse.

arbiter, är'bit-èr, *n.* A person appointed by parties in controversy to decide their differences; an umpire.

arbitrate, är'bi-trāt, *vi.* (arbitrating, arbitrated). To act as an arbiter; to decide.

arbor, är'bèr, *n.* A bower; a shelter in a garden, formed of trees, etc.

arboreous, är-bō 'rē -us, *a.* Belonging to trees.

arboretum, är-bo-rē'tum, *n.* A place where trees are cultivated for scientific purposes.

arbutus, är'bu-tūs, *n.* An evergreen shrub, with berries like the strawberry.

arc, ärk, *n.* A part of a circle or curve.

arch, ärch, *a.* Chief; cunning; sly; roguish.

arch, ärch, *n.* A concave structure supported by its own curve, a vault.—*vt.* To cover with an arch; to form with a curve.

archaic, är-kā 'ik, *a.* Antiquated; obsolete.

archaism, är'kā-izm, *n.* Obsolete word or expression.

Archangel, ärk-ā n'jel, *n.* An angel of the highest order.

Archeology, är-kē-ol'o-ji, *n.* The science of antiquities; knowledge of ancient art.

Archipelago, är-ki-pel'a-gō, *n.* The Aegean Sea; a sea abounding in small islands.

architect, är'ki-tekt, *n.* One who plans buildings, etc., a contriver.

architecture, är'ki-tek-tū r, *n.* The art or science of building; structure.

ardor, är'dèr, *n.* Warmth; fervency; eagerness.

arduous, är'du-us, *a.* Difficult; laborious.

are, är, The plural pres. indic. of the verb to be.

area, a'rē-a, *n.* Any open surface; superficial contents; any enclosed space.

argue, är'gū *vi.* (arguing, argued). To offer reasons; to dispute.—*vt.* To show reasons for, to discuss.

argument, är'gūment, *n.* A reason offered,

a plea, subject of a discourse; heads of contents; controversy.

Argus, är'gus, *n.* A fabulous being with a hundred eyes; a watchful person.

Arian, ā'ri-an, *a.* Pertaining to Arius, who denied the divinity of Christ.—*n.* One who adheres to the doctrines of Arius.

arid, a'rid, *a.* Dry; dried; parched.

Aries, ā'ri-ēz, *n.* The Ram, the first of the twelve signs of the zodiac.

aristocracy, a-ris-tok'ra-si, *n.* Government by the nobility; the nobility.

aristocrat a'ris-to-krat, *n.* A noble one who favors aristocracy.

Arithmetic, a-rith'met-ik, *n.* The science of numbering; the art of computation.

ark, ärk, *n.* A chest; a large floating vessel.

armadillo, är-ma-dil'lō, *n.* A quadruped of the southwestern U.S. with a hard bony shell.

armament, ärm'a-ment, *n.* A force armed for war; war-munitions of a ship.

armory, ärm 'e-ri, *n.* A repository of arms.

armpit, ärm'pit, *n.* The hollow place under the shoulder.

army, är'mi, *n.* A body of men armed for war; a great number.

aroma, a-rō 'ma, *n.* Perfume, the fragrant principle in plants, etc.

aromatic, a-rō -mat'ik, *a.* Fragrant; spicy.—*n.* A fragrant plant or drug.

around, a-round', *prep.* About; on all sides of; encircling.—*adv.* On every side.

arrest, a-rest', *vt.* To stop; to apprehend.—*n.* A seizure by warrant; stoppage.

arrive, a-rīv', *vi.* (arriving, arrived). To come, to reach, to attain.

arson, är'son, *n.* The malicious setting on fire of a house, etc.

art, ärt, *n.* Practical skill; a system of rules for certain actions; cunning; profession of a painter, etc.

artery, är'tè-ri, *n.* A tube which conveys blood from the heart.

artful, ärt'ful, *a.* Full of art; skillful; crafty.

arthritis, är-thrī 'tis, *n.* Gout.

article, är'ti-kl, *n.* A separate item; stipulation, a particular commodity; a part of speech used before nouns, as *the.*—*vt.* To bind by articles.—*vi.* To stipulate.

articulate, är-tik'ū-lāt, *a.* Distinct; clear.—*vi.* To utter distinct sound syllables, or words.—*vt.* To speak distinctly.

artifice, ärt'i-fis, *n.* An artful device; fraud; stratagem.

as, az, *adv.* and *conj.* Like; even; equally;

while; since; for example.

asbestos, as-bes'tos, *n*. A mineral fibrous substance which is incombustible.

ascend, as-send', *vi*. To rise; to go backward in order of time.—*vt*. To move upward upon; to climb.

aseptic, a-sep'tik, *a*. Not liable to putrefy.

ash, ash, *n*. A well-known timber tree.

ashamed, a-shāmd', *a*. Affected by shame.

ashes, ash'ez, *n.pl*. The dust produced by combustion; the remains of a dead body.

ashore, a-shōr', *adv*. or *pred.a*. On shore.

askance, askant, a-skans', a-skant', *adv*. Awry, obliquely.

aslant, a-slant'. *Pred.a*. or *adv*. On slant; obliquely; not perpendicular.

asleep, a-slēp', *pred.a*. or *adv*. Sleeping, at rest.

aslope, a-slōp', *pred.a*. or *adv*. On slope; obliquely.

asp, asp, *n*. A small venomous serpent of Egypt.

asparagus, as-pa'ra-gus, *n*. A well-known esculent plant.

aspect, as'pekt, *n*. Appearance; situation.

Aspen, asp'en, *n*. A species of the Poplar.

asperse as-pèrs', *vt*. (aspersing, aspersed). To calumniate; to slander.

asphalt, as-falt', *n*. A bituminous, hard substance, used for pavement, etc.

aspirant, as-pî'r'ant, n. A candidate.

asquint, a-skwint', *adv*. Out of the corner or angle of the eye; obliquely.

ass, as, *n*. A well-known animal akin to the horse; a dolt.

assail, as-sāl', *vt*. To attack; to assault.

assemble, as-sem'bl, *vt*. (assembling, assembled). To bring together.—*vi*. To come together.

assembly, as-sem'bli, *n*. An assemblage; a convocation.

assent, as-sent', *n*. Act of agreeing to anything, consent.—*vi*. To agree; to yield.

assert, as-sèrt', *vt*. To affirm; to maintain, to vindicate.

assiduous, as-sid'ū -us, *a*. Constantly diligent.

assign, as-sīn', *vt*. To designate, to allot; to make over to another.—*n*. A person to whom property or any right may be or is transferred.

assignment, as-sīn'ment, *n*. Act of assigning; thing assigned; a writ of transfer.

assimilate, as-sim'il-āt, *vt*. (assimilating, assimilated). To make like to; to digest.—*vi*. To become similar or of the same substance.

assist, as-sist', *vt*. To help.—*vi*. To lend help, to contribute.

assistance, as-sist'ans, *n*. Help aid.

assuage, as-swā j', *vt*. (assuaging, assuaged). To allay, to calm.—*vi*. To abate or subside.

assume, as-sūm', *vt*. (assuming, assumed). To take for granted, to usurp.—*vi*. To claim more than is due; to be arrogant.

assurance, a-shör'ans, *n*. Act of assuring, secure confidence, impudence; positive declaration; insurance.

assure, a-shör', *vt*. (assuring, assured) To make sure; to confirm; to insure.

astern, a-stè rn', *adv*. In or at the hinder part of a ship.

asteroid, as'tèr-oid, *n*. A small planet.

asthma, as'ma or as'thma, *n*. A disorder of respiration, characterized by difficulty of breathing, cough, and expectoration.

astonish, as-ton'ish, *vt*. To surprise; to astound.

astound, as-tound', *vt*. To astonish; to stun; to strike dumb with amazement.

Astrology, as-trol'o-ji, *n*. The pretended art of foretelling future events from the stars.

Astronomy, as-tron'o-mi, *n*. The science of the heavenly bodies.

astute, as-tūt', *a*. Shrewd; crafty.

asunder, a-sun'dèr, *adv*. or *pred.a*. Apart; into parts; in a divided state.

at, at, *prep*. Denoting presence or nearness; in a state of; employed in, on, or with; with direction towards.

athlete, ath-lēt', *n*. One skilled in exercises of agility or strength.

athletics, ath-let'iks, *n.pl*. Athletic exercises.

Atlantean, at-lan-tē'an, *a*. Gigantic.

Atlantic, at-lan'tik, *a*. Pertaining to the ocean between Europe, Africa, and America.—*n*. This ocean.

atlas, at'las, *n*. A collection of maps.

atmosphere, at'mos-fēr, *n*. The mass of gas around the earth; air pervading influence.

atom, a'tom, *n*. A minute particle of matter; anything extremely small.

atone, a-tōn', *vi*. (atoning, atoned). To make satisfaction.—*vt*. To expiate.

attache, at-ta-shā', *n*. One attached to the suite of an ambassador. **Attache case**, *n*. A small oblong case of leather or fiber, for carrying documents, books, etc.

attack, at-tak', *vt*. To assault; to assail.— *n*. An assault; seizure by a disease.

attain, at-tān', *vi*. To come or arrive. —*vt*. To reach; to gain; to obtain.

attention, at-ten'shon, *n*. Act of attending,

heed; courtesy.

attentive, at-tent'iv, *a.* Heedful.

attenuate, at-ten'ū-āt, *vt.* (attenuating, attenuated). To make slender or thin (as liquids).—*vi.* To diminish.

attest, at-test', *vt.* To bear witness to; to certify; to call to witness.

attestation, at-test-ā'shon, *n.* Testimony.

attic, at'tik, *a.* Pertaining to Attica or to Athens; pure; elegant in style or language.—*n.* The dialect of Attica or Athens; the uppermost story of a building; garret.

attire, at-tī r', *vt.* (attiring, attired) To dress; to array.—*n.* Dress.

attitude, at'ti-tūd, *n.* Posture.

attorney, at-tėr'ni, *n.* One who acts in place of another; one who practices in law-courts.

attractive, at-trakt'iv, *a.* Having the power of attracting; enticing.

attrition, at-tri 'shon, *n.* Act of wearing, or state of being worn, by rubbing.

audit, ä'dit, *n.* An official examination of accounts.—*vt.* To examine and adjust, as accounts.

auditory, ä'di-tō-ri, *a.* Pertaining to the sense or organs of hearing.— *n.* An audience; an auditorium.

auger, ä'gėr, *n.* An instrument for boring holes.

August, ä'gust, *n.* The eighth month of the year.

auk, äk, *n.* A swimming bird found in the British seas, with very short wings.

aunt, änt, *n.* The sister of one's father or mother.

aureate, ä-rē'āt, *a.* Golden.

aurelia, ä-rē 'li-a, *n.* The chrysalis of an insect.

aureola, aureole, ä-rē 'ō -la, ä'rē -ō l *n.* An illumination represented as surrounding a holy person, as Christ, a halo.

Aurora Borealis, ä-rō'ra bō-rē-a'lis *n.* The northern lights or streamers.—**Aurora Australis,** a similar phenomenon in the S. hemisphere.

auspice, ä'spis, *n.* Augury from birds; protection; influence.

auspicious, ä-spi'shus, *a.* Fortunate; propitious.

austere, ä-ster', *a.* Rigid; sour; stern; severe.

autocracy, ätok'ra-si, *n.* Absolute government by one man.

autograph, ä'tō-graf, *n.* A person's own handwriting; signature.

automatic, ä-tō-mat'ik.—*a.* Self-acting; moving spontaneously.— *n.* A pistol

which is reloaded by force of the recoil.

automaton, ä-tōm'ä-ton, *n;* pl. **-ta.** A self-moving machine, or one which moves by invisible machinery.

automobile, ä'tō-mo-bēl'', *n.* A motor-car or similar vehicle.

autonomy, ä-ton'o-mi, *n.* The power or right of self-government.

autopsy, ä'top-si, *n.* Personal observation, post-mortem examination.

Autumn, ä'tum, *n.* The third season of the year, between summer and winter.

avail, a-vāl', *vt.* To profit; to promote. —*vi.* To be of use; to answer the purpose.—*n.* Advantage, use.

avalanche, av'a-lansh, *n.* A large body of snow or ice sliding down a mountain.

avarice, av'a-ris, *n.* Covetousness.

average, av'ėr-ā j, *n.* Medium; mean proportion.—*a.* Medial, containing a mean proportion.—*vt.* To find the mean of.— *vi.* To form a mean.

avidity, a-vid'i-ti, *n.* Eager desire; greediness; strong appetite.

avocation, av-ēkā'shon, *n.* Business; occupation.

avoid, a-void', *vt.* To shun; to evade; to make void.

avow, a-vou', *vt.* To declare with confidence, to confess frankly.

await, a-wāt', *vt.* To wait for; to expect, to be in store for.

award, a-wärd', *vt.* To adjudge.—*vi.* To make an award.—*n.* A judgment; decision of arbitrators.

aware, a-wā r', *a.* Informed; conscious.

away, a-wā ', *adv.* Absent; at a distance; in motion from; by degrees in continuance.—*exclam.* Begone!

awe, ä, *n.* Fear; fear mingled with reverence.—*vt.* (awing, awed). To strike with fear and reverence.

awhile, a-whīl ', *adv.* For some time.

awkward, ak'wėrd, *a.* Inexpert; inelegant.

awkwardly, ak'wėrd-li, *adv.* In a bungling manner, inelegantly.

awn, än, *n.* The beard of corn or grass.

awning, än'ing, *n.* A cover of canvas, etc.; to shelter from the sun or wind.

awry, arī, *pred.a.* or *adv.* Twisted toward one side; distorted; asquint.

axe, aks, *n.* An instrument for hewing and chopping.

axilla, aks-il'la, *n.* The arm-pit.

axiom, aks'i-om, *n.* A self-evident truth.

azoic, a-zō'ik, *a.* Destitute of organic life.

azure, ä'zhūr, *a.* Sky-colored.—*n.* The fine blue color of the sky; the sky.

B

Baccarat, bak-ka-rä, *n.* A game of cards played by any number and a banker.
Bacchanal, bak'ka-nal, *n.* A votary of Bacchus; a revel.— *a.* Characterized by intemperate drinking.
bachelor, bach'el-èr, *n.* An unmarried man; one who has taken the university degree below that of Master or Doctor.
bacillus, ba-sil'lus, *n.*- *pl.* **-illi.** A microscopic organism which causes disease.
backbite, bak'bīt, *vt.* To speak evil of secretly.
backbone, bak'bōn, *n.* The spine; strength.
bacon, bā'kn, n. Swine's flesh cured and dried.
Bacteriology, bak-tē'ri-ol''o-ji, *n.* The doctrine or study of bacteria.
bacterium, bak-tē'ri-um, *n.; pl.* **-ia.** A disease germ.
bad, bad, *a.* Not good; wicked; immoral; injurious; incompetent.
badge, baj, *n.* A mark or cognizance worn.
badger, baj'èr, *n.* A burrowing quadruped, nocturnal in habits.— *vt.* To worry; to pester.
bagnio, ban'yō, *n.* A bath; brothel; prison.
bagpipe, bag'pīp, *n.* A musical wind-instrument.
bail, bā l, *vt.* To liberate from custody on security for reappearance, to free (a boat) from water; to bale.— *n.* Security given for release; the person who gives such security.
bailiff, bā 'lif, *n.* A subordinate civil officer, a steward.
bailiwick, bā'li-wik, *n.* The extent or limit of a bailiffs jurisdiction.
balcony, bal'ko-ni, *n.* A platform projecting from a window.
bald, bäld, *a.* Wanting hair; unadorned; bare; paltry.
bale, bā l, *n.* A bundle or package of goods.— *vt.* (baling, baled). To make up in a bale; to free from water; to bail. **Bale out,** *vi.* To leave aircraft by parachute.
baleful, bāl'fül, *a.* Calamitous, deadly.
balk, bäk, *n.* A bridge of land left unploughed; a great beam; a barrier; a disappointment.— *vt.* To baffle; to disappoint.
ball, bäl, *n.* A round body, a globe; a bullet, an entertainment of dancing.— *vi.* To form, as snow, into balls, as on horses' hoofs.
ballad, bal'lad, *n.* A short narrative poem; a popular song.
ballot, bal'lot, *n.* A ball, paper, etc., used for voting in private; the system of voting by such means.— *vi.* To vote by ballot.
balm, bäm, *n.* Balsam; that which heals or soothes, the name of several aromatic plants.— *vt.* To anoint with balm, to soothe.
balsam, bäl'sam, *n.* An oily, aromatic substance got from trees; a soothing ointment.
band, band, *n.* That which binds, a bond; a fillet; a company; a body of musicians.— *vt.* To bind together, to unite in a troop or confederacy.— *vi.* To unite in a band.
bandage, band'āj, *n.* A band; a cloth for a wound, etc.— *vt.* (bandaging, bandaged). To bind with a bandage.
bandbox, band'boks, *n.* A slight box for caps, bonnets, etc.
bandit, ban'dit, *n.; pl.* **-itti, -its.** An outlaw, a robber, a highwayman.
bandolier, ban-dō-lēr', *n.* A shoulder-belt for carrying cartridges.
bank, bangk, *n.* Ground rising from the side of a river, lake, etc.; any heap piled up; a bench of rowers. place where money is deposited; a banking company.— *vt.* To fortify with a bank; to deposit in a bank.
bankrupt, bangk'rupt, *n.* One who cannot pay his debts.— *a.* Unable to pay debts.
banner, ban'nè r, *n.* A flag bearing a device or national emblem; a standard.
banquet, bang'kwet, *n.* A feast; a sumptuous entertainment.— *vt.* To treat with a feast.— *vi.* To feast.
banshee, ban'shē, *n.* An Irish fairy believed to attach herself to a house or family.
bantam, ban'tam, *n.* A small breed of domestic fowl with feathered shanks.
banter, ban'tèr, *vt.* To attack with jocularity; to rally.— *n.* Raillery; pleasantry.
barb, bärb, *n.* The points which stand backward in an arrow hook, etc.; a Barbary horse.— *vt.* To furnish with barbs or points.
barbarian, bär-ba'ri-an, *a.* Belonging to savages; uncivilized.— *n.* A savage.
barbarous, bär'bär-us, *a.* In a state of barbarism; cruel; inhuman.
barbecue, bär-be-kū, *n.* A hog, etc. roasted whole; a feast in the open air.— *vt.* To dress and roast whole.
barber, bär'bèr, *n.* One who shaves beards and dresses hair.

barge, bärj, *n.* A boat of pleasure or state; a flat-bottomed boat of burden.

baritone, ba'ri-tōn, *a.* Having a voice ranging between tenor and bass.—*n.* A male voice between tenor and bass.

bark, bärk, *n.* The outer rind of a tree, a barque, the noise made by a dog, wolf, etc.—*vt.* To strip bark off; to treat with bark; to make the cry of dogs, etc.

barley, bär'li, *n.* A species of grain used especially for making malt.

barmaid, bär'mād, *n.* A woman who tends a bar where liquors are sold.

barn, bärn, *n.* A building for grain, hay, etc.

barnacle, bär'na-kl, *n.* A shell-fish, often found on ships' bottoms, a species of goose.

barren, ba'ren, *a.* Sterile; unfruitful; unsuggestive.

barricade, ba-ri-kad', *n.* A temporary fortification to obstruct an enemy; a barrier.—*vt.* To obstruct; to bar.

barrier, ba'ri-ėr, *n.* Fence; obstruction.

barrister, ba'ris-tē r, *n.* A counselor at law; a lawyer whose profession is to speak in court on behalf of clients.

barrow, ba'rō, *n.* A small hand or wheel carriage; a sepulchral mound.

barter, bär'tėr, *vi.* To traffic by exchange.—*vt.* To exchange in commerce.—*n.* Traffic by exchange.

basalt, ba-zält', *n.* A dark volcanic rock, often found in columnar form.

bascule, bas'kūl, *n.* An arrangement in bridges by which one part balances another.

basilisk, baz'il-isk, *n.* A fabulous serpent, lizard, or cockatrice; a genus of crested lizards; an old kind of cannon.

basin, bā'sn, *n.* A broad circular dish, a reservoir, a clock; tract of country drained by a river.

basis, bās'is, *n.; pl.* -ses. A base; foundation; groundwork.

bask, bask, *vt.* To lie in warmth, or in the sun, to enjoy ease and prosperity.—*vt.* To warm by exposure to heat.

basket, bas'ket, *n.* A domestic vessel made of twigs, etc.- the contents of a basket.—*vt.* To put in a basket.

bass, bäs, *n.* The American linden a mat made of bast; a fish allied to the perch.

bass, bā s, *n.* The lowest part in musical harmony; the lowest male voice.

bastion, bas'ti-on, *n.* A large mass of earth or masonry standing out from a rampart.

bat, bat, *n.* A flying mammal, like a mouse; a heavy stick; a club used to strike the ball in cricket, etc.— vi. (batting, batted). To play with a bat.

batch, bach, *n.* Quantity of bread baked at one time; a quantity.

bath, bäth, *n.* Place to bathe in; immersion in water, etc.; a Jewish measure.

bathe, bā TH, *vt.* (bathing, bathed). To immerse in water, etc.—*vi.* To take a bath.

battle, bat'1, *n.* Encounter of two armies, a combat.—vi. (battling, battled). To contend in fight.

be, bē, *vi. substantive* (being, been; pres. am, art, is, are; pret. was, wast or wert, were). To exist; to become, to remain.

beach, bēch, *n.* The shore of the sea.—*vt. To* run (a vessel) on a beach.

beacon, bē'kn, *n.* A light to direct seamen, a signal of danger.—*vt.* To afford light, as a beacon; to light up.

beaker, bēk'ėr, *n.* A large drinking cup.

beam, bēm, *n.* A main timber in a building. Part of a balance which sustains the scales; pole of a carriage; a ray of light.—*vt.* to send forth, as beams: to emit.—*vi.* To shine.

bean, bēn, *n.* A name of several kinds of pulse.

bear, bär, *n.* A large carnivorous plantigrade quadruped; one of two constellations, the Greater and Lesser; an uncouth person; one who tries to bring down the price of stock.

beard, bē rd, *n.* The hair on the chin, etc.; the awn of corn.—vt. To defy to the face.

beast, bēst, *n.* Any four-footed animal; a brutal man.

beatify, bē-at'i-fi, *vt.* (beatifying, beatified). To make happy; to declare a person blessed.

beating, bēt'ing, *n.* Act of striking; chastisement by blows; a conquering; defeat.

Beatitude, bē-at'i-tūd, *n.* Blessedness bliss, one of the declarations of blessedness to particular virtues made by Christ.

beauty, bū'ti, *n.* Loveliness; elegance; grace a beautiful woman.

because, bē-käz', By cause; on this account that.

bed, bed, *n.* Something to sleep or rest on, the channel of a river, place where anything is deposited; a layer, a stratum.—*vt.* (bedding, bedded). To lay in a bed; to sow; to stratify.—*vi.* To go to bed.

Bedouin, bed'ö-in, *n.* A nomadic Arab living in tents in Arabia, Syria, Egypt, etc.

bedraggle, bē-drag'l, *vt.* To soil by drawing along on mud.

bedrid, bedridden, bed'rid, bed' rid-n, *a.* Confined to bed by age or infirmity.

bedroom, bed'röm, *n.* A sleeping apartment.

bedstead, bed'sted, *n.* A frame for supporting a bed.

bee, bē, *n.* The insect that makes honey.

beech, bēch, *n.* A large smoothbarked tree yielding a hard timber and nuts.

beef, bēf, *n.* The flesh of an ox, bull or cow.—*a.* Consisting of such flesh.

befit, bē-fit', *vt.* To suit; to become.

before, bē-fōr', *prep.* In front of; in presence of, earlier than; in preference to.—*adv.* In time preceding further, onward; in front

beforehand, bē-fōr'hand, *a.* In good pecuniary circumstances.— *adv.* In advance.

beg, beg, *vt.* (begging, begged). To ask in charity; to ask earnestly; to take for granted. *vi.* To ask or live upon alms.

beget, bē-get', *vt.* (begetting, pp. begot, begotten, pret. begot). To procreate; to produce.

beggar, beg'gėr, *n.* One who begs.—*vt.* To impoverish.

begin, bē-gin', *vi.* (pp. begun, pret. began). To take rise; to do the first act, to commence.—*vt.* To enter on to originate.

beige, bā zh, *n.* A fabric made of unbleached or undyed wool; a greyishbrown color.

being, bē'ing, *n.* Existence; a creature.

belabor, bē-lā'bėr, *vt.* To beat soundly; to thump.

belated, bē-lāt'ed, *p.a.* Made late benighted.

believe, bē-lēv', *vt.* (believing, believed). To give belief to; to credit; to expect with confidence.—*vi.* To have a firm persuasion.

belittle, bē -lit'l, *vt.* To make smaller; to speak disparagingly.

belle, bel, *n.* A lady of great beauty.

bellicose, bel'li-kōs, *a.* Warlike; pugnacious.

belligerent, bel-lij'er-ent, *a.* Waging war.—*n.* A nation or state wag ing war.

bellow, bel'ō, *vi.* To make a hollow loud noise, as a bull; to roar.—*n.* A roar.

bellows, bel'ōz, *n.sing.* and *pl.* An instrument for blowing fires, sup plying wind to organ-pipes, etc.

bell-wether, bel'weTH-ér, *n.* A sheep which leads the flock with a bell on his neck.

belly, bel'li, *n.* That part of the body which contains the bowels.—*vt.* and *i.* (bellying, bellied). To swell, bulge.

belong, bē -long', *vi.* To be the property; to appertain; to be connected, to have original residence.

below, bē-lō', *prep.* Under in place beneath; unworthy of—*adv.* In a lower place; beneath; on earth; in hell.

belt, belt, *n.* A girdle; a band.—*vt.* To encircle.

bemoan, bēmōn', *vt.* To lament; bewail.

bemused, bē-mū zd', *a.* Muddled stupefied.

bench, bensh, *n.* A long seat; seat of justice; body of judges.—*vt.* To furnish with benches.

bend, bend, *vt.* (pp. and pret. bent and bended). To curve, to direct to a certain point; to subdue.—*vi.* To become crooked; to lean or turn; to yield.—*n.* A curve.

beneath, bē-nē th', *prep.* Under lower in place, rank, dignity, etc., unworthy of.—*adv.* Ina, lower, place, below.

benediction, ben-ē-dik'shon, *n.* Act of blessing; invocation of happiness.

benefaction, ben-ē-fak'shon, *n.* The doing of a benefit; a benefit conferred.

benefactor, ben-ē-fak 'tėr, *n.* He who confers a benefit.

benefit, ben-ē-fit, *n.* An act of kindness; a favor; advantage.—*vt.* To do a service to.—*vi.* To gain advantage.

benevolent, bē-nev'ō-lent, *a.* Kind charitable.

benumb, bē-num', *vt.* To deprive of sensation; to make torpid; to stupefy.

Benzene, ben'zēn, *n.* A liquid used to remove grease spots, etc.

beset, bē-set', *vt.* (besetting beset). To surround, to press on ail sides.

beside, besides, bē-sīd', bē-sīdz' *prep.* By the side of, near, over and above; distinct from.—*adv.* Moreover, in addition.

besiege, bē-sēj', *vt.* (besieging, besieged). To lay siege to; to beset.

besom, be'zum, *n.* A brush of twigs; a broom.

besot, bē-sot', *vt.* (besotting, besotted). To make sottish.

bespangle, bē-spang'gl, *vt.* To adorn with spangles.

bespatter, bēspat'tėr, *vt.* To spatter over.

bespeak, bē-spē k', *vt.* (pp. bespoke, bespoken, pret. bespoke). To speak for beforehand; to indicate.

Bessemer-steel, bes'e-mer-stēl *n.* Steel made directly from molten cast-iron by driving through it air to carry off impurities.

bestial, bes'ti-al, *a.* Belonging to a beast; brutish; vile.

Bestiary, bes'ti-a-ri, *n.* A book of the middle ages treating fancifully of beasts.

bestir, bē-stėr', *vt.* To stir up to put into brisk action. (Usually with refl. pron.)

bestow, bē-stō', *vt.* To lay up; to give; to confer; to dispose of; to apply.

bestride, bē-strīd', *vt.* (pp. bestrid, bestridden, pret. bestrid, bestrode). To stride over, to place a leg on each side of.

bet, bet, *n.* A wager; that which is pledged in a contest.—*vt.* (betting, betted). To wager.

betray, bē-trā', *vt.* To disclose treacherously, to entrap.

betroth, bē-trō TH', *vt.* To affiance; to pledge to marriage.

between, bē-twēn', *prep.* In the middle, from one to another of, belonging to two.

beverage, bev'ėr-āj, *n.* Drink; liquor.

bevy, be'vi, *n.* A flock of birds; a company of females.

bewail, bē-wā l', *vt.* To lament.—*vi.* To utter deep grief.

beware, bē-wār', *vi.* To take care (with *of*).

bewilder, bē-wil'dė r *vt.* To confuse; to perplex.

bewitch, bē-wich', *vt.* To enchant; to fascinate; to overpower by charms.

beyond, bē-yond', *prep.* On the further side of; farther onward than; out of the reach of, above.—*adv.* At a distance.

Bible, bī'bl, *n.* The Holy Scriptures.

bibliography, bib-li-og'ra-fi, *n.* A history of books and their editions; list of books by one author or on one subject.

bicycle, bī'si-kl, *n.* A two-wheeled vehicle propelled by the rider.

bid, bid, *vt.* (bidding, pp. bid, bidden, pret. bid, bade). To ask, to order; to offer.—*n.* An offer, as at an auction.

bidding, bid'ing, *n.* Invitation; order; offer.

bide, bīd, *vi.* (biding, bode). To dwell; to remain.—*vt.* To endure; to abide.

bier, bē r, *n.* A carriage or frame for conveying a corpse to the grave.

bile, bīl, *n.* A yellowish bitter liquid secreted in the liver; spleen; anger.

bilingual, bī-lin 'gwal, *a.* In two languages.

biliteral, bī-lit 'er-al, *a.* Consisting of two letters.

bilk, bilk, *vt.* To defraud, to elude.

bimonthly, bī-munth'li, *a.* Occur-ring every two months.

bin, bin, *n.* A receptacle for corn, etc., a partition in a wine-cellar.

binary, bi'na-ri, *a.* Twofold.

biographer, bī-og'ra-fē r, *n.* A writer of biography.

Biography, bī-og'ra-fi, *n.* An account of one's life and character.

Biology, bī-ol'o-ji, *n.* The science of life.

bioplasm, bī'ō-plazm, *n.* The germinal matter in plants and animals.

bipartite, bī-pärt'-īt, *a.* Having two parts.

biped, bī'ped, *n.* An animal with two feet.

birch, bė rch, *n.* A tree having small leaves, white bark, and a fragrant odor.

bismuth, bis'muth, *n.* A brittle yellowish or reddish-white metal.

bison, bī'zon, *n.* A quadruped of the ox family; the American buffalo.

bisque, bisk, *n.* Unglazed white porcelain; odds given at tennis, etc.

bit, bit, *n.* A morsel, fragment, the metal part of a bridle inserted in a horse's mouth; a boring tool.—*vt.* (bitting, bitted). To put the bit in the mouth.

bitch, bich, *n.* A female dog; a name of reproach for a woman.

biting, bī-t'ing, *p.a.* Sharp; severe; sarcastic.

bitter, bit'ėr, *a.* Sharp to the taste severe; painful; calamitous; distressing.

biweekly, bī-wek'li, *a.* Occurring every two weeks.

bizarre, bi-zär', *a.* Odd, fantastical.

blab, blab, *vt.* (blabbing, blabbed). To tell indiscreetly.—*vi.* To talk indiscreetly.

blackberry, blak'be-ri, *n.* A plant of the bramble kind, and its fruit.

blackbird, blak'bė rd, *n.* A species of thrush.

blackboard, blak'bō-rd, *n.* A board for writing on with chalk for instruction.

blacken, blak'n, *vt.* To make black; to defame.—*vi.* To grow black or dark.

blackguard, blak'gärd or bla'gärd, *n.* A scoundrel.—*vt.* To revile in scurrilous language.

black-sheep, blak'shēp, *n.* One whose conduct is discreditable.

blacksmith, blak'smith, *n.* A smith who works in iron.

blackthorn, blak'thorn, *n.* The sloe.

bladder, blad'ėr, *n.* A thin sac in animals containing the urine, bile, etc.; a blister; anything like the animal bladder.

blade, blā d, *n.* A leaf; cutting part of a sword, knife, etc.; flat part of an oar.

blame, blā m, *vt.* (blaming, blamed). To censure, to reprimand.—*n.* Censure;

fault.

blanch, blansh, *vt*. To make white.—*vi*. To grow white; to bleach.

blare, blā r, *vi*. (blaring, blared). To give forth a loud sound.—*vt*. To sound loudly; to proclaim noisily.—*n*. Sound like that of a trumpet; roar.

blarney, blär'ni, *n*. Excessively complimentary language; gammon.—*vt*. To flatter.

blase, blä-zā, *a*. Satiated; used up; bored.

blaspheme, blas-fēm', *vt*. (blaspheming, blasphemed). To speak irreverently of, as of God; to speak evil of.—*vi*. To utter blasphemy.

blatant, blā́tant, *a*. Bellowing; noisy.

blemish, blem'ish, *vt*. To mar, to tarnish.—*n*. A mark of imperfection; dishonor.

blend, blend, *vt*. To mix together.— *vi*. To be mixed.—*n*. A mixture.

blindfold, blīnd'fō ld, *a*. Having the eyes covered.—*vt*. To cover the eyes of.

blindness, blīnd'nes, *n*. Want of sight or discernment, ignorance.

blink, blingk, *vi*. To wink; to twinkle.—*vt*. To shut the eyes upon; to avoid.—*n*. A twinkle; a glimpse or glance.

blinker, bling'kėr, *n*. A flap to prevent a horse from seeing sideways.

bliss, blis, *n*. Blessedness; perfect happiness.

blister, blis 'tèr, *n*. A thin bladder on the skin; a pustule, something to raise a blister.—*vi*. To rise in blisters.—*vt*. To raise a blister or blisters on, to apply a blister to.

blithe, blīTH, *a*. Joyful; gay; mirth.

blockade, blok-ā d', *n*. A close siege by troops or ships.—*vt*. (blockading, blockaded). To besiege closely.

blockhead, blok'hed, *n*. A stupid fellow.

blond, blonde, blond, *a*. Of a fair complexion.—*n*. A person of fair complexion.

blood-hound, blud'hound, *n*. A hound of remarkably acute smell.

blossom, blos 'om, *n*. The flower of a plant.—*vi*. To bloom: to flower; to flourish.

blot, blot, *vt*. (blotted, blotting). To spot, to stain, to cancel (with out) to dry.—*n*. A spot or stain; an obliteration.

blotch, bloch, *n*. Pustule upon the skin; an eruption; a confused patch of color.

blotter, blot'ėr, *n*. One who blots; a piece of blotting-paper.

blouse, blouz, *n*. A light loose upper garment.

bluebell, blü'bel, *n*. The wild hyacinth (in England), the harebell (in Scotland).

blue-stocking, blü'stok-ing, *n*. A learned and pedantic lady.

blue-stone, blü'stōn, *n*. Sulphate of copper.

bluff, bluf, *a*. Steep; blustering; burly, hearty.—*n*. A steep projecting bank.— *vt*. and *i*. To impose on by a show of boldness or strength.

blunder, blun'dè r, *vi*. To err stupidly; to stumble.—*vt*. To confound.—*n*. A gross mistake, error.

blunt, blunt, *a*. Dull on the edge or point; not sharp; dull in understanding, unceremonious.—*vt*. To make blunt or dull.

blur, blèr, *n*. A stain; a blot.—*vt*. (blurring, blurred). To stain, to obscure; to render indistinct.

boarder, bord'ėr, *n*. One who receives food and lodging at a stated charge; one who boards a ship in action.

boarding-school, bō rd'ing-skōl, *n*. A school which supplies board as well as tuition.

boast, bō st, *vi*. To brag; to talk ostentatiously.—*vt*. To brag of; to magnify.—*n*. A vaunting; the cause of boasting.

boat, bōt, *n*. A small open vessel usually impelled by oars, a small ship.—*vt*. To transport in a boat.— *vi*. To go in a boat.

boatswain, bō'sn, *n*. A ship's officer who has charge of boats, sails, etc.

body, bo'di, *n*. The trunk of an animal; main part, matter, a persona system; strength; reality; any solid figure.—*vt*. (bodying, bodied). To give a body to; to embody (with *forth*).

boisterous, bois'tèr-us, *a*. Stormy; noisy.

bold, bō ld, *a*. Daring; courageous; impudent, steep and abrupt.

bole, bōl, *n*. The body or stem of a tree; a kind of fine clay.

Bolero, bō-lär'ō, *n*. A Spanish dance.

bolster, bō l'stér, *n*. A long pillow; a pad.—*vt*. To support with a bolster; to hold up; to maintain.

bondage, bond'āj, *n*. Slavery; thraldom.

bonded, bond'ed, *a*. Secured by bond; under a bond to pay duty containing goods liable to duties.

bonfire, bon'fīr, *n*. A large fire in the open air expressive of joy.

book-maker, bük'mak-ėr, *n*. One who compiles books, one who bets systematically.

bookworm, bük'wėrm, *n*. A worm that eats holes in books, a close student of books.

boomerang, bōm'e-rang, *n.* An Australian missile of hard wood, which can return to hit an object behind the thrower.

boon, bön, *n.* Answer to a prayer; a favor, gift, or grant.—*a.* Merry; pleasant.

boor, bör, *n.* A rustic; an ill-mannered or illiterate fellow.

boot, böt, *vt.* To benefit; to put on boots.—*n.* Profit, a covering for the foot and leg; *pl.* a male servant in a hotel.

bore, bōr, *vt.* (boring, bored). To make a hole in, to weary.—*vi.* To pierce.—*n.* The hole made by boring; the diameter of a round hole; a person or thing that wearies; a sudden rise of the tide in certain estuaries.

bosky, bosk'i, *a.* Woody or bushy.

bosom, bö'zum, *n.* The breast; the seat of the affections.—*vt.* To conceal.—*a.* Much beloved; confidential.

boss, bos, *n.* A knob; an ornamental projection; a master.

Botany, bot'a-ni *n.* The science which treats of plants.

botch, boch, *n.* A swelling on the skin; a clumsy patch; bungled work.—*vt.* To mend or perform clumsily.

both, bōth, *a.* and *pron.* The two taken by themselves; the pair.— *conj.* As well; on the one side.

bother, boTH'er, *vt.* To annoy.—*vi.* To trouble oneself.—*n.* A trouble, vexation.

bothersome, boTH'ér-sum, *a.* Causing trouble.

bott, bot, bot, *n.* A maggot found in the intestines of horses, etc.: generally in *pl.*

bound, bound, *n.* A boundary; a leap.—*vt.* To limit, to restrain.—*vi.* To leap, to rebound.—*p.a.* Obliged; sure.—*a.* Ready; destined.

boundary, bound'a-ri, *n.* A mark designating a limit, border.

bountiful, boun'ti-ful, *a.* Munificent, generous.

bounty, boun'ti, *n.* Liberality; generosity; a gratuity; premium to encourage trade.

bow, bō , *n.* An instrument to shoot arrows; the rainbow; a curve; a fiddlestick an ornamental knot.

bowel, bou'el, *n.* One of the intestines; *pl.* the intestines; the seat of pity, compassion.

bower, bou'ér, *n.* An anchor carried at the bow; a shady recess; an arbor.

Bowie-knife, bō'i-nîf, *n.* A knife from 10 to 15 inches long and about 2 inches broad.

bowler, bō l'é r, *n.* One who bowls; a round-shaped felt hat.

bowling, bōl'ing, *n.* Act or art of playing with bowls; art or style of a bowler.

bowman, bō̌man, *n.* An archer.

bowsprit, bō'sprit, *n.* A large spar which projects over the bow of a ship.

boxwood, boks'wüd, *n.* The hardgrained wood of the box-tree; the plant itself.

boy, boi, *n.* A male child, a lad.

brackish, brak'ish, *a.* Salt; saltish.

bract, brakt, *n.* An irregularly developed leaf at the base of a flower.

brad, brad, *n.* A small nail with no head.

brag, brag, *vi.* (bragging, bragged). To bluster; to talk big.—*n.* A boast.

brake, brāk, *n.* A place overgrown with brushwood, etc., a thicket; the bracken; an instrument to break flax; a harrow for breaking clods; a contrivance for retarding the motion of wheels; a large wagonette.

bramble, bram'bl, *n.* A prickly shrub of the rose family; its berry.

bran, bran, *n.* The husks of ground corn.

branch, bransh, *n.* The shoot of a or plant; the offshoot of anything, as of a river, family, etc.; a limb.—*vi.* To spread in branches.—*vt.* To divide or form into branches.

bravado, bra-vā'dō, *n.* A boast or rag; would-be boldness.

brave, brāv, *a.* Daring; bold; valiant; noble.—*n.* A daring person, a savage warrior.—*vt.* (braving, braved). To challenge; to defy; to encounter with courage.

brawl, bräl, *vi.* To quarrel noisily.—*n.* A noisy quarrel, uproar.

brawn, brän, *n.* The flesh of a boar; the muscular part of the body; muscle.

bray, brā, *vt.* To beat or grind small.—*vi.* To make a loud harsh sound, as an ass.—*n.* The cry of an ass.

braze, brā z, *vt.* (brazing, brazed). To cover with brass; to solder with brass.

breaker, brā k'ér, *n.* One who or that which breaks; a rock; a wave broken by rocks.

breakwater, brā k 'wa-tè r, *n.* A mole to break the force of the waves.

bream, brēm, *n.* A fish.—*vt.* To clean a ship's bottom by means of fire.

breath, breth *n.* The air drawn into and expelled from the lungs; life; a single respiration; pause; a gentle breeze.

breech, brē ch, *n.* The lower part of the body behind; the hinder part of a gun, etc.—*vt.* To put into breeches.

bribe, brîb, *n.* A gift to corrupt the conduct or judgment.—*vt.* (bribing bribed).

To gain over by bribes.

bric-a-brac, brik-a-brak, *n.* Articles of interest or value from rarity, antiquity, etc.

brick, brik, *n.* A rectangular mass of burned clay, used in building, etc., a loaf shaped like a brick.—*a.* Made of brick.—*vt.* To lay with bricks.

bridal, brī'd'al, *n.* A wedding-feast a wedding.—*a.* Belonging to a bride or to a wedding.

bride, brīd, *n.* A woman about to be or newly married.

bridegroom, brī'd'gröm, *n.* A man about to be or newly married.

bride's-maid, brī'dz'mād, *n.* A woman who attends on a bride at her wedding.

bridge, brij, *n.* A structure across a river, etc., to furnish a passage; the upper part of the nose.—*vt.* (bridging, bridged). To build a bridge over.

brier, brī'ėr, *n.* A prickly shrub, species of the rose.

brig, brig, *n.* A vessel with two masts, square-rigged.

brigand, bri'gand, *n.* A freebooter.

brigantine, brig'an-tīn, *n.* A light swift vessel two-masted and square-rigged.

bright, brīt, *a.* Clear; shining; glittering; acute; witty; lively; cheer-

brim, brim, *n.* The rim of anything; the upper edge of the mouth of a vessel.—*vi.* (brimming, brimmed). To be full to the brim.

brimstone, brim'stön, *n.* sulphur.

brindled, brind'ld, *a.* Marked with brown streaks.

brine, brīn, *n.* Salt water, the sea.

bring, bring, *vt.* (bringing, brought). To lead or cause to come; to fetch; to produce; to attract; to prevail upon.

brink, bringk, *n.* The edge of a steep place.

broach, brōch, *n.* A spit a brooch.—*vt.* To pierce, as with a spit; to tap; to open up; to publish first.

broad, bräd, *a.* Having extent from side to side; wide; unrestricted; indelicate.

broaden, bräd'n, *vi.* To grow broad.—*vt.* To make broad.

broadside, brad'sīd, *n.* A discharge of all the guns on one side of a ship; a sheet of paper printed on one side.

brocade, brō-kād', *n.* A silk or satin stuff variegated with gold and silver.

broccoli, brok'o-li, *n.* A kind of cauliflower.

bronchial, brong'ki-al, *a.* Belonging to the tubes branching from the windpipe through the lungs.

bronchitis, brong-kī'tis *n.* Inflammation of the bronchial tubes.

brother, bruTH'ėr, *n.; pl.* **brothers, brethren,** bruTH'ėrz, breTH'ren. A male born of the same parents, an associate a fellow-creature.

browse, brouz, *vt.* (browsing, browsed). To pasture or feed upon.—*vi.* To crop and eat food.

bruin, brö'in, *n.* A familiar name of a bear.

brusque, brusk, *a.* Abrupt in manner, rude.

brussels-sprouts, brus'elz-sprouts, *n.pl.* A variety of cabbage.

brutal, bröt'al, *a.* Cruel, ferocious.

brute, bröt, *a.* Senseless; bestial; uncivilized.—*n.* A beast; a brutal person.

bubo, bū'bō, *n.*, pl. **-oes.** A swelling or abscess in a glandular part of the body.

bubonic, bū·bon'ik, *a.* Pertaining to bubo.

buccaneer, buk-a-nēr', *n.* A pirate.

buck, buk, *n.* The male of deer goats, etc., a gay young fellow; a lye for steeping clothes in.—*vt.* To steep in lye.—*vi.* To leap, as a horse, so as to dismount the rider.

bucket, buk 'et, *n.* A vessel in which water is drawn or carried.

buck-shot, buk'shot, *n.* A large kind of shot used for killing large game.

buckwheat, buk'whēt, *n.* A plant bearing small seeds which are ground into meal.

bucolic, bū-kol'ik, *a.* Pastoral.—*n.* A pastoral poem.

buffalo, buf'fa-lō, *n.* A species of ox larger than the common ox; the American bison.

buffer, buf'ėr, *n.* An apparatus for deadening concussion.

buffet, buf'et, *n.* A cupboard for wine, glasses, etc.; a place for refreshments (pron. bu-fe).

buffet, buf'et, *n.* A blow; a slap.—*vt.* To beat; to box; to contend against.

buffoon, buf-fön', *n.* One who makes sport by low jests and antic gestures; a droll.

bug, bug, *n.* A name for various insects, particularly one infesting houses and inflicting severe bites.

bulb, bulb, *n.* A round root; a round protuberance.

bulbul, bül'bül, *n.* The Persian nightingale.

bulge, bulj, *n.* A swelling, bilge.—*vi.* (bulging, bulged). To swell out, to be protuberant.

bulk, bulk, *n*. Magnitude; the majority; extent.

bull-frog, bül'frog, *n*. A large species of frog in N. America, with a loud bass voice.

bullion, bül'yon, *n*. Uncoined gold or silver.

bull's-eye, bülz'ï, *n*. A circular opening for light or air; the center of a target.

bully, bül'i, *n*. An overbearing quarrelsome fellow.—*vt*. (bullying bullied). To insult and overbear.— *vi*. To bluster or domineer.

bulrush, bül'rush, *n*. A large strong kind of rush.

bulwark, bül'werk, *n*. A bastion, a fortification; a means of defense or safety.

bumble-bee, bum'bl-bē, *n*. A large bee.

bumpkin, bump'kin, *n*. An awkward rustic; a lout.

bun, bun, *n*. A kind of cake or sweet bread.

bunch, bunsh, *n*. A knob or lump; a cluster.—*vi*. To swell out in a protuberance; to cluster.

bundle, bun'dl, *n*. A number of things bound together; a package.—*vt*. (bundling, bundled). To tie in a bundle; to dispose of hurriedly.—*vt*. To depart hurriedly.

bung, bung, *n*. The stopper of a cask.—*vt*. To stop with a bung; to close up.

bungalow, bung'ga-lō, *n*. A single-storied house.

buoy, boi, *n*. A floating mark to point out shoals, etc.; something to keep a person or thing up in the water.—*vt*. To keep afloat; to bear up.—*vi*. To float.

buoyant, boi'ant, *a*. Floating; light; elastic.

burglar, bėrg'lėr, *n*. One who robs a house by night.

burgundy, bėr'gun-di, *n*. A kind of wine, so called from Burgundy in France.

burnish, bėr'nish, *vt*. To polish.—*vi*. To grow bright or glossy.—*n*. Gloss; luster.

burr, bėr, *n*. A guttural sounding of the letter r; a rough or projecting ridge; bur

burrow, bu'rō , *n*. A hole in the earth made by rabbits, etc.— *vi*. To excavate a hole underground; to hide.

bury, be'ri, *vt*. (burying, buried). To put into a grave; to overwhelm; to hide.

bush, büsh, *n*. A shrub with branches; a thicket; the backwoods of Australia, a lining of hard metal in the nave of a wheel, etc.—*vi*. To grow bushy.

bushel, büsh'el, *n*. A dry measure containing eight gallons or four pecks.

business, biz'nes, *n*. Occupation concern; trade.—*a*. Pertaining to traffic, trade, etc.

butter, but'tėr, *n*. An oily substance obtained from cream by churning, any substance resembling butter. —*vt*. To spread with butter; to flatter grossly.

butterfly, but'tėr-flï, *n*. The name of a group of winged insects.

buttermilk, but'ėr-milk, *n*. The milk that remains after the butter is separated.

buttock, but'tok, *n*. The protuberant part of the body behind; the rump.

button, but'n, *n*. A knob to fasten the parts of dress; a knob or stud; *pl*. a pageboy.—*vt*. To fasten with buttons.

buxom, buks'um, *a*. Gay; brisk; wanton.

buy, bï, *vt*. (buying, bought). To acquire by payment' to purchase; to bribe.—*vi*. To negotiate or treat about a purchase.

buzz, buz, *vi*. To hum, as bees; to whisper.—*vt*. To whisper.—*n*. The noise of bees, a confused humming noise.

by, bï, *prep*. Used to denote the instrument, agent, or manner, at near, beside, through or with, in, for; according to; at the rate of; not later than.—*adv*. Near; passing. In *composition,* secondary, side.

Byzantine, biz-an'tïn or biz', *a*. Pertaining to Byzantium or Constantinople and the Greek Empire of which it was the capital.

C

cabal, ka-bal', *n.* An intrigue; persons united in some intrigue. —*vi.* (caballing, caballed). To combine in plotting.

cabaret, kab-a-ret, ka-ba-rā, *n.* A tavern; a restaurant in which singing and dancing performances are given.

cabbage, kab'ā j, *n.* A culinary vegetable.—*vt.* (cabbaging, cabbaged). To purloin, especially pieces of cloth.

cabin, kab'in, *n.* A hut; an apartment in a ship.—*vt.* To confine, as in a cabin.

cabinet, kab'in-et, *n.* A closet; a small room; a set of drawers for curiosities; the ministers of state.

cacophony, ka-kof'ō-ni, *n.* Unpleasant vocal sound; a discord.

cactus, kak'tus, *n.*; pl. **-tuses** or **-ti.** A spiny shrub of numerous species.

caisson, kas'son, *n.* An ammunition chest; a structure to raise sunken vessels; a structure used in laying foundations in deep water.

cajole, ka-jōl', *vt.* (cajoling, cajoled). To coax; to court; to deceive by flattery.

Caledonian, kal-i-dō'ni-an, *a.* Pertaining to Scotland.—*n.* A Scot.

Calends, ka'lendz, *n.pl.* Among the Romans, the first day of each month.

calf, käf, *n.*, pl. **calves,** kävz. The young of the cow, a kind of leather the fleshy part of the leg below the knee.

calico, ka'li-kō, *n.* Cotton cloth.

calligraphy, kal-lig'ra-fi, *n.* The art of beautiful writing; penmanship.

calling, käl'ing, *n.* Vocation; profession.

calipers, kal'i-pė rz, *n.pl.* Compasses for measuring caliber.

callosity, ka-los'i-ti, *n.* Hardness of skin; horny hardness.

callous. kal'us, *a.* Hardened; unfeeling; obdurate.

caloric, ka-lo'rik, *n.* The principle or simple element of heat, heat.

calumet, kal'ū -met, *n.* The North American Indians' pipe of peace.

camera, kam'ė -ra, *n.* An arched roof; a council chamber; an apparatus for taking photographs.

camomile kam'ō-mil, *n.* A bitter medicinal plant.

camouflage, kam-ö-fläzh, *n.* The art of disguising; especially the art of disguising material in warfare.

camp, kamp, *n.* The ground on which an army pitch their tents; an encampment.—*vi.* To pitch a camp; to encamp.

campaign, kam-pān', *n.* The time an army keeps the field every year, during a war; its operations.—*vi.* To serve in a campaign.

campanile, kam-pa-nē'lā or kam' pa-nîl, *n.*; pl. **-ili** or **-iles.** A belltower.

campion, kam'pi-on, *n.* A popular name of certain plants of the Pink family.

can, kan, *n.* A cup or vessel for liquors.

can, kan, *vi.* (pret. could). To be able, to have sufficient moral or physical power.

canal, ka-nal', *n.* A channel; an artificial water-course for boats; a duct of the body.

canard, ka-när or ka-närd', *n.* An absurd story; a false rumor.

cancel, kan'sel, *vt.* (cancelling cancelled). To obliterate, to revoke, to set aside.—*n.* Act of cancelling.

Cancer, kan'sėr, *n.* One of the signs of the zodiac, a malignant growth in the body.

candid, kan'did, *a.* Sincere; ingenuous.

candidate, kan'di-dā t, *n.* One who proposes himself, or is proposed for some office; one who aspires after preferment.

candied, kan'did, *a.* Preserved with sugar, or incrusted with it.

candle, kan'dl, *n.* A cylindrical body of tallow wax, etc., surrounding a wick and used for giving light.

candlestick, kan'dl-stik, *n.* An instrument to hold a candle.

cane, kān, *n.* A reed; a walking-stick.—*vt.* (caning, caned). To beat with a cane.

canine, ka'nîn, *a.* Pertaining to dogs.

cannon, kan'un, *n.* A great gun the striking of a ball on two other balls successively.—*vi.* To strike with rebounding collision; to make a cannon at billiards.

canny, cannie, kan'i, *a.* Cautious; wary.

canoe, ka-nö', *n.* A boat made of the trunk of a tree, or of bark or skins; a light boat propelled by Paddles.

cantankerous, kan-tang'kėr-us, *a.* Ill-natured; cross; contentious.

cantata, kan-tä'ta, *n.* A short musical composition in the form of an oratorio.

canteen, kan-tēn', *n.* A vessel used by soldiers for carrying liquor, a place in barracks where provisions, etc., are sold.

canvas, kan'vas, *n.* A coarse cloth; sailcloth, sails of ships, cloth for painting on, a painting.

canvass, kan'vas, *vt.* To scrutinize; to solicit the votes of—*vi.* To solicit votes or interest, to use efforts to obtain.—*n.*

Scrutiny; solicitation of votes.

capable, kā'pa-bl, *a.* Having sufficient skill or power; competent; susceptible.

capacious, ka-pā'shus, *a.* Wide; large; comprehensive.

capacitate, ka-pas'i-tāt, *vt.* To make able; to qualify.

capacity, ka-pas'i-ti, *n.* Power of holding; extent of space; ability; state.

capital, kap'it-al, *a.* First in importance, metropolitan, affecting the head, punishable with death.—*n.* The uppermost part of a column; the chief city, the stock of a bank tradesman, etc.; a large letter or type.

capitalist, kap'it-al-ist, *n.* A man who has a capital or wealth.

capsicum, kap'si-kum, *n.* The generic name of some tropical plants yielding chilies and cayenne pepper.

capsize, kap-sīz', *vt.* (capsizing, capsized). to upset or overturn.

captain, kap'tin, *n.* A head officer the commander of a ship, troop of horse, or company of infantry; a leader.

caption, kap'shon, *n.* Seizure; arrest; heading or short title of a division of a book, or of a scene in a cinematograph film.

captious, kap'shus, *a.* Ready to find fault; carping.

captive, kap'tiv, *n.* One taken in war, one ensnared by love, beauty etc.—*a.* Make prisoner; kept in bondage.

capture, kap'tūr, *n.* Act of taking the thing taken.—*vt.* (capturing' captured). To take by force or stratagem.

caravan, ka'ra-van, *n.* A company of travelers associated together for safety, a large close carriage.

caraway, ka'ra-wā, *n.* A biennial, aromatic Plant whose seeds are used in baking, etc.

carbide, kär'bīd, *n.* A compound of carbon with a metal.

carbine, kär'bīn, *n.* A short-barreled rifle used by cavalry, police, etc.

carbolic, kär-bol'ik, *a.* An antiseptic and disinfecting acid obtained from coal-tar.

carbon, kär'bon, *n.* Pure charcoal an elementary substance, bright and brittle.

carbonate, kär'bon-āt, *n.* A salt formed by the union of carbonic acid with a base.

carbuncle, kär'bung-kl, *n.* A fiery red precious stone; an inflammatory tumor.

carburetor, kär'bū-ret-èr, *n.* A device for vaporizing the light oil fuel used in the engines of motorcars, airplanes, etc.

carcas, kär'kas, *a.* A dead body anything decayed; a framework; a kind of bomb

care, kār, *n.* Solicitude; attention; object of watchful regard.—*vi.* (caring, cared). To be solicitous; to be inclined; to have regard.

caress, ka-res', *vt.* To fondle, to embrace affectionately.—*n.* An act of endearment.

caret, ka'ret, *n.* In writing, this mark, A, noting insertion.

carious, kā'ri-us, *a.* Ulcerated; decayed.

carminative, kär'min-āt-iv, *n.* A medicine for flatulence, etc.

carmine, kär'min, *n.* A bright crimson color.

carnage, kär'nāj, *n.* Great slaughter in war, massacre, butchery.

carnal, kär'nal, *a.* Fleshly; sensual.

carotid, ka-rot'id, *a.* Pertaining to the two great arteries in the neck conveying the blood to the head.

carrion, ka'ri-on, *n.* Dead and putrefying flesh.—*a.* Relating to putrefying carcasses; feeding on carrion.

carrot, ka'rot, *n.* A yellowish or reddish esculent root of a tapering form.

carry, ka'ri, *vt.* (carrying, carried). To bear, convey, or transport, to gain, to capture, to import, to behave.—*vi.* To convey; to propel.—*n.* Onward motion.

cart, kärt, *n.* A carriage of burden with two wheels.—*vt.* To carry or place on a cart.

carte-blanche, kärt-blänsh, *n.* A blank paper; unconditional terms.

cartel, kär'tel, *n.* A challenge; an agreement for the exchange of prisoners.

cartography, kär-tog'ra-fi, *n.* The art or practice of drawing up charts.

cartoon, kär-tön', *n.* A drawing for a fresco or tapestry; a pictorial sketch relating to a prevalent topic.

cartouch, kär-tösh', *n.* A cartridge or cartridge-box; a sculptured ornament.

cartridge, kär'trij, *n.* A case containing the charge of a gun or any firearm.

carve, kärv, *vt.* (carving, carved). To cut, to engrave, to shape by cutting.—*vi.* To cut up meat; to sculpture.

cash, kash, *n.* Money; ready money; coin.—*vt.* To turn into money.

cashmere, kash'mēr *n.* A rich kind of shawl, a fine woolen stuff.

casino, ka-sē'nō , *n.* A public dancing, singing, or gaming saloon.

castor, kas'tèr, *n.* A small cruet, a small wheel on the leg of a table, etc.

castor-oil, kas'tèr-oil, *n.* A medicinal oil obtained from a tropical Plant.

castrate, kas'trā t, *vt.* (castrating, castrated). To geld; to emasculate; to expurgate.

cast-steel, kast'stē l, *n.* Steel melted and cast into ingots and rolled into bars.

casual, ka'zhū-al, *a.* Happening by chance; occasional; contingent.

casualty, ka'zhū-al-ti, *n.* Accident, especially one resulting in death or injury; death or injury caused by enemy action.

casuistry, ka'zū -is-tri, *n.* The science of determining cases of conscience; sophistry.

cataclysm, kat'a-klizm, *n.* A deluge; a sudden overwhelming catastrophe.

catapult, kat'a-pult, *n.* An apparatus for throwing stones, etc.

cataract, kat'a-rakt, *n.* A great waterfall; a disease of the eye.

catarrh, ka-tär', *n.* A flow of mucus from the nose, etc.; a cold.

catastrophe, ka-tas'trō-fē, *n.* Calamity or disaster, final event.

catechism, ka'tē-kizm, *n.* A manual of instruction by questions and answers, especially in religion.

catgut, kat'gut, *n.* The intestines of a cat; intestines made into strings for musical instruments, etc.; a kind of linen or canvas.

cathartic, ka-thär'tik, *a.* Purging.—*n.* A medicine that purges.

cathedral, ka-thē'dral, *n.* The principal church in a diocese.

catheter, kath'e-tėr, *n.* A tubular instrument, to be introduced into the bladder.

cathode, kath'ōd, *n.* The negative pole of an electric current.

cattle, kat'tl, *n.pl.* Domestic quadrupeds serving for tillage or food; bovine animals.

caucus, kä'kus, *n.* A Private committee to manage election matters.

caudal, kä'dal, *a.* Pertaining to a tail.

caul, käl, *n.* A net for the hair; a membrane investing some part of the intestines.

caulk, käk, *vt.* To drive oakum into the seams of (a ship) to prevent leaking.

causative, käz'a-tiv, *a.* That expresses a cause or reason that effects.

cause, käz, *n.* That which produces an effect, reason, origin, sake, purpose, a suit in court; that which a person or party espouses.—*vt.* (causing, caused). To effect; to bring about.

causeway, causey, käz'wā , käz'i, *n.* A raised road, a paved way.

caustic, käs'tik, *a.* Burning; corroding; cutting.—*n.* A substance which burns the flesh.

cauterization, kä'ter-īz-ā"shon, *n.* Act of cauterizing.

cavern, ka'vėrn, *n.* A large cave.

caviare, caviar, ka-vi-är', *n.* The roe of the sturgeon salted and prepared for food.

cavil, ka'vil, *vi.* (caviling, caviled). To carp, to find fault with insufficient reason.—*n.* A captious objection.

cavity, ka'vi-ti, *n.* A hollow place.

cayenne, kā-en', *n.* A pepper made from capsicum seeds.

cease, sēs, *vi.* (ceasing, ceased). To leave off, to fail, to stop, to become extinct.—*vt.* To put a stop to.

celestial, sē-les'ti-al, *a.* Heavenly pertaining to heaven.—*n.* An inhabitant of heaven.

celibacy, se'li-ba-si, *n.* The unmarried state; a single life.

celibate, se'li-bāt, *n.* One who intentionally remains unmarried.— *a.* Unmarried.

cell, sel, *n.* A small room, a cave, a small mass of protoplasm forming the structural unit in animal tissues.

cemetery, se'mē-te-ri, *n.* A burial place.

cenotaph, sen'ō-taf, *n.* A monument to one who is buried elsewhere.

censorious, sen-sō'ri-us, *a.* Addicted to censure.

census, sen'sus, *n.* An enumeration of the inhabitants of a country.

cent, sent, *n.* A hundred; a copper coin in America etc., the hundredth part of a dollar. *Per cent,* a certain rate by the hundred.

centipede, sen'ti-pēd, *n.* An insect having a great number of feet.

central, sen'tral, *a.* Placed in the center, relating to the center.

centripetal, sen-trip'et-al, *a.* Tending toward the center.

cereal, sē'rē-al, *a.* Pertaining to corn.—*n.* A grain plant.

cerebral, se're-bral, *a.* Pertaining to the brain.

ceremony, se'rē-mō-ni, *n.* Outward rite, form, observance, formality.

cerise, se-rēz', *n.* Cherry-color.

certain, sėr'tān, *a.* Sure; undeniable; decided; particular; some; one.

certificate, sėr-tif'i-kāt, *n.* A written testimony a credential.

certify, sėr-ti-fī, *vt.* (certifying, certified). To give certain information to testify to in writing.

chafe, chāf, *vt.* (chafing, chafed). To make

warm by rubbing; to fret by rubbing, to enrage.—*vi.* To be fretted by friction; to rage.—*n.* A heat; a fretting.

chaff, chaf, *n.* The husk of corn and grasses; banter.—*vt.* To banter.

chagrin sha-grēn', *n.* Ill-humor; vexation.—*vt.* To vex, to mortify.

chain, chān, *n.* A series of links; a line of things connected, that which binds, a line formed of links 66 feet long; (*pl.*) bondage; slavery. —*vt.* To bind with a chain; to confine.

chairman, chā r'man, *n.* The presiding officer of an assembly; a President.

chalybeate, ka-lib'ē-āt, *a.* Impregnated with particles of iron.—*n.* A liquid into which iron or steel enters.

chameleon, ka-mē'lē-on, *n.* A species of lizard, whose color changes.

chamfer, cham'fèr, *n.* A small furrow in wood, etc., a bevel.—*vt.* To cut a chamfer in, to bevel

chamois, sham'i or sham'wä, *n.* A species of antelope; a soft leather.

champ, champ, *vt.* To devour with violent action of the teeth, to bite the bit, as a horse.—*vi.* To keep biting.

champagne, sham-pān', *n.* A kind of brisk sparkling wine.

champion, cham'pi-on, *n.* A combatant for another, or for a cause; a hero, one victorious in contest.— *vt.* To fight for.

chance, chans, *n.* That which happens; accident; possibility of an occurrence, opportunity.—*vi.* (chancing, chanced). To happen.—*a.* Happening by chance, casual.

changeling, chānj'ling, *n.* A child substituted for another; a fool; one apt to change.

chaplain, chap'lān, *n.* A clergyman of the army, navy, court, etc.

chapter, chap'tèr, *n.* Division of a book; a society of clergymen belonging to a cathedral or collegiate church; an organized branch of some fraternity.

charade, sha-räd', *n.* A species of riddle upon the syllables of a word.

charcoal, chär'kōl, *n.* Coal made by charring wood, the residue of animal, vegetable, and many mineral substances, when heated to redness in close vessels.

charity, cha'ri-ti, *n.* A disposition to relieve the wants of others; benevolence; alms; a charitable institution.

charlatan, shär 'la-tan, *n.* A quack.

charm, chärm, *n.* A spell; fascination; a locket, etc.—*vt.* To enthrall; to delight.

chart, chärt, *n.* A map, delineation of coasts, etc., tabulated facts.

charter, chär'tè r, *n.* A writing given as evidence of a grant, contract etc.—*vt.* To establish by charter; to hire or to let (a ship).

chauffeur, shō'fèr, *n.* A person regularly employed to drive a private motor-car.

cheap, chēp, *a.* Of a low price; common, not respected.

cheat, chēt, *vt.* To defraud; to deceive.—*n.* A deceitful act; a swindler.

checkmate, chek'māt, *n.* A move in chess which ends the game; defeat.—*vt.* to give checkmate to, to frustrate; to defeat.

cheddar, ched'èr, *n.* A rich English cheese.

cheek, chēk, *n.* The side of the face below the eyes on each side; impudence.

Chemistry, kem'ist-ri, *n.* The science which treats of the properties and nature of elementary substances.

cherish, che'rish, *vt.* To treat with tenderness; to encourage.

cheroot, shē-röt', *n.* A kind of cigar with both ends cut square off.

cherry, che'ri, *n.* A tree and its fruit, of the plum family.—*a.* Like a cherry in color.

cherub, che'rub, *n.*; pl. **-ubs** and **-ubim.** An angel of the second order, a beautiful child.

chicory, chik'o-ri, *n.* A common English plant, often used to mix with coffee.

chide, chīd, *vt.* and *i.* (chiding, pret. chid, pp. chid, chidden). To reprove, to scold.

chief, chēf, *a.* Being at the head first; leading.—*n.* A principal person; a leader.

chilblain, chil'blān, *n.* A blain or sore produced on the hands or feet by cold.

childbirth, child'bé rth, *n.* The act of bringing forth a child; travail; labor.

chill, chil, *n.* A shivering with cold; a cold fit, that which checks or disheartens.—*a.* Cold, tending to cause shivering, dispiriting.—*vt.* To make cold; to discourage.

chime, chīm, *n.* A set of bells tuned to each other; their sound; harmony; the brim of a cask.—*vi.* (chiming, chimed). To sound in consonance; to agree.—*vt.* To cause to sound in harmony; to cause to sound.

chin, chin, *n.* The lower part of the face, the point of the under jaw.

china, chī'na, *n.* A species of fine porcelain.

chinchilla, chin-chil'la, *n.* A genus of S. American rodent animals; their fur.

chiropodist, kīr-op'od-ist, *n.* One who

extracts corns, removes bunions, etc.

chirp, chêrp, *vi.* To make the lively noise of small birds.—*n.* A short, shrill note of birds.

chisel, chiz'el, *n.* A cutting tool used in wood-work, masonry, sculpture, etc.—*vt.* (chiselling chiselled). To cut gouge, or engrave with a chisel.

chit, chit, *n.* A note; an order or pass.

chlorophyll, klō'rō-fil, *n.* The green coloring matter of plants.

chocolate, cho 'ko-lā t, *n.* A preparation from the kernels of the cacaonut.—*a.* Dark, glossy brown.

choice, chois, *n.* Act of choosing oPtion, the thing chosen, best part of anything; the object of choice.—*a.* Select, Precious.

chop, chop, *vt.* (chopping chopped). To cut into small pieces, to barter or exchange.—*vi.* To change; to turn suddenly.—*n.* A piece chopped off; a small piece of meat, a crack or cleft, a turn or change; the jaw; the mouth.

chopsticks, chop'stiks, *n.* Two sticks of wood, ivory, etc., used by the Chinese in eating.

chord, kord, *n.* String of a musical instrument, the simultaneous combination of different sounds; a straight line joining the ends of the arc of a circle or curve.

chorus, kō'rus, *n.* A company of singers, a piece performed by a company in concert; verses of a song in which the company join the singer; any union of voices in general.

chosen, chōz'n, *a.* Select, eminent.

chrism, krizm, *n.* Consecrated oil.

christen, kris'n, *vt.* To baptize; to name.

Christian, kris'ti-an, *n.* A professed follower of Christ.—*a.* Pertaining to Christ or Christianity.

Christmas, kris'mas, *n.* The festival of Christ's nativity, observed annually on 25th December.—*a.* Belonging to Christmas time.

chromatic, krō-mat'ik, *a.* Relating to color; proceeding by semitones.

chrome, chromium, krōm, krō 'mium, *n.* A steel-gray, hard metal, from which colored preparations are made.

chronic, kron'ik, *a.* Continuing a long time, lingering, continuous.

chronology, kro-nol'o-ji, *n.* Arrangement of events according to their dates.

chrysalis, kris'a-lis, *n.*, pl. **-ides** or **-ises.** The form of certain insects before they arrive at their winged state.

chrysanthemum, kri-san'thē-mum, *n.* The name of numerous composite plants.

chub, chub, *n.* A small river fish of the carp family.

cider, sī'dèr, *n.* A fermented drink prepared from the juice of apples.

cigar, si-gär', *n.* A roll of tobacco for smoking.

cigarette, sig-a-ret', *n.* A little cut tobacco rolled up in rice paper, used for smoking.

cilia, sil'i-a, *n.pl.* Minute hairs on plants or animals.

ciliary, sil'i-a-ri, *a.* Belonging to or of the nature of eyelashes.

Cimmerian, sim-mē'ri-an, *a.* Pertaining to the fabulous Cimmerians, who dwelt in perpetual darkness; extremely dark.

cinnamon, sin'na-mon, *n.* The inner bark of a tree, a native of Ceylon; a spice.

circle, sêr'kl, *n.* A plane figure contained by a curved line, every point of which is equally distant from a point within the figure, called the center the curved line itself, a ring; enclosure; a class; a coterie.—*vt.* (circling circled). To move round, to enclose.—*vi.* To move circularly.

circuit, sêr'kit, *n.* Act of going round; space measured by travelling round; the journey of judges to hold courts the district visited by judges; path of an electric current.

circular, sêr'kū-lêr, *a.* Round; addressed to a number of persons.—*n.* A paper addressed to a number of persons.

circulate, sêr'kū-lāt, *vi.* (circulating, circulated). To move in a circle, to have currency.—*vt.* To spread; to give currency to.

circumcise, sêr'kum-sīz *vt.* (circumcising, circumcised). To cut off the foreskin, according to Jewish and Mohammedan law.

circumference, sêr-kum'fē-rens, *n.* The bounding line of a circle.

circumstance, sêr'kum-stans, *n.* Something attending, or relative to a main fact or case; event; *(pl.)* state of affairs, condition.

circumvent, sêr-kum-vent', *vt.* To encompass; to outwit.

circus, sêr'kus, *n.*; pl. **-ses.** Among the Romans, a place for horseraces; a place for feats of horsemanship and acrobatic displays.

cirrus, sir'rus, *n.*; pl. **cirri.** A tendril; a light fleecy cloud at a high elevation.

cistern, sis'têrn, *n.* An artificial receptacle for water, etc.; a natural reservoir.

citadel, si'ta-del, *n*. A fortress in or near a city.

citation, sī-tā'shon, *n*. Quotation; a summons.

citizen, si'ti-zen, *n*. An inhabitant of a city; one who has full municipal and political privileges.—*a*. Having the qualities of a citizen.

civilian, si-vil'i-an, *n*. One skilled in the civil law, one engaged in civil, not military or clerical pursuits.

civility, si-vil'i-ti, *n*. Quality of being civil; good breeding; (pl.) acts of politeness.

civilize, si'vil-īz, *vt*. (civilizing, civilized). To reclaim from a savage state.

clamp, klamp, *n*. A piece of timber or iron, used to strengthen or fasten, a heavy footstep.—*vt*. To fasten or strengthen with clamps; to tread heavily.

clan, klan, *n*. A family; a tribe; a sect.

clandestine, klan-des'tin, *a*. Secret; underhand.

clang, klang, *vt*. or *i*. To make a sharp sound, as by striking metallic substances.—*n*. A loud sound made by striking together metallic bodies.

clank, klangk, *n*. The loud sound made by the collision of metallic bodies.—*vi*. or *t*. To sound or cause to sound with a clank.

clasp, klasp, *n*. An embrace; a hook for fastening; a catch; a bar added to a military medal to commemorate a particular battle or campaign.—*vt*. To fasten together with a clasp, to inclose in the hand; to embrace closely.

clasp-knife, klasp'nīf, *n*. A knife the blade of which folds into the handle.

class, klas, *n*. A rank of persons or things; an order; a group.—*vt*. To arrange in classes.

clause, klāz, *n*. A member of a sentence; a distinct part of a contract, will, etc.

claustrophobia, kläs'trō-fo"bē-a, *n*. Morbid fear of confined spaces.

clavicle, klav'i-kl, *n*. The collarbone.

claw, klä, *n*. The sharp hooked nail of an animal; that which resembles a claw.—*vt*. To scrape, scratch, or tear.

clay, klā, *n*. A tenacious kind of earth, earth in general; the body. —*vt*. To cover with clay; to purify and whiten with clay, as sugar.

clean, klēn, *a*. Free from dirt; pure. —*adv*. Quite; fully.—*vt*. To purify; to cleanse.

cleat, klēt, *n*. A piece of wood or iron in a ship to fasten ropes upon; a wedge.

clement, kle'ment, *a*. Mild; humane.

clench, klensh, *vt*. To secure; to confirm; to grasp.

clergy, klėr'ji, *n.pl*. The body or order of men set apart to the service of God, in the Christian church.

clericalism, kle'rik-al-izm, *n*. Clerical power to influence; sacerdotalism.

clerk, klärk, *n*. A clergyman; one who reads the responses in church; one who is employed under another as a writer.

cliche, klē'shā, *n*. A hackneyed phrase.

click, klik, *vi*. To make a small sharp noise, or a succession of such sounds.— *n*. A small sharp sound.

client, klī'ent, *n*. A person under patronage; one who employs a lawyer.

cliff, klif, *n*. A precipice; a steep rock.

climacteric, kli-mak-te'rik, *n*. A critical period in human life.

climate, klī'māt, *n*. The condition of a country in respect of temperature, dryness, wind, etc.

climb, klīm, *vi*. To creep up step by step; to ascend.—*vt*. To ascent.

clock, klok, *n*. An instrument which measures time.

clod, klod, *n*. A lump of earth; a stupid fellow.—*vt*. (clodding, clodded). To pelt with clods.

clog, klog, *vt*. (clogging, clogged). To hinder; to impede; to trammel.—*vi*. To be loaded.—*n*. Hindrance; a shoe with a wooden sole.

cloister, klois'tėr, *n*. A monastery or nunnery; an arcade round an open court.— *vt*. To shut up in a cloister; to immure.

close, klōs, *a*. Shut fast; tight; dense; near; stingy, trusty, intense; without ventilation; disposed to keep secrets.—*adv*. Tightly, in contact, or very near.—*n*. An inclosed place; precinct of a cathedral.

clot, klot, *n*. A mass of soft or fluid matter concreted.—*vi*. (clotting, clotted). To become thick; to coagulate.

cloud, kloud, *n*. A collection of visible vapor, suspended in the air; something similar to this; what obscures, threatens, etc.; a great multitude, a mass.—*vt*. To obscure; to darken; to sully; to make to appear sullen.—*vi*. To grow cloudy.

cloy, kloi, *vt*. To glut; to fill to loathing.

club-footed, klub'fut-ed, *a*. Having short, crooked, or deformed feet.

cluck, kluk, *vi*. To make the noise of the hen when calling chickens.—*n*. Such a sound.

clue, klö, *n*. A ball of thread; a thread serving to guide; something helping to unravel a mystery.

coast, kōst, *n*. The sea-shore; the country near the sea.—*vi*. To sail along a shore; to sail from port to port.

coax, kōks, *vt*. To wheedle; to persuade by fondling and flattering.

cob, kob, *n*. A round knob; the head of clover or wheat; a smallish thick-set horse; a mile swan.

cobalt, kō'bält, *n*. A mineral of grayish color, and a metal obtained from it yielding a permanent blue; the blue itself.

cobble, kob'l, *vt*. (cobbling, cobbled). To mend coarsely, as shoes; to botch.—*n*. A roundish stone.

coco, cocoa, kō'kō, *n*. A tropical palm-tree.

cocoa, kō'kō, *n*. The seed of the cacao prepared for a beverage; the beverage itself.

cocoon, kō'kön', *n*. The silky case in which the silkworm involves itself when still a larva; the envelope of other larvae.

cod, kod, *n*. A species of sea fish allied to the haddock; a husk; a pod.

coddle, kod'l, *vt*. (coddling, coddled). To fondle.

code, kōd, *n*. A digest of laws; a collection of rules; a system of signals, etc.

codicil, ko'di-sil, *n*. A writing by way of supplement to a will.

coffee, kof'i, *n*. A tree and its fruit or berries; a beverage made from the seeds.

coffee-house, kof'i hous, *n*. A house where coffee and refreshments are supplied.

coffer, kof'ėr, *n*. A chest for holding gold, jewels etc.

coffin, kof'fin, *n*. The chest in which a dead human body is buried.—*vt*. To inclose in a coffin.

cog, kog, *n*. The tooth of a wheel. —*vt*. (cogging, cogged). To furnish with cogs; to trick, deceive; to manipulate dice unfairly.—*vi*. To cheat; to lie.

cogent, kō'jent, *a*. Forcible; convincing.

cogitate, ko'jit-āt, *vi*. (cogitating cogitated) To ponder; to meditate.

cognac, kō'nyak, *n*. A kind of brandy.

cognate, kog'nāt, *a*. Born of the same stock; akin; of the same nature.

cognition, kog-ni'shon, *n*. Knowledge from personal view or experience.

cohesion, kō-hē'zhon, *n*. Act of sticking together; the attraction by which bodies are kept together; coherence.

coiffure, koif'ūr, *n*. Mode of dressing the hair in women.

coil, koil, *vt*. To wind into a ring.

—*n*. A ring or rings into which a rope, etc., is wound.

coin, koin, *n*. A piece of metal stamped, as money, that which serves for payment.—*vt*. To stamp and convert metal into money; to mint; to invent; to fabricate.

coition, kō-i'shon, *n*. Sexual intercourse.

colitis, kō-lī'tis, *n*. Inflammation of the large intestine, especially of its mucous membrane.

collar, kol'ėr, *n*. A part of dress that surrounds the neck, something worn round the neck.—*vt*. To seize by the collar; to put a collar on; to roll up and bind with a cord.

collect, kol'ekt, *n*. A short comprehensive prayer; a short prayer adapted to a particular occasion.

collected, kol-lekt'ed, *p.a*. Cool; self-possessed.

collectivism, kol-lek'tiv-izm, *n*. The doctrine that the state should own or control the land and all means of production.

collide, kol-līd', *vi*. (colliding, collided). To strike against each other; to meet in opposition.

collie, kol'i, *n*. A dog common in Scotland, much used for sheep.

colophon, ko'lo-fōn, *n*. An inscription or device formerly on the last page of a book, now usually in its preliminary pages.

color-blindness, kul'ėr-blī nd-nes, *n*. Inability to distinguish colors.

colossal, kō-los'al, *a*. Huge; gigantic.

colure, kō-lūr', *n*. Either of two great circles of the heavens, passing through the solstitial and the equinoctial points of the ecliptic.

coma, kō'ma, *n*. Deep sleep; stupor; the hair-like envelope round the nucleus of a comet.

comb, kōm, *n*. An instrument for separating hair, wool, etc.; the crest of a cock, honeycomb.—*vt*. To separate and adjust with a comb.

combine, kom-bīn', *vt*. (combining, combined). To cause to unite; to join.—*vi*. To come into union, to coalesce; to league together.—kom' bin, *n*. A union.

combustible, kom-bust'i-bl, *a*. Capable of catching fire; inflammable.—*n*. A substance easily set on fire.

come, kum, *vi*. (coming, pret. came, pp. come). To move hitherward; to draw nigh; to arrive; to happen, to appear; to rise, to result.

comedian, ko-mē'di-an, *n*. An actor in or

writer of comedies.

coming, kum'ing, *p.a.* Future.—*n.* Approach.

comity, ko'mi-ti, *n.* Courtesy; civility.

comma, kom'ma, *n.* A mark of punctuation, thus (,) an interval in music.

commend, kom-mend', *vt.* To commit to the care of; to recommend; to praise.

commensal, kom-men'sal, *n.* One that eats at the same table; one living with another.

commensurate kom-men'sūr-ā t *a.* Proportional; having equal measure.

comment, kom-ment', *vi.* To make remarks or criticisms.—*vt.* To annotate.—*n.* kom'-ment. An explanatory note; criticism.

commentary, kom'ment-a-ri, *n.* Book of comments, an historical narrative.

commerce, kom'mėrs, *n.* Exchange of goods by barter or purchase; trade; intercourse.

commercial, kom-mėr'shal, *a.* Pertaining to commerce, trading; mercantile.

commissure, kom'mis-sūr, *n.* A joint or seam; juncture.

commit, kom-mit', *vt.* (committing, committed). To intrust; to consign; to send to prison, to perpetrate; to endanger or compromise (oneself).

committee, kom-mit'tē, *n.* A body of persons appointed to manage any matter.

commix, kom-miks', *vt.* To blend; to mix.

commodious, kom-mō'di-us, *a.* Convenient; spacious and suitable.

commodore, kom'mo-dōr, *n.* A captain in the navy who is discharging duties rather more important than those usually assigned to a captain.

communicable, kom-mū'ni-ka-bl *a.* Capable of being imparted to another.

communicant, kom-mūni-kant, *n.* One who communicates, a partaker of the Lord's supper.

communicate, kom-mū'ni-kāt, *vt.* (communicating, communicated). To cause to be common to others; to impart, as news disease, etc.to bestow, to reveal.—*vi.* To share with others; to partake of the Lord's supper; to have intercourse, to correspond.

communion, kom-mūn'yon, *n.* A mutual participation in anything mutual intercourse; concord; celebration of the Lord's supper.

Communism, kom'mūn-izm, *n.* The doctrine of a community of property by which the state owns and controls all means of production.

Communist, kom'mūn-ist, *n.* One who holds the doctrines of communism; member of the communist party.

community, kom-mū'ni-ti, *n.* Mutual participation; the public; a society of persons under the same laws.

company, kum'pa-ni, *n.* Companionship; an assembly of persons; partners in a firm; a division of a battalion, consisting of four platoons, and commanded by a major or mounted captain, with a captain as second-in-command the crew of a ship.—*vi.* To associate with.

comparative, kom-pa'ra-tiv, *a.* Estimated by comparison; not positive or absolute.

compatriot, kom-pā'tri-ot, *n.* One of the same country.

compete, kom-pēt', *vi.* (competing, competed). To strive for the same thing as another; to contend.

competent, kom'pē-tent *a.* Suitable, sufficient, qualified, having adequate right.

competition, kom-pē-ti'shon, *n.* Contest for the same object, rivalry.

complacence, complacency, komplā ' sens, komplā'sen-si, *n.* A feeling of quiet satisfaction; complaisance.

complain, kom-plān', *vi.* to express grief or distress, to lament to express dissatisfaction; to make a formal accusation.

complaisance, kom'plā-zans, *n.* A pleasing deportment; courtesy; urbanity.

complement, kom'plē-ment, *n.* That which fills up; full quantity or number.

complete, kom-plēt', *a.* Having no deficiency; finished; total; absolute.—*vt.* (completing, completed). To make complete; to finish; to fulfill.

complexion, kom-plek'shon, *n.* The color of the face; general appearance.

comply, kom-plī', *vi.* (complying, complied). To yield; to assent; to acquiesce.

component, kom-pōn'ent, *a.* Composing; forming an element of a compound.—*n.* A constituent part; ingredient.

composer, kom-pōz'ėr, *n.* An author, especially a musical author.

compost, kom'pōst, *n.* A mixture for manure.

compress, kom-pres', *vt.* To press together; to squeeze; to condense.—*n.* kom'pres. A soft mass or bandage used in surgery.

compressible, kom-pres'i-bl, *a.* Capable of being compressed.

comprise, kom-prīz, *vt.* (comprising, comprised). To embrace; to contain; to inclose.

compromise, kom'prō-mîz, *n.* An amicable agreement to settle differences, mutual concession.—*vi.* To settle by mutual concessions; to involve; to endanger the interests of.

comptroller, kon-trōl'er, *n.* A controller, an officer who examines the accounts of collectors of public money.

compulsion, kom-pul'shon, *n.* Act of compelling; state of being compelled; force.

compulsory, kom-pul'so-ri, *a.* Constraining; coercive; obligatory.

compunction, kom-pungk'shon, *n.* Remorse; contrition.

concave, kon'kāv, *a.* Hollow, as the inner surface of a sphere; opposed to convex.—*n.* A hollow; an arch or vault.

conceal, kon-sēl', *vt.* To hide; to secrete; to disguise.

concede, kon-sēd', *vt.* (conceding, conceded). To yield; to grant.—*vi.* To make concession.

conceit, kon-sēt', *n.* Conception; fancy; self-flattering opinion; vanity.

concentrate, kon'sen-trāt, *vt.* (concentrating, concentrated). To bring together; to direct to one object, to condense.

concentric, kon-sen'trik, *a.* Having a common center.

concept, kon'sept, *n.* An object conceived by the mind; a general notion of a class of objects.

concert, kon-sėrt', *vt.* to plan together; to contrive.—*n.* kon'sert. Agreement in a design; harmony; performance of a company of players, singers, etc.

concise, kon-sīs', *a.* Brief; abridged; comprehensive.

conclave, kon'klā v, *n.* A private apartment; the assembly of cardinals for the election of a pope; a close assembly.

conclude, kon-klūd', *vt.* (concluding, concluded). To end; to decide; to deduce.—*vt.* To end; to form a final judgment.

concomitance, concomitancy, kon-kom'i-tans, kon-kom'i-tan-si, *n.* A being together or in connection with another thing.

concubine, kong'kū-bīn, *n.* A woman who cohabits with a man; a mistress.

concupiscence, kon-kū'pis-ens, *n.* Lust.

concur, kon-kėr', *vt.* (concurring, concurred). To unite; to agree; to assent.

concussion, kon-ku'shon, *n.* A violent shock.

concussive, kon-kus'iv, *a.* Having the power or quality of shaking; agitating.

condemn, kon-dem', *vt.* To pronounce to be wrong; to censure; to sentence.

conditionally, kon-di'shon-al-li, *adv.* With certain limitations.

condone, kon-don', *vt.* (condoning condoned). To pardon; to imply forgiveness of.

condor, kon'dor, *n.* A S. American vulture.

conduce, kon-dūs', *vi.* (conducing conduced). To lead; to tend, to contribute.

conduct, kon'dukt, *n.* Personal behavior, management; escort.—*vt.* kon-dukt'. To read or guide; to escort; to manage; to behave (oneself), to transmit, as heat, etc.

confection, kon-fek'shon, *n.* A mixture; a sweetmeat.

confectioner, kon-fek'shon-ėr, *n.* One who makes or sells sweetmeats.

Confederacy, kon-fe'de-ra-si, *n.* A confederation; the parties united by a league.

confederate, kon-fe'de-rā t, *a.* Allied by treaty.—*n.* One united with others in a league.—*vt.* and *i.* (confederating, confederated). To unite in a league.

confederation, kon-fe'de-rā''shon, *n.* A league; alliance, particularly of states, etc.

conference, kon'fėr-ens, *n.* A meeting for consultation, or for the adjustment of differences; bestowal.

confidence, kon'fī-dens, *n.* Firm belief or trust; self-reliance; boldness; assurance; a secret.

confidential, kon-fī-den'shal, *a.* Enjoying confidence; trusty; private; secret.

confirm, kon-fėrm', *vt.* To make firm or more firm; to establish; to make certain; to administer the rite of confirmation to.

confirmation, kon-fėrm-ā'shon, *n.* Act of confirming; additional evidence; ratification; the laying on of a bishop's hands in the rite of admission to the privileges of a Christian.

confiscate, kon'fis-kā t, *vt.* (confiscating, confiscated). To seize as forfeited to the public treasury.

conflagration, kon-fla-grā'shon, *n.* A great fire.

conflict, kon'flikt, *n.* a struggle; clashing of views or statements.—*vi.* kon-flikt'. To meet in opposition; to be antagonistic.

confluence, kon'flū-ens, *n.* A flowing together; meeting, or place of meeting, of rivers; a concourse; a crowd.

conform, kon-form', *vt.* To cause to be of the same form; to adapt.—*vi.* To comply.

conformation, kon-for-mā'shon, *n.* The act of conforming; structure; configuration.

conformist, kon-for'mist, *n.* One who conforms; one who complies with the worship of the established church.

confound, kon-found', *vt.* To confuse; to astound; to overthrow; to mistake.

confute, kon-fū t', *vt.* (confuting confuted). To prove to be false; to refute.

congeniality, kon-jē 'ni-al''i-ti, *n.* Natural affinity; suitableness.

congenital, kon-jen'it-al, *a.* Pertaining to an individual from his birth.

congeries, kon-jē 'ri-ēz, *n.* A head or pile; a collection of several bodies in one mass.

congest, kon-jest', *vt.* and *i.* To accumulate to excess, as blood, population, etc.

congestion kon-jest'shon *n.* Excessive accumulation; undue fullness of blood-vessels in an organ.

Congregation, kong-grē -gā'shon, *n.* Act of congregating; an assembly; an assembly met for divine worship.

Congregationalist, kong-grē-gā' shon-al-ist, *n.* One who adheres to the system in which each separate congregation or church forms an independent body

congress, kong'gres, *n.* An assembly; a meeting of ambassadors etc., for the settlement of affairs between different nations; the legislature of the United States.

congruence, congruency, kong' grü-ens, kong'grü-en-si, *n.* Accordance; consistency.

congruity, kon-grü'i-ti, *n.* Suitableness accordance; consistency.

conic, conical, kon'ik, kon'ik-al, *a.* Having the form of a cone; pertaining to a cone.

conjugate, kon'jū-gā t, *vt.* (conjugating, conjugated). To join together; to inflect (a verb) through its several forms.—*a.* Joined in pairs; kindred in origin and meaning.

conjunction, kon-jungk'shon, *n.* Act of joining; state of being joined; connection; a connecting word.

connect, kon-nekt', *vt.* To conjoin; to combine, to associate,—*vi.* To unite or cohere together; to have a close relation.

connection, kon-nek'shon, *n.* Act of connecting; state of being connected; a relation by blood or marriage; relationship.

connective, kon-nekt'iv, *a.* Having the power of connecting; tending to connect.—*n.* A word that connects other words and sentences; a conjunction.

connivance, kon-nīv'ans, *n.* Voluntary blindness to an act; pretended ignorance.

connive, kon-nīv', *vi.* (conniving connived). To wink; to pretend ignorance or blindness, to forbear to see (with at).

conscience, kon'shens, *n.* Internal knowledge or judgment of right and wrong; the moral sense; morality.

conscionable, kon'shon-a-bl, *a.* Reasonable.

conscious, kon 'shus, *a.* Knowing in one's own mind; knowing by sensation or perception; aware; sensible; self-conscious.

consciousness, kon'shus-nes, *n.* State of being conscious; perception of what passes in one's own mind; sense of guilt or innocence.

consequence, kon'sē-kwens, *n.* That which follows as a result, inference; importance.

consequent, kon'sē-kwent, *a.* Following, as the natural effect, or by inference.— *n.* Effect; result; inference.

consequential, kon-sē -kwen'shal, *a.* Following as the effect; pompous.

conservation, kon-sé rv-ā 'shon, *n.* Preservation, the keeping of a thing entire.

considerable, kon-si'dèr-a-bl, *a.* Worthy of consideration; moderately large.

considerate, kon-si'dèr-āt, *a.* Given to consideration; mindful of others; deliberate.

considerately, kon-si'dèr-āt-li, *adv.* In a considerate manner.

consideration, kon-si'dèr-ā''shon n. Mental view; serious deliberation; importance; motive of action; an equivalent.

considering, kon-si'dèr-ing, *prep.* Taking into account; making allowance for.

consign, kon-sīn', *vt.* To deliver over to another by agreement; to intrust; to commit; to deposit.

consolation, kon-sōl-ā'shon, *n.* A solace; alleviation of misery, what helps to cheer; what gives comfort.

console, kon-sōl', *vt.* (consoling, consoled). To comfort; to soothe; to cheer.

consolidate, kon-sol'id-āt, *vt.* (consolidating, consolidated). To make solid or firm, to unite into one; to compact.—*vi.* To grow firm and solid.

conspiracy, kon-spi'ra-si, *n.* A plot; a treasonable combination.

conspire, kon-spīr', *vi.* (conspiring, conspired). To plot; to combine for some evil purpose; to tend to one end.

constable, kun 'sta-bl, *n.* An officer of the peace; policeman.

constant, kon'stant, *a.* Stead-fast; perpetual; assiduous; resolute.—*n.* That which remains unchanged; a fixed quantity.

constellation, kon-stel-lā'shon, *n.* A group of fixed stars; an assemblage of splendors or excellences.

constipate, kon'sti-pāt, *vt.* (constipating, constipated). To make costive.

constituent, kon-stit'ū-ent, *a.* Forming; existing as an essential part.—*n.* An elector; an essential part.

constitute, kon'sti-tū t, *vt.* (constituting, constituted). To set up or establish; to compose; to appoint; to make and empower.

constitution, kon-sti-tū'shon, *n.* The particular frame or character of the body or mind, established form of government, a system of fundamental laws; a particular law.

constitutional, kon-sti-tū'shon-al, *a.* Adherent in the human constitution, consistent with the civil constitution; legal.—*n.* A walk for the sake of health.

constrain, kon-strā n', *vt.* To urge by force; to necessitate; to restrain.

constructive, kon-strukt'iv, *a.* Having ability to construct; created or deduced by construction; inferred.

construe, kon'strū , *vt.* (construing, construed). To arrange words so as to discover the sense of a sentence to interpret.

consult, kon-sult', *vi.* To seek the opinion of another; to deliberate in common; to consider.—*vt.* To ask advice of; to refer to for information; to have regard to.

consume, kon-sūm', *vt.* (consuming, consumed). To reduce to nothing; to burn up; to squander.—*vi.* To waste away slowly; to be exhausted.

consummate, kon'sum-āt, *vt.* To finish; to perfect.—*a.* kon-sum'at. Complete; perfect.

consumption, kon-sum'shon, *n.* Act of consuming; quantity consumed; a gradual wasting away of the body.

contact, kon'takt, *n.* A touching together; close union or juncture of bodies.

contagion, kon-tā'jon, *n.* Communication of a disease by contact; poisonous emanation; infection.

contain, kon-tān', *vt.* To hold, to be able to hold; to comprise; to restrain.

contaminate, kon-tam'in-āt, *vt.* To corrupt; to taint; to vitiate.

contemptible, kon-tem'ti-bl, *a.* Worthy of contempt; despicable; vile; mean.

contemptuous, kon-tem'tū -us, *a.* Manifesting contempt; scornful; insolent.

contend, kon-tend', *vi.* To strive; to vie; to dispute; to wrangle.

contest, kon-test', *vt.* To call in question; to strive for.—*vi.* To strive; to contend; to emulate.—*n.* kon'test. Struggle for victory; encounter; debate; competition.

context, kon'tekst, *n.* The parts which precede or follow a passage quoted.

contiguous, kon-tig'ū-us, *a.* Touching one another; in contact; adjacent.

continence, continency, kon'ti-nens, kona-ti-nen-si, *n.* Restraint of the desires and passions; chastity; temperance.

continent, kon'ti-nent, *a.* Chaste; moderate.—*n.* A connected tract of land of great extent; the mainland of Europe.

contingence, contingency, kon-tin'jens, kon-tin'jen-si, *n.* Quality of being contingent; an event which may occur; chance; juncture.

continue, kon-tin'ū, *vi.* (continuing continued). To remain in a state or place; to be durable; to persevere; to be steadfast.—*vt.* To prolong; to extend, to persevere in.

continuity, kon-ti-nū 'i-ti, *n.* Close union of parts; unbroken texture; cohesion.

continuous, kon-tin'ū-us, *a.* Joined together closely; conjoined; continued.

contort, kon-tort', *vt.* To twist; to writhe, to draw or pull awry.

contortionist, kon-tor'shon-ist, *n.* An acrobat who practices contortions of the body.

contour, kontör', *n.* The line that bounds a body; outline.

contractile, kon-traktīl, *a.* Having the power of contracting, as living fibers.

contraction, kon-trak'shon, *n.* Shrinking; shortening; abbreviation.

contractor, kon-trakt'èr, *n.* One who contracts to perform any work or service, or to furnish supplies, at a certain price or rate.

contradict, kon-tra-dikt', *vt.* To assert to be the contrary; to deny; to oppose.

contradiction, kon-tra dik 'shon, *n.* A contrary assertion; inconsistency with itself.

contradictory, kon-tra-dik'to-ri, *a.* Implying contradiction; inconsistent.

contradistinction, kon'tra-distingk"shon, *n.* Distinction by opposites.

contravene, kon-tra-vēn' *vt.* (contravening, contravened). To oppose; to transgress.

contribute, kon-trib'ūt, *vt.* (contributing, contributed). To give in common with others.—*vi.* To give a part; to conduce.

contribution, kon-tri-bū'shon, *n.* Act of contributing; that which is contributed; an article sent to a periodical, etc.

contrite, kon'trīt, *a.* Brokenhearted for sin; penitent.

contrition, kon-tri'shon, *n.* Grief of heart for sin.

contrivance, kon-trīv'ans, *n.* Scheme; invention; artifice.

control, kon-trōl', *n.* Restraint; superintendence, authority.—*vt.* (controlling, controlled). To restrain; to regulate.

controller, kon-trōl'ėr, *n.* An officer who checks the accounts of collectors of public moneys.

controversy, kon'trō-vėr-si, *n.* A disputation, particularly in writing; litigation.

controvert, kon'trō-vėrt, *vt.* To dispute by reasoning; to attempt to disprove or confute.

conundrum, kō-nun'drum, *n.* A sort of riddle turning on some odd resemblance between things quite unlike.

convalesce, kon-va-les', *vi.* (convalescing, convalesced). To recover health.

convalescence, kon-va-les'ens, *n.* The state of one convalescent; gradual recovery after illness.

convene, kon-vēn', *vi.* (convening convened). To assemble.—*vt.* To cause to assemble, to convoke.

convenience, conveniency, kon-vē' niens, kon-vē'ni-en-si, *n.* Ease; comfort; suitable opportunity; an appliance or utensil.

convenient, kon-vė'ni-ent, *a.* Suit-able, adapted opportune.

convent, kon-vent, *n.* A body of monks or nuns; a monastery; a nunnery.

conventicle, kon-ven'ti-kl, *n.* A secret meeting, a meeting of religious dissenters; their meeting place.

convention, kon-ven'shon, *n.* An assembly; an agreement; recognized social custom.

conventional, kon-ven'shon-al, *a.* Formed by agreement, tacitly understood; resting on mere usage.

convergent, kon-vėrj'ent, *a.* Tending to one point or object; approaching.

conversant, kon'vėrs-ant, *a.* Having intercourse or familiarity; versed in; proficient; occupied or concerned.

conversation, kon-vė r-sā 'shon, *n.*

Familiar intercourse; easy talk.

converse, kon-vėrs', *vi.* (conversing, conversed). To hold intercourse; to talk familiarly; to commune.—*n.* kon'vers. Conversation, familiarity, something forming a counterpart.—*a.* Put the opposite or reverse way.

conversion, kon-vėr'shon, *n.* Change from one state, religion, or party to another; interchange of terms in logic.

convert, kon-vėrt', *vt.* and *i.* To change from one state, use, religion, or party to another; to turn from a bad life to a good; to interchange conversely.—*n.* kon'vert. One who has changed his opinion, practice, or religion.

convict, kon-vikt', *vt.* To prove or decide to be guilty.—*n.* kon'vikt. A person found guilty; one undergo ing penal servitude.

convince, kon-vins', *vt.* (convincing, convinced). To persuade by argument; to satisfy by evidence or proof.

convocation, kon-vō-ka'shon, *n.* Act of convoking; an assembly, particularly of clergy or heads of a university.

convoke, kon-vōk', *vt.* (convoking, convoked). To call together; to summon to meet.

convolution, kon-vō-lū'shon, *n.* Act of rolling together or on itself, a winding; a spiral.

convolve, kon-volv', *vt.* To roll together or on itself, to coil up.

cool, kōl, *a.* Moderately cold, dispassionate; self-possessed; impudent.—*n.* A moderate degree or state of cold.—*vt.* To make cool; to moderate; to calm; to render indifferent.—*vi.* To lose heat, ardor, affection, etc.

cope, kōp, *n.* A sacerdotal cloak; the arch of the sky; the roof of a house; the arch over a door, etc.— *vt.* (coping, coped). To cover, as with a cope, to strive, or contend to oppose with success (with *with*).

Copernican, kō-pėr'ni-kan, *a.* Pertaining to Copernicus, or to his astronomical system.

copper, kop'ėr, *n.* A reddish colored ductile and malleable metal; a large boiler; a copper coin.—*a.* Consisting of or resembling copper.—*vt.* To cover with sheets of copper.

copulate, kop'ū-lāt, *vi.* (copulating, copulated). To come together, as different sexes.

copulative, kop'ū-lāt-iv, *a.* That unites. *n.* A conjunction.

copy, ko'pi, *n.* An imitation; a transcript; a pattern; a single example of a book, etc.; matter to be set up in type.—*vt.* (copying copied). To imitate; to transcribe.

copyright, kop'i-rīt, *n.* The exclusive right to print or produce, given for a limited number of years to an author, artist, etc., or his assignee.—*a.* Relating to, or protected by copyright.—*vt.* To secure by copyright.

coralline, ko'ral-īn, *a.* Consisting of, like, or containing coral.—*n.* A sea-weed; an orange-red color; a coral zoophyte.

corbel, kor'bel, *n.* A piece projecting from a wall as a support.—*vt.* (corbelling, corbelled). To support on corbels; to provide with corbels.

cord, kord, *n.* A small rope; a band; a sinew; a pile of wood, 8 feet long, 4 high, and 4 broad.—*vi.* To bind with a cord.

corduroy, kor-dė-roi', *n.* A thick cotton stuff corded or ribbed.

core, kōr, *n.* The heart or inner part; the central part of fruit.

co-respondent, kō-rē-spond'ent, *n.* A joint respondent; a man charged with adultery in a divorce case.

corn, korn, *n.* Grain; the seeds of plants which grow in ears, and are made into bread; a horny excrescence on a toe or foot.—*vt.* To preserve with salt in grains; to granulate.

cornea, kor'nē-a, *n.* The horny transparent membrane in the fore part of the eye.

corned, korned, *a.* Cured by salting.

corner, kor'nėr, *n.* A projecting extremity; angle; a secret or retired place; a nook.—*vt.* To buy up the whole stock of a commodity.

corner-stone, kor'nėr-stōn, *n.* The stone which lies at the corner of two walls, and unites them; the principal stone.

cornet, kor'net, *n.* A sort of trumpet, formerly a cavalry officer, of the lowest commissioned rank, who bore the standard.

cornice, kor'nis, *n.* A molded projection crowning a part; uppermost molding of a pediment, room, etc.

Cornish, korn'ish, *a.* Pertaining to Cornwall.—*n.* The language of Cornwall.

cornucopia, kor-nū-kō'pi-a, *n.* The representation of a horn filled with fruit, flowers, and grain, a symbol of plenty and peace.

coronet, ko'rō-net, *n.* A small crown worn by peers and peeresses; an ornamental headdress; something that surmounts.

corporal, kor'po-ral, *n.* A non-commissioned officer ranking below a sergeant.—*a.* Belonging or relating to the body; material.

corporate, kor'po-rāt, *a.* Formed into a legal body, and empowered to act in legal processes as an individual.

corporation, kor-po-rā'shon, *n.* A body corporate, empowered to act as an individual; the human body or frame.

corporeal, kor-pō'rē-al, *a.* Having a body; material; opposed to spiritual.

corps, kōr, *n.,* pl. **corps,** kōrz. A body of troops. Army Corps. Two or more divisions.

corpse, korps, *n.* The dead body of a human being; a carcass; remains.

corpulence, corpulency, kor' pū-lens, kor'-pū-len-si, *n.* The state of being corpulent; excessive fatness.

corpuscle, kor'pus-l, *n.* A minute particle or physical atom; a minute animal cell.

corral, kor-rāl', *n.* A pen for cattle; an inclosure formed by wagons; a stockade for capturing elephants.

correct, ko-rekt', *a.* Right; accurate; exact.—*vt.* To make right; to chastise; to counteract.

correction, ko-rek'shon, *n.* Act of correcting; state of being corrected; discipline; chastisement; counteraction.

correctness, ko-rekt'nes, *n.* Freedom from faults or errors; accuracy; exactness.

correlate, kor'ē-lāt, *n.* A correlative.—*vi.* (correlating, correlated). To be reciprocally related.—*vt.* To place in reciprocal relation; to determine the relations between.

correlative, ko-rel'at-iv, *a.* Having a mutual relation, as father and son.—*n.* One who or that which stands in reciprocal relation.

correspond, ko-rē-spond', *vi.* To answer one to another, to be congruous; to fit; to hold intercourse by letters.

correspondence, ko-rē-spond'ens *n.* Act or state of corresponding, fitness; congruity; intercourse by letters; the letters interchanged.

correspondent, ko-rē-spond'ent, *a.* Corresponding; suitable; congru*ous*.—*n.* One who has intercourse by letters.

corridor, ko'ri-dör, *n.* A passage in a building, or round a court.

corrosion, ko-rō'zhon, *n.* Action of corroding; state of being corroded.

corrugate, ko'rū-gāt, *vt.* To wrinkle; to contract into folds or furrows.

corrugation, ko-rū-gā'shon, *n.* A wrinkling; contraction into wrinkles.

corrupt, ko-rupt', *vt.* To make putrid; to deprave; to taint; to bribe; to infect with errors.—*vi.* To become putrid or vitiated.—*a.* Tainted; depraved; infected with errors.

corruptible, ko-rupt'i-bl, *a.* That may be corrupted; subject to decay, destruction, etc.

corruption, ko-rup'shon, *n.* Act or process of corrupting; depravity; pollution, taint of blood, bribe-taking; bribery.

corset, kor'set *n.* An article of dress laced closely round the body; stays.

cortege, kor'tāzh, *n.* A train of attendants.

cortex, kor'teks, *n.* The bark of a tree; a membrane enveloping part of the body.

cortical, kor'tik-al, *a.* Belonging to consisting of, or resembling bark, belonging to the external covering.

coruscate, ko-rus'kā t *vi.* (coruscating, coruscated). To flash intermittently; to glitter.

cosmetic, koz-met'ik, *a.* Improving beauty.—*n.* An application to improve the complexion.

cosmic, cosmical, koz'mik, koz' mik-al, *a.* Relating to the whole frame of the universe.

Cosmos, koz'mos, *n.* The universe; the system of order and harmony in creation.

cost, kost, *vt.* (costing, cost). To be bought for; to require to be laid out or borne.—*n.* That which is paid for anything; expenditure; loss *(pl.)* expenses of a lawsuit.

cough, kof *n.* A violent convulsive effort of the lungs to throw off offending matter.—*vi.* To make a violent effort, with noise, to expel the airs from the lungs, and throw off any offensive matter.—*vt.* To expel from the lungs by a violent effort with noise; to expectorate.

could, küd, *pret.* of *can.* Was able.

council, koun'sil, *n.* An assembly for consultation, a body of men designated to advise a sovereign or chief magistrate; a convocation.

counter, count-êr *n.* One who or that which counts; anything used to reckon, as in games; a shop table.—*adv.* Contrary; in an opposite direction.—*a.* Adverse; opposing.

counteract, koun-têr-akt', *vt.* To act in opposition to; to render ineffectual.

counterbalance, koun-têr-bal'ans, *vt.* To weigh against with an equal weight; to act against with equal power.—*n.* Equal weight, power, or agency, acting in opposition.

countercheck, koun-têr-chek', *vt.* To oppose by some obstacle; to check.—*n.* Check, check that controls another check.

counterfeit, koun'têr-fit, *vt.* and *i.* To forge; to copy; to feign.—*a.* Made in imitation; fraudulent.—*n.* An imposter; a forgery.

counterpoise, koun'têr-poiz, *vt.* To counterbalance.—*n.* A weight which balances another; equivalence of power or force; equilibrium.

countryman, kun'tri-man, *n.* One born in the same country with another; one who dwells in the country; a rustic.

county, koun'ti, *n.* A particular portion of a state or kingdom; a shire.—*a.* Pertaining to a county.

couplet, kup'let, *n.* Two lines that rhyme.

coupling, kup'ling, *n.* The act of one who couples; that which couples; a hook, chain, or other contrivance forming a connection.

courage, ku'rij, *n.* Intrepidity; dauntlessness; hardihood.

courageous, ku-rā'jē-us. *a.* Bold; brave, heroic, fearless.

courier, kö'rē-er, *n.* A messenger sent express with dispatches; a travelling attendant.

courthouse, kört'hous, *n.* A house in which established courts are held.

cove, kōv, *n.* A small inlet or bay; a sheltered recess in the sea-shore a concave molding; a man, fellow.—*vt.* To arch over.

covenant, kuv'en-ant, *n.* A contract; compact; a writing containing the terms of an agreement.— *vi.* To enter into a formal agree ment; to stipulate.—*vt.* To grant by covenant.

coverlet, kuv'êr-let, *n.* The cover of a bed.

covert, kuv'êrt, *a.* Kept secret; private; insidious.—*n.* A shelter; a thicket.

cowardice, kou'êrd-is, *n.* Want of courage to face danger.

cow-catcher, kou'kach-êr, *n.* A frame in front of locomotives to remove obstructions.

cower, kou'êr, *vi.* To crouch; to sink by bending the knees; to shrink through fear.

cowhide, kou'hīd. *n.* The hide of a cow; a leather whip.—*vt.* To flog with a leather whip.

crab, krab, *n.* A crustaceous fish with strong claws, a portable windlass, etc.; Cancer, a sign of the zodiac; a wild sour apple; a morose person.

crabbed, krab'ed, *a.* Perverse; peevish, perplexing.

crack, krak, *n.* A chink or fissure, a sudden or sharp sound; a sounding blow, a chat.—*vt.* and *i.* To break with a sharp, abrupt sound; to break partially: to snap: to boast of, to utter with smartness; to chat.

cracked, krakt, *a.* Having fissures but not in pieces, impaired, crazy.

cracker, krak'ér, *n.* One who or that which cracks, a small firework; a hard biscuit.

crackle, krak'l, *vi.* (crackling, crackled). To make small abrupt noises rapidly repeated.

crackling, krak'ling, *n.* The act or noise of the verb to crackle, the brown skin of roasted pork.

cradle, krā'dl, *n.* A small bed in which infants are rocked, a frame to support or hold together.—*vt.* (cradling, cradled). To lay or rock in a cradle.

Craniology, krā-ni-ol'o-ji, *n.* The knowledge of the cranium or skull.

cranium, krā'ni-um, *n.* The skull; the bones which inclose the brain.

crank, krangk, *n.* A contrivance for producing a horizontal or perpendicular motion by means of a rotary motion, or the contrary; a bend or turn.—*a.* Liable to be overset, loose.

cravat, kra-vat', *n.* A neck-cloth.

craven, krā'vn, *n.* A coward; a weak-hearted, spiritless fellow.—*a.* Cowardly.

craw, krä, *n.* The crop or first stomach of fowls.

crawl, kräl, *vi.* To creep; to advance slowly, slyly, or weakly.

crayfish, crawfish, krā'fish. krä'fish, *n.* A crustacean found in streams; also the spiny lobster, a sea crustacean.

crayon, krā'on, *n.* A pencil of colored clay, chalk, or charcoal, used in drawing; a drawing made with crayons.—*vt.* To sketch.

craze, krāz, *vt.* (crazing, crazed). To shatter; to impair the intellect of —*vi.* To become crazy.—*n.* An inordinate desire.

crazy, krā z'i, *a.* Decrepit; deranged; weakened or disordered in intellect.

create, kre-āt', *vt.* (creating, created). To bring into being from nothing; to cause

to be; to shape; to beget, to bring about; to invest with a new character; to constitute or appoint.

creation, krē-ā'shon, *n.* Act of creating; the aggregate of created things; the universe; conferring of a title or dignity.

creature, krē'tur, *n.* Something created; a human being, something imagined; a person who owes his rise to another; a mere tool.

credential, krē-den'shi-al, *n.* That which gives a title to credit; *(pl.)* documents showing that one is entitled to credit, or is invested with authority.

credit, kred'it, *n.* Reliance on testimony; faith, reputed integrity; transfer of goods, etc., in confidence of future payment; reputation for pecuniary worth; time given for payment of goods sold on trust, side of an account in which payment is entered; money possessed or due.—*vt.* To trust, to believe; to sell or lend to, in confidence of future payment; to procure credit or honor to, to enter on the credit side of an account; to attribute.

credulity, kred-du'li-ti, *n.* A disposition to believe on slight evidence.

creed krēd, *n.* A system of principles believed or professed; a brief summary of the articles of Christian faith.

creek, krēk, *n.* A small bay; a small harbor, a brook.

creep, krēp, *vi.* (creeping, crept). To move as a reptile; to crawl; to grow along the ground, or on another body; to move secretly, feebly, or timorously; to be servile; to shiver.

cress, kres, *n.* The name of various plants, mostly cruciferous, used as a salad.

crib, krib, *n.* A child's bed; a small habitation; a rack a stall for oxen a framework; a literal translation.—*vt.* (cribbing, cribbed). To shut up in a narrow habitation; to pilfer.

Cribbage, krib'āj, *n.* A game of cards.

crick, krik, *n.* A local spasm or cramp; a stiffness of the neck.

cricket, krik'et, *n.* An insect which makes a creaking or chirping sound; an open-air game played with bats, ball, and wickets.

cringe, krinj, *vi.* (cringing, cringed). To bend, to bend with servility; to fawn.— *n.* A bow; servile civility.

crinkle, kring'kl, *vi.* (crinkling, crinkled). To bend in little turns; to wrinkle.—*vt.* To form with short turns or wrinkles.— *n.* A winding or turn; a wrinkle.

criterion, krī-tē'ri-un, *n.;* pl. **-ia.** Standard of judging; a measure, test.

critic, kri'tik, *n.* One skilled in judging literary or artistic work; a reviewer; a severe judge.—*a.* Relating to criticism.

critical, kri'tik-al, *a.* Relating to or containing criticism; nicely judicious, inclined to find fault, relating to a crisis; momentous.

crochet, krō'shā, *n.* A species of knitting performed by means of a small hook.

crockery, krok'é-ri, *n.* Earthenware, vessels formed of clay glazed and baked.

crop, krop, *n.* The first stomach of birds; the craw; harvest; corn, etc., while growing; act of cutting, as hair; a short whip without a lash.—*vt.* (cropping, cropped). To cut off the ends of; to cut close; to browse, to gather before it falls; to cultivate.

crop-eared, krop'ērd, *a.* Having the ears cut short.

croquet, krō'kā, *n.* An open-air game played with mallets, balls, hoops, and pegs.

cross, kros, *n.* An instrument of death, consisting of two pieces of timber placed transversely; the symbol of the Christian religion; the religion itself, a monument or sign in the form of a cross; anything that thwarts; a hybrid.—*a.* Athwart, adverse; fretful.—*vt.* To draw a line or lay a body across; to mark with a cross, to cancel; to pass from side to side of, to thwart; to perplex; to interbreed.—*vi.* To be athwart; to move across.

crotch, kroch, *n.* A fork or forking.

crotchet, kroch'et, *n.* A note in music, half the length of a minim; a whim; a perverse conceit; a bracket in printing.

crow, krō, *n.* A black bird of the genus Corvus, including the raven, rook, jackdaw, etc., a crowbar, the sound which a cock utters.—*vi.* (crowing, *pret.* crew, crowed, *pp.* crowed). To cry as a cock; to exult; to boast.

crowbar, krō'bar, *n.* A bar of iron with a bent or forked end, used as a lever.

crowd, kroud, *n.* A number of persons or things; a throng; the populace.—*vt.* To fill by pressing together, to fill to excess.—*vi.* To press in numbers; to throng.

crowded, kroud'ed, *a.* Filled by a promiscuous multitude.

crow's-feet, krōz'fēt, *n.pl.* The wrinkles at corners of the eyes, the effects of age.

crucial, krō'shi-al, *a.* Relating to a cross,

severe searching, decisive.

crucible, krō'si-bl, *n.* A melting pot, used by chemists and others.

Crucifix, krö 'si-fiks, *n.* A cross with the figure of Christ crucified on it.

Crucifixion, krö-si-fik'shon, *n.* The act of crucifying; the death of Christ.

crucify, krö'si-fī, *vt.* (crucifying crucified). To put to death by nailing the hands and feet of to a cross, to mortify; to torment.

crude, kröd, *a.* Raw, unripe; in its natural state; not brought to perfection.

cruel, krö'el, *a.* Unmerciful; hardhearted; ferocious; brutal; severe.

cruet, krö'et, *n.* A vial or small glass bottle for holding vinegar, oil, etc.

cruise, kröz, *vi.* (cruising, cruised). To sail hither and thither.—*n.* A sailing to and fro in search of an enemy's ships, or for pleasure.

cruiser, kröz'ér, *n.* A person or a ship that cruises; a swift armed vessel to protect or destroy shipping.

crumb, krum, *n.* A fragment; a small piece of bread broken off the soft part of bread.—*vt.* To break into small pieces with the fingers; to cover with breadcrumbs.

crush, krush, *vt.* To squeeze; to bruise; to pound; to overpower; to oppress.—*vi.* To be pressed; to force one's way amid a crowd.—*n.* A violent pressing or squeezing; a crowding.

crust, krust, *n.* The hard outer coat of anything; the outside of a loaf, a piece of hard bread; a deposit from wine.—*vt.* and *i.* To cover with a crust or hard coat.

cry, krī, *vi.* (crying, cried). To utter the loud shrill sounds of weeping joy, fear, surprise, etc.; to clamor; to weep.—*vt.* To shout; to proclaim.—*n.* The loud voice of man or beast; a shriek or scream; acclamation, weeping, importunate call, a political catchword.

crypt, kript, *n.* A subterranean cell for burying purposes; a subterranean chapel.

ctenoid, ten'oid, *a.* Comb-shaped; having the posterior edge with teeth: said of the scales of fishes; having scales of this kind.

cub, kub, *n.* The young of certain quadrupeds, as the bear and fox. —*vi.* (cubbing, cubbed). To bring forth cubs.

cube, kūb, *n.* A regular solid body, with six equal square sides, the third power, or the product from multiplying a number twice by itself.—*vt.* To raise to the third power.

cubicle, kū-bi-kl, *n.* A sleeping place, a compartment for one bed in a dormitory.

cubit, kū'bit, *n.* The forearm; the length from the elbow to the extremity of the middle finger, usually taken as 18 inches.

cuckold, kük'öld, *n.* A man whose wife is false to his bed.—*vt.* To make a cuckold of.

cuckoo, kü'kö, *n.* A migratory bird so named from the sound of its note.

cucumber, kū'kum-bér, *n.* An annual plant of the gourd family.

cud, kud, *n.* The food which ruminating animals bring up from the first stomach to chew.

cue, kū, *n.* The last words of an actor's speech, catch-word, hint, the part which any man is to play in his turn; humor; the straight rod used in billiards.

cuff, kuf, *n.* A blow; slap; part of a sleeve near the hand.—*vt.* To beat; to strike with talons or wings, or with fists.

culprit, kul'prit, *n.* A person arraigned in court for a crime, or convicted of a crime; a criminal; an offender.

cult, kult, *n.* A system of belief and worship; a subject of devoted study.

cultivate, kul'ti-vāt, *vt.* To till; to refine, to foster, to improve.

culture, kul'tūr, *n.* Cultivation, the rearing of certain animals, as oysters; the application of labor, or other means of improvement, the result of such efforts; refinement.—*vt.* To cultivate.

culvert, kul'vèrt, *n.* An arched drain under a road, railway, etc., for the passage of water.

cumulation, kū-mu-lā'shon, *n.* A heaping up; a heap; accumulation.

cumulus, kū'mū-lus, *n.*, pl. -li. A cloud in the form of dense convex or conical heaps.

cuneiform, kū-nē'i-form, *a.* Wedge-shaped; applied to the arrowheaded characters on old Babylonian and Persian inscriptions.

cunning, kun'ing, *a.* Astute; artful.—*n.* Faculty or act of using stratagem; craftiness; artifice.

cupboard, kup'bōrd, *n.* A case or inclosure for cups, plates, dishes, etc.

curate, kū'rāt, *n.* One to whom the cure of souls is committed, a clergyman employed to assist in the duties of a rector or vicar.

curative, kū'rāt-iv, *a.* Relating to the cure of diseases; tending to cure.

curb, kèrb, *vt.* To control; to check; to restrain with a curb, as a horse to strengthen by a curb-stone.—*n.* Check; restraint; part of a bridle; a curb-stone.

curio, kū'ri-ō, *n.; pl.* -os, A curiosity; an interesting and curious article.

curiosity, kūri-os'i-ti, *n.* Inquisitiveness; a thing unusual; a rarity.

curl, kèrl, *vt.* To form into ringlets, —*vi.* To take a twisted or coiled form; to play at the game of curling.—*n.* A ringlet of hair, or anything of a like form, a waving; flexure.

curriculum, ku-rik'ū-lum, *n.* A course of study in a university, school, etc.

currier, ku'ri-èr, *n.* A man who dresses leather after it is tanned.

curry, ku'ri, *n.* A highly spiced sauce or mixture; a dish cooked with curry.—*vt.* (currying, curried). To flavor with curry, to dress leather; to rub and clean (a horse) with a comb, to seek (favor).

curse, kèrs, *vt.* (cursing, cursed). To utter a wish of evil against; a blight, to torment with calamities. —*vi.* To utter imprecations, to blaspheme.—*n.* Imprecation of evil, execration, torment.

curve, kè rv, *a.* Bending, inflected. —*n.* A bending without angles; a bent line.—*vt.* (curving, curved). To bend.

cushion, kush'on, *n.* A pillow for a seat, something resembling a pillow.—*vt.* To seat on a cushion; to furnish with cushions.

cusp, kusp, *n.* The point of the moon, or other luminary; a point formed by the meeting of two curves.

custodian, kus-tō'di-an, *n.* One who has care of a library, public building, etc.

custody, kus'tō-di, *n.* A keeping; guardianship; imprisonment; security.

custom, kus'tum, *n.* Habit, established practice, fashion, a buying of goods; business support; a tax on goods, *pl.* duties on merchandise imported or exported.

custom-house, kus'tum-hous, *n.* The office where customs are paid.

cut, kut, *vt.* (cutting, cut). To divide into pieces, to fell or mow, to clip to carve; to affect deeply; to intersect, to castrate, to divide, as cards, to refuse to recognize.—*vi.* To make an incision; to be severed by a cutting instrument, to pass straight and rapidly.—*a.* Gashed carved; intersected; deeply affected.—*n.* The action of an edged instrument; a wound; a stroke with a whip, a severe remark; a channel; any small piece; a lot; a near passage, a carving or engraving; act of dividing a pack of cards; form; fashion; refusal to recognize a person.

cyanide, sī'an-id, *n.* A combination of cyanogen with a metallic base.

cyanogen, sī-an'ō-jen, *n.* A poisonous gas of a strong and peculiar odor.

cycle, sī'kl, *n.* An orbit in the heavens; a circle of years; a bicycle or tricycle.—*vi.* To recur in a cycle, to ride a bicycle.

cylinder, si'lin-dèr, *n.* An elongated round body of uniform diameter.

cymbal, sim'bal, *n.* A basin-shaped musical instrument of brass, used in pairs.

cynic, sin'ik, *n.* One of a sect of Greek philosophers who professed contempt of riches, arts, etc.; a morose man.

cypress, sī'pres, *n.* An evergreen tree, the emblem of mourning.

cyst, sist, *n.* A bag in animal bodies containing matter.

D

dabble, dab'bl, vt. (dabbling, dabbled). To wet, to sprinkle.—vi. To play in water, to do anything in a superficial manner, to meddle.

dais, dā'is, n. The high table at the upper end of the dining-hall, the raised floor on which the table stood; a canopy.

damage, dam'āj, n. Hurt; injury; money compensation (generally in pl.).—vt. (damaging, damaged). To injure, to impair.

damn, darn, vt. To send to hell; to condemn.

damnation, dam-nā'shon, n. Condemnation; sentence to punishment in the future state.

dandelion, dan'di-lī-un, n. A composite plant bearing a bright yellow flower.

dandle, dan'dl, vt. (dandling, dandled). To shake on the knee, as an infant, to fondle, to trifle with.

dandruff, dan'druff, n. A scurf on the head.

danger, dān'jèr, n. Exposure to injury; jeopardy; risk.

dangerous, dān'jèr-us, a. Perilous causing risk of harm; unsafe; insecure.

dangle, dang'gl, vi. (dangling, dangled). To hang loose, to follow officiously.— vt. To carry suspended loosely, to swing.

darkness, därk'nes, n. Absence of light; blackness; gloom; ignorance, privacy.

darling, där'ling, a. Dearly beloved.—n. One much beloved; a favorite.

darn, därn, vt. To mend by imitating the texture of the stuff with thread and needle, to sew together.—n. A place so mended.

dauby, däb'i, a. Viscous; glutinous.

daybreak, dā'brak, n. The dawn; first appearance of light in the morning.

daydream, dā'drēm, vt. A vision to the waking senses, a reverie.

daylight, dā'līt, n. The light of the day.

daze, dāz, vt. (dazing, dazed). To stupefy, to stun.

dead, ded, a. Without life; deceased, perfectly still, dull, cold tasteless; spiritless; utter; unerring.

deaden, ded'n, vt. To abate in vigor force, or sensation; to darken, dull or dim.

deaf, def, a. Wanting the sense of hearing, not listening or regarding.

dearth, dèrth, n. Scarcity; want; famine.

debauch, dē-bäch', vt. To corrupt to pervert.—vi. To riot; to revel.—n. Excess in eating or drinking; lewdness.

debit, deb'it, n. A recorded item of debt, the left-hand page or debtor side of a ledger or account.—vt. To charge with debt.

debonair, de-bō-nār', a. Gracious; courteous.

debouch, dē-bösh', vi. To issue or march out of a narrow place.

debris, dē-brē', n.sing. or pl. Fragments; rubbish.

debt, det, n. That which is due from one person to another; obligation; guilt.

debut, dā-bü', n. First appearance in public.

decade, de'kād, n. The number of ten, a period of ten Years.

decapod, dek'a-pod, n. A crustacean having ten feet, as a crab; also a cuttle-fish with ten prehensile arms.

deceit, dē-sēt', n. Fraud; guile; cunning.

deceitful, dē-sēt'ful, a. Fraudulent delusive; false; hollow.

December, dē-sem'bèr, n. The twelfth and last month of the year.

decency, dē'sen-si, n. The state or quality of being decent; decorum; modesty.

decennial, dē-sen'ni-al, a. Consisting of ten years; happening every ten years.

decent, dē'sent, a. Becoming seemly; respectable; modest, moderate.

decentralize, dē-sen'tral-īz, vt. To remove from direct dependence on a central authority.

decide, dē-sīd', vt. (deciding, decided). To determine, to settle, to resolve.—vi. To determine; to pronounce a judgment.

deck, dek, vt. To clothe; to adorn; to furnish with a deck, as a vessel.—n. The platform or floor of a ship.

declaim, dē-klam', vi. To make a formal speech; to harangue; to inveigh.

declamation, de-kla-mā'shon, n. The art or act of declaiming; a harangue.

declaration, de-kla-rā'shon, n. Act of declaring, that which is declared; an explicit statement; a solemn affirmation.

declarative, dē-klār'at-iv, a. Explanatory; making proclamation.

decoration, dek'ō-rā'shon, n. Act of decorating; that which adorns; a badge or medal.

decorum, dē-kō'rum, n. Propriety of speech or behavior; seemliness.

decoy, dē-koi', n. An enclosure for catching ducks or wild fowls, a lure.—vt. To lure into a snare; to entice.

decrement, de'krĕ-ment, *n.* De-crease; quantity lost by diminution or waste.

decrepit, dē-krep'it, *a.* Broken down with age; being in the last stage of decay.

dedicate, ded'i-kāt, *vt.* (dedicating, dedicated). To consecrate to a sacred purpose, to devote (often refl.); to inscribe to a friend.

dedication, ded-i-kā'shon, *n.* Act of devoting to some person, use, or thing; inscription or address.

deem, dēm, *vt.* To judge, to think.— *vi.* To judge; to be of opinion; to estimate.

deface, dē'fās', *vt.* To destroy or mar the surface of a thing; to disfigure; to erase.

defeat, dē-fet', *n.* Frustration; overthrow, loss of battle.—*vt.* To frustrate; to foil, to overthrow; to conquer.

defect, dē-fekt', *n.* Want, a blemish fault; flaw.

defective, dē-fekt'iv *a.* Having a defect; deficient; faulty.

defendant, dē-fen'dant, *n.* A defender; in law, the person that opposes a charge, etc.

defer, dē-fũr', *vt.* (deferring, deferred). To put off to a future time; to postpone.— *vi.* To yield to another's opinion, to submit courteously or from respect.

deference, de'fer-ens, *n.* A yielding in opinion; regard; respect; submission.

deferment, dē-fer-ment, *n.* Postponement.

defiance, dē-fī'ans, *n.* Act of defying; a challenge to fight; contempt of opposition or danger.

deficient, de-fi'shent, *a.* Defective; imperfect; not adequate.

defunct, dē-fungkt', *a.* Dead; deceased.— *n.* A dead person; one deceased.

defy, dē-fī', *vt.* (defying, defied). To provoke to combat, to dare, to challenge, to set at nought.

degrade, dē-grād', *vt.* (degrading, degraded). To reduce to a lower rank; to strip of honors, to debase; to depose; to dishonor.

dehydration, dē-hî-drā'shon, *n.* Process of freeing a compound from water.

delectable, dē-lekt'a-bl, *a.* Delightful.

deliberation, dē-lib'ė-rā"shon, *n.* Thoughtful consideration, prudence, discussion of reasons for and against a measure.

delicacy, de'li-ka-si, *n.* The quality of being delicate- fineness of texture; tenderness; minute accuracy, refined taste, a dainty.

deliverance, dē-liv'ėr-ans, *n.* Re-lease; rescue; an authoritative judgment.

delusive, de-lũ'siv, *a.* Apt to deceive.

delve, delv, *vt.* and *i.* (delving delved). To dig.

demagnetize, dē-mag'net-ĩz, *vt.* To deprive of magnetic polarity.

demagogue, dem'a-gog, *n.* A leader of the people; a factious orator.

demarcation, de-mär-kā'shon, *n.* Act of setting a limit; a limit fixed.

demean, dē-mēn', *vt.* To conduct, to behave, to debase (oneself).

demeanor, dē-mēn'ėr, *n.* Manner of conducting oneself; behavior.

demobilize, dē-mō'bil-ĩz, *vt.* To disband.

demolish, dē-mol'ish, *vt.* To pull down; to destroy.

demon, dē'mon, *n.* A spirit, holding a place below the celestial deities of the pagans, an evil spirit, a devil; a fiend-like man.

demoralize, dē-mo'ral-ĩz, *vt.* To corrupt the morals of, to deprave.

demoralizing, dē-mo'ral-ĩz-ing, *p.a.* Tending to destroy morals or moral principles.

demure, dē-mūr', *a.* Consciously grave, affectedly modest.

den, den, *n.* A cave; a dell; a haunt.

denary, dē-na-ri, *a.* Containing ten; proceeding by tens.—*n.* The number ten.

dendriform, den'dri-form, *a.* Having the form or appearance of a tree.

denial, dē-nī'al, *n.* Act of denying contradiction; refusal to grant or acknowledge.

denigrate, den'i-grāt, *vt.* To blacken; to sully.

denim, den'im, *n.* A coarse cotton drill used for making aprons, overalls, etc.

denizen, de'ni-zn, *n.* A stranger admitted to residence in a foreign country.

denominate, dē-nom'in-āt, *vt.* (de-nominating, denominated). To name, to designate.

denomination, dē-nom'in-ā"shon, *n.* Act of naming; title; class; religious sect.

denominationalism, dē-nom'in-ā" shon-al-izm, *n.* A class spirit; system of religious sects having each their own schools.

denominative, dē-nom'in-āt-iv, *a.* That confers a distinct appellation.

denote, dē-not', *vt.* To indicate; to imply.

denouement, dā-nö'mäng, *n.* The winding up of a plot in a novel or drama; solution of a mystery; issue, the event.

denounce, dē-nouns', *vt.* (denouncing, denounced). To threaten; to accuse publicly, to stigmatize.

dentition, den-ti'shon, *n.* The cutting of teeth in infancy; the system of teeth peculiar to an animal.

denture, den'tūr, *n.* A set of false teeth.

denude, dē-nūd', *vt.* (denuding, denuded). To make bare; to divest; to uncover.

denunciation, dē-nun'si-ā"shon, *n.* Act of denouncing; public menace; arraignment.

deodorize, dē-ō'dėr-īz, *vt.* (deodorizing, deodorized). To deprive of fetid odor.

deoxidate, deoxidize, dē-ok'sid-āt, de-ok'sïd-iz, *vt.* To reduce from the state of an oxide.

depart, de-pärt', *vi.* To go away; to desist, to abandon; to deviate; to die.

department, dē-pärt'ment, *n.* A separate part; a division of territory; a distinct branch, as of science, etc.

depend, dē-pend, *vi.* To hang from; to be contingent or conditioned; to rest or rely solely; to trust.

deplorable, dē -plō r'a-bl, *a.* To be deplored; lamentable; grievous; pitiable.

deplore, dē-plōr', *vt.* (deploring, deplored). To feel or express deep grief for; to bewail.

deploy, dē-ploi', *vt.* To open out; to extend from column to line as a body of troops.—*vi.* To form a more extended front or line.

deportation, dē-pōrt-ā'shon, *n.* Removal from one country to another; exile.

depot, dep'ō, *n.* A place of deposit; headquarters of a regiment; a railway-station.

deprave, dē -prā v', *vt.* (depraving, depraved). To make bad or worse to impair the good qualities of; to corrupt; to vitiate.

depredate, de'pre-dāt, *vt.* To plunder, to waste.

depress, dē-pres', *vt.* To press down; to lower; to humble; to deject.

derangement, dē-rānj'ment, *n.* A putting out of order; disorder; insanity.

derelict, de're-likt, *a.* Abandoned.—*n.* Anything forsaken or left, especially a ship.

dereliction, de-re-lik 'shon, *n.* Act of forsaking; state of being forsaken; neglect.

deride, dē-rīd', *vt.* (deriding, derided). To laugh at in contempt; to ridicule, to jeer.

derision, dē-ri'zhon, *n.* Act of deriding; scorn; ridicule, mockery.

derivation, de-ri-vā'shon, *a.* Act of deriving, the tracing of a word from its root; deduction.

derivative, de-riv'āt-iv, *a.* Derived sec-

ondary.—*n.* That which is derived; a word which takes its origin in another word.

derive, de-rīv', *vt.* (deriving, derived). To draw or receive, as from a source or origin, to trace the etymology of.—*vi.* To come from.

derma, dermis, derm, dėr'ma, dėr'mis, dē rm, *n.* The true skin, or under layer of the skin.

descant, des'kant, *n.* A discourse discussion, a song or tune with various modulations.—*vi.* deskant'. To discourse or animadvert freely; to add a part to a melody.

descend, dē-send, *vi.* To pass or move down, to invade, to be derived; to pass to an heir.—*vt.* To pass or move down, on, or alone.

desecrate, de'se-krāt, vt. (desecrating, desecrated). To divert from a sacred purpose, to profane.

desiderate, dē-sid'er-āt, *vt.* To desire; to want, to miss.

despair, dē-spār', *n.* A hopeless state, despondency, that which causes despair; loss of hope.—*vi.* To give up all hope; to despond.

despite, dē-spīt', *n.* Extreme malice, defiance with contempt, an act of malice. — *vt.* To despise, to spite. —*prep.* In spite of; notwithstanding.

despoil, dē-spoil', *vt.* To take from by force; to rob; to bereave; to rifle.

despond, dē-spond', *vi.* To be cast down or dejected; to lose heart, hope, or resolution.

dessert, dē-zėrt', *n.* That which is served at the close of a dinner, as fruits, etc.

destination, des-tin-ā'shon, *n.* Act of destining; ultimate design; predetermined end.

destine, des'tin, *vt.* (destining, destined). To set or appoint to a purpose; to design; to doom; to ordain.

destroy, dē-stroi', *vt.* To pull down to overthrow; to devastate; to annihilate.

detain, dē-tān', *vt.* To keep back or from; to withhold; to arrest, to check, to retard.

detect, dē-tekt', *vt.* To discover, to bring to light.

detergent, dē-tėrj'ent, *a.* Cleansing; purging.—*n.* That which cleanses.

deteriorate, dē-tē'ri-ō-rā t, *vi.* (deteriorating, deteriorated). To grow worse, to degenerate.—*vt.* To reduce in quality.

detest, dē-test', *vt.* To abhor; to loathe.

detestable, dē-test'a-bl, *a.* Extremely hateful; abominable; odious.

dethrone, de-thrōn', *vt.* (dethroning dethroned). To divest of royal authority and dignity; to depose.

detonate, de'tō-nāt, *vt.* (detonating, detonated). To cause to explode, to cause to burn with a sudden repot.—*vi.* To explode.

detract, de-trakt', *vt.* To draw away, to disparage.—*vi.* To take away from (especially reputation).

devastate, de'vas-tāt, *vt.* (devastating, devastated). To lay waste; to ravage.

deviate, de'vi-āt, *vi.* (deviating, deviated). To stray; to wander; to swerve, to err.

device, de-vîs', *n.* That which is devised, contrivance; scheme; an emblem.

devotee, dev-o-tē', *n.* One wholly devoted, particularly to religion; a votary.

devout, de-vout', *a.* Pious, expressing devotion; earnest; solemn.

diagnose, dī-ag-nōs', *vt.* To ascertain from symptoms the true nature of.

diagnosis, dī-ag-nō'sis, *n.* The ascertaining from symptoms the true nature of diseases.

diagram, dī'a-gram, *n.* A drawing to demonstrate the properties of any figure; an illustrative figure in outline.

dial, dī'al, *n.* An instrument for showing the hour by the sun's shadow; face of a clock, etc.

dialect, dī'a-lekt, *n.* The idiom of a language peculiar to a province; language; manner of speaking.

diapason, dī-a-pā'zon, *n.* The entire compass of a voice or instrument; an organ stop.

diaphanous, dī-af'an-us, *a.* Having power to transmit rays of light transparent.

diarrhea, dī-a-rē'a, *n.* A morbidly frequent evacuation of the intestines.

diary, dī'a-ri, *n.* A register of daily events or transactions; a journal.

dibble, dib'bl, *n.* A pointed instrument to make holes for planting seeds, etc.—*vt.* (dibbling, dibbled). To make holes for planting seeds, etc.

dickey, dicky, dik'i, *n.* A false shirtfront; the driver's seat in a carriage.

dicotyledon, dī'kot-i-lē''don, *n.* A plant whose seeds contain a pair of cotyledons.

dictaphone, dik'ta-fon, *n.* Trade name for an instrument into which correspondence is dictated to be transcribed afterwards.

dictator, dik-tāt'èr, *n.* One invested with absolute authority.

diction, dik'shon, *n.* Choice of words;

mode of expression, style.

die, dī, *vi.* (dying, died). To cease to live, to expire; to sink gradually; to vanish.

dietetics, dī-et-et'iks, *n.* Principles for regulating the diet.

differ, dif'èr, *vi.* To be unlike or distinct; to disagree; to be at variance.

digit, di'jit, *n.* A finger; three-fourths of an inch, the twelfth part of the diameter of the sun or moon; any integer under 10.

dignify, dig'ni-fi, *vt.* (dignifying, dignified). To invest with dignity, to exalt in rank or office; to make illustrious.

digress, di-gres' or di'gres, *vi.* To depart from the main subject; to deviate.

diligence, di'li-jens, *n.* Steady application; assiduity; a four-wheeled stage-coach.

diluvium, di-lū'vi-um, *n.* A deluge or inundation; a deposit of sand, gravel, etc., caused by a flood.

dim, dim, *a.* Not seeing clearly; not clearly seen; mysterious; tarnished. —*vt.* (dimming, dimmed). To dull, to obscure, to sully.

dime, dim, *n.* A silver coin the tenth of a dollar.

diminish, di-min'ish, *vt.* To reduce to abate, to degrade.—*vi.* To become less.

dinner, din'nèr, *n.* The principal meal of the day.

diocese, dī'ō-sēs, *n.* An ecclesiastical division of a state, subject to a bishop.

diorama, dī-ō-rä'ma, *n.* A contrivance for giving a high degree of optical illusion to painted scenes.

diphtheria, dif-thē'ri-a, *n.* An epidemic inflammatory disease of the throat.

diphthong, dif'thong, *n.* A union of two vowels pronounced in one syllable.

diploma, di-plō-ma, *n.* A document conferring some power, privilege, or honor.

disagree, dis-a-grē', *vi.* To be of a different opinion, to dissent; to be unfriendly, to be unsuitable.

disapprove, dis-ap-prōv', *vt.* To censure as wrong, to regard with dislike; to reject.

disarrange, dis-a-ranj', *vt.* To put out of arrangement or order; to derange.

disarray, dis-a-rā', *vt.* To undress; to throw into disorder.—*n.* Disorder, undress.

disband dis-band', *vt.* To dismiss from military service; to dis perse.—*vi.* To retire from military service; to dissolve connection.

disbar, dis-bär', *vt.* To expel from being a member of the bar.

discard, dis-kärd', *vt.* To throw away; to cast off; to dismiss; to dis charge.

discernment, dis-sèrn'ment, *n.* Act or power of discerning; judgment; sagacity.

disciple, dis-sī'pl, *n.* A learner, a pupil, an adherent to the doctrines of another.

disconsolate, dis-kon'sō-lāt, *a.* Comfortless, hopeless; gloomy, cheerless.

discontent, dis-kon-tent', *n.* Want of content, uneasiness of mind dissatisfaction.

discontinuance, dis-kon-tin'ū-ans, *n.* A breaking off- cessation.

discord, dis'kord, *n.* Want of concord; disagreement; disagreement of sounds.

discountenance, dis-koun'ten-ans *vt.* To restrain by censure, cold treatment, etc.

discourage, dis-ku'rāj, *vt.* (discouraging, discouraged). To dishearten, to dissuade.

discouragement, dis-ku'rā j-ment, *n.* Act of discouraging; that which discourages.

discourse, dis-kōrs', *n.* A speech; treatise, sermon- conversation.— *vi.* (discoursing, discoursed). To talk; to converse; to treat of formally, to expatiate.—*vt.* To utter.

discourtesy, dis-kōr'te-si, *n.* In-civility, rudeness, act of disrespect.

discovery, dis-kuv'èri, *n.* Act of discovering; disclosure; that which is discovered.

discreet, dis-krēt, *a.* Prudent; wary; judicious.

discrete, dis'kret, *a.* Separate; distinct.

disembroil, dis-em-broil', *vt.* To disentangle, to free from perplexity.

disentangle, dis-en-tang'gl, *vt.* To free from entanglement; to clear.

disfavor, dis-fa'vèr, *n.* Want of favor, unfavorable regard.—*vt.* To withhold favor from; to discountenance.

disfigure, dis-fi'gūr, *vt.* (disfiguring, disfigured). To mar the figure of; to impair the beauty, symmetry, or excellence of.

disfranchise, dis-fran'chiz, *vt.* To deprive of the rights of a free citizen.

disgust, dis-gust', *n.* Distaste; loathing; repugnance.—*vt.* To cause distaste in; to offend the mind or moral taste of.

dishearten, dis-härt'n, *vt.* To discourage to depress.

dishevel, di-she'vel, *vt.* (dishevelling, dishevelled). To put out of order, or spread loosely, as the hair.

disjoint, disjoint', *vt.* To separate as parts united by joints; to put out of joint; to make incoherent.

dislocate, dis'lō-kāt, *vt.* To displace, to put out of joint.

disloyal, dis-loi'al, *a.* Void of loyalty, false to a sovereign, faithless.

dismal, diz'mal, *a.* Dark; gloomy; doleful, calamitous sorrowful.

dismantle, dis-man'tl, *vt.* To strip; to divest, to unrig; to deprive or strip, as of military equipment or defenses, to break down.

disobedience, dis-ō-bē'di-ens, *n.* Neglect or refusal to obey.

disobey, dis-ō-bā', *vt.* To neglect or refuse to obey; to violate an order.

disorganize, dis-or'gan-īz, *vt.* To destroy organic structure or connected system in; to throw into confusion.

disperse, dis-pèrs', *vt.* To scatter; to dispel, to diffuse, to distribute.— *vi.* To be scattered; to vanish.

displease, dis-plēz, *vt.* To offend, to dissatisfy; to provoke.—*vi.* To disgust.

displeasure, dis-ple'zhŭr, *n.* Dissatisfaction, resentment.

disproportionate, dis-prō-pōr' shon-āt, *a.* Not proportioned; unsymmetrical, inadequate.

disprove, dis-prōv', *vt.* To prove to be false, to confute.

disputation, dis-pūt-ā'shon, *n.* Act of disputing; controversy in words; debate.

disqualify, dis-kwo'li-fī, *vt.* To divest of qualifications; to incapacitate.

disquiet, dis-kwī'et, *n.* Uneasiness anxiety.—*vt.* To make uneasy or restless.

disreputable, dis-rē'pūt-a-bl, *a.* Discreditable, low, mean.

disrepute, dis-rē-pūt', *n.* Loss or want of reputation; disesteem; disgrace.

disrespect, dis-rē-spekt', *n.* Want of respect; incivility.—*vt.* To show disrespect to.

disroot, dis-röt', *vt.* To tear up the roots.

dissatisfaction, dis-sa'tis-fak''shon, *n.* Want of satisfaction; discontent.

dissatisfy, dis-sa'tis-fī, *vt.* To fail to satisfy, to render discontented.

dissect, dis-sekt', *vt.* To cut up; to anatomize, to divide and examine minutely.

dissertation, dis-sèr-tā'shon, *n.* A formal discourse; treatise; disquisition.

disservice, dis-sèr'vis, *n.* An ill-service, injury, harm, mischief

dissever, dis-sev'er, *vt.* To part in two; to disunite.

dissident, dis'si-dent, *a.* Dissenting. —n. A dissenter.

dissimilitude, dis-si-mil'i-tū d, *n.* Unlikeness; want of resemblance.

dissolvent, diz-zolv'ent, *a.* Having power

to dissolve.—*n.* That which has the power of melting; a solvent.

distaste, dis-tāst', *n.* Aversion of the taste or mind, dislike.—*vt.* To dislike.

distend, dis-tend', *vt.* To stretch by force from within, to swell.—*vi.* To swell; to dilate.

distinguish, dis-ting'gwish, *vt.* To mark out by some peculiarity; to perceive, to make eminent, to signalize.—*vi.* To make a distinction; to find or show the difference.

distort, dis-tort', *vt.* To twist; to pervert.

distortion, dis-tor'shon, *n.* Act of distorting, a writhing motion, deformity; perversion of the true meaning of words.

distract, dis-trakt', *vt.* To draw towards different objects; to perplex; to disorder the reason of; to render furious.

distraught, dis-trät', *a.* Distracted.

distress, dis-tres', *n.* Anguish of body or mind, affliction, state of danger or destitution; act of distraining.—*vt.* To afflict with pain or anguish; to perplex.

distributive, dis-tri'būt-iv, *a.* That distributes; expressing separation or division.—*n.* A word that divides or distributes, as *each, every, either.*

district, dis'trikt, *n.* A limited extent of country; a circuit; a region.

distrust, dis-trust', *vt.* To have no trust in; to doubt; to suspect.—*n.* Want of trust; doubt; suspicion; discredit.

disturb, dis-tėrb ', *vt.* To throw into disorder; to agitate; to hinder; to move.

disturbance, dis-tėrb'ans, *n.* State of being disturbed; commotion; excitement- interruption of a right.

ditch, dich, *n.* A trench in the earth for drainage or defense.—*vi.* To dig a ditch.—*vt.* To dig a ditch in; to drain by a ditch; to surround with a ditch.

ditto, dit'tō, *n.* A word used in lists, etc., meaning same as above; often written *Do.*

dive, dīv, *vi.* (diving, dived). To plunge into water head-foremost; to go under water to execute some work- to go deep.

diverge, di-vėrj', *vi.* (diverging, diverged). To proceed from a point in different directions; to deviate; to vary.

diversity, di-vėrs'i-ti, *n.* State of being diverse; contrariety, variety.

divert, di-vėrt', *vt.* To turn aside; to amuse.

divide, di-vīd', *vt.* (dividing, divided). To part asunder; to separate; to keep apart; to distribute, allot; to set at variance.—*vi.* To part; to be of different opinions;

to vote by the division of a legislative house into parties.

dividend, di'vi-dend *n.* A number which is to be divided; share of profit; share divided to creditors.

divination, di-vin-ā'shon, *n.* Act of divining; a foretelling future events, or discovering things secret, by magical means.

divulsion, di-vul'shon, *n.* A pulling tearing, or rending asunder, or separating.

dizziness, diz'zi-nes, *n.* Giddiness; vertigo.

dizzy, diz'zi, *a.* Having a sensation of whirling in the head; giddy causing giddiness.—*vt.* (dizzying dizzied). To make giddy.

docket, dok'et, *n.* A summary; a bill tied to goods; a list of cases in a court.—*vt.* To make an abstract of; to mark the contents of papers on the back; to attach a docket to.

dockyard, dok'yärd, *n.* A yard near a dock for naval stores.

doctor, dok'ter, *n.* A person who has received the highest degree in a university faculty, one licensed to practice medicine; a physician.—*vt.* To treat medically; to adulterate.

dodge, doj, *vt.* (dodging, dodged). To start aside; to quibble.—*vt.* To evade by a sudden shift of place.—*n.* An artifice, an evasion.

dodo, dō'dō, *n.* An extinct bird of Mauritius, having a massive, clumsy body, short strong legs and wings useless for flight.

doe, dō, *n.* A female deer.

dogmatism, dog'mat-izm, *n.* Positiveness in assertion; arrogance in opinion.

dogmatize, dog'mat-īz, *vi.* (dogmatizing, dogmatized). To assert with undue confidence; to advance principles with arrogance.

doily, doi'li, *n.* A small ornamental mat for glasses, etc.

doldrums, dol'drumz, *n.pl.* The dumps.

dole, dōl, *n.* That which is dealt out share; gratuity, grief, sorrow.—*vt.* (doling, doled). To deal out to distribute.

doleful, dōl'fül, *a.* Full of pain grief, etc.; expressing or causing grief; gloomy.

dolomite, dōl'o-mīt, *n.* A granular crystalline or schistose rock compounded of carbonate of magnesia and carbonate of lime.

dolor, dō'lèr, *n.* Sorrow; lamentation.

dolorous, dō'lèr-us, *a.* Sorrowful; doleful.

dolphin, dol'fin, *n.* A small species of

whale remarkable for gambolling in the water; a fish celebrated for its changes of color when dying.

dolt, dōlt, *n*. A blockhead.

domain, dō-mān', *n*. Territory governed; estate, a demesne.

dome, dōm, *n*. A hemispherical roof of a building; a large cupola.

domestic, dō-mes'tik, *a*. Belonging to the house or home tame, not foreign.—*n*. A household servant.

domesticate, do-mes'tik-āt, *vt*. To accustom to remain much at home; to tame.

domicile, do'mi-sîl, *n*. A habitation; family residence.—*vt*. (domiciling domiciled). To establish in a residence.

dominant, dom'in-ant, *a*. Governing; predominant; ascendant.

dominate, dom'in-āt, *vt*. (dominating, dominated). To rule; to predominate over.

Don, don, *n*. A Spanish title, corresponding to Eng. Mr.; an important personage, a resident Fellow of a college at Oxford or Cambridge.—*vt*. (donning, donned). To put on; to invest with.

donate, dō'nāt, *vt*. To bestow.

donation, dō-nā'shon, *n*. Act of giving; that which is given; a gift; a present.

donkey, dong'ki, *n*. An ass.

donna, don'na, *n*. A lady, as, *prima donna*, the first female singer in an opera, etc.

doomsday, dömz'dā, *n*. The day of judgment.

door, dōr, *n*. The entrance of a house or room, the frame of boards that shuts such an entrance; avenue; means of approach.

dossier, dos'ē-ā, *n*. A collection of documents of information about a person or incident.

dot, dot, *n*. A small point, as made with a pen, etc.; a speck.—*vt*. (dotting, dotted). To mark with a dot to diversify with small objects.—*vi*. To make dots.

dotal, dōt'al, *a*. Pertaining to dower.

dotard, dōt'ėrd, *n*. One whose mind is impaired by age; one foolishly fond.

dote, dōt, *vi*. (doting, doted). To have the intellect impaired by age; to be foolishly fond.

doubling, du'bl-ing, *n*. Act of making double, a fold, a lining.

doubt, dout, *vi*. To waver in opinion or judgment; to question; to suspect.—*vt*. To deem uncertain; to distrust.—*n*. A wavering in opinion; uncertainty; suspicion.

dowager, dou'ā-jėr, *n*. A title given to the widow of a person of title provided that she is mother grandmother, or stepmother of the successor.

dowdy, dou'di, *n*. An awkward, illdressed woman.—*a*. Ill-dressed vulgar-looking.

dowel, dou'el, *n*. A pin of wood or iron to join boards, etc.—*vt*. (dowelling, dowelled). To fasten by dowels.

downy, doun'i, *a*. Covered with, or pertaining to, down, soft; soothing.

dowry, dou'ri, *n*. The property which a woman brings to her husband in marriage; a dower; gift.

dozen, du'zn, *n*. Twelve things regarded collectively.

Draconic, Draconian, drā-kon'ik, drā-kō'ni-an, *a*. Relating to Draco, the Athenian lawgiver; extremely severe.

draft, dräft, *n*. A detachment of men or things; an order for money; the first sketch of any writing; a sketch.—*vt*. To make a draft of; to sketch, to select.

drake, drāk, *n*. The male of ducks.

dram, dram, *n*. The eighth part of an ounce, or sixty grains apothecaries' measure; the sixteenth part of an ounce avoirdupois; as much spirituous liquor as is drunk at once.

drama, drä'ma, *n*. A representation on a stage; a play; dramatic literature.

dramatist, drä'mat-ist, *n*. The author of a dramatic composition.

dramaturgy, dräm'a-ter-ji, *n*. The science of dramatic composition and representation.

drape, drāp, *vt*. (draping, draped). To cover with cloth or drapery.

drapery, dräp'ė-ri, *n*. The occupation of a draper; fabrics of wool or linen; clothes or hangings.

drastic, dras'tik, *a*. Acting with strength or violence.—*n*. A strong purgative.

drawer, drä'ėr, *n*. One who or that which draws; he who draws a bill; a sliding box in a case, etc., *pl*. an under-garment for the lower limbs.

drawing, drä'ing, *n*. Act of one who draws; representation of objects by lines and shades; delineation.

drawl, dräl, *vi*. To speak with slow prolonged utterance.—*vt*. To utter in a slow tone.—*n*. A lengthened utterance.

dread, dred, *n*. Fear, united with respect; terror; the person or the thing dreaded.—*a*. Exciting great fear; terrible; venerable.—*vt*. and *i*. To fear in a great degree.

drill, dril, *n*. A kind of coarse linen or cotton cloth.

drone, drōn, *n.* The male or nonworking bee, an idler, a low humming sound; a large tube of the bagpipe.—*vi.* (droning, droned). To give a low dull sound; to hum.

drowse, drouz, *vi.* (drowsing drowsed). To nod in slumber; to doze, to look heavy.—*vt.* To make heavy with sleep, or stupid.

dual, dū'al, *a.* Expressing the number two; existing as two; twofold.

dubious, dū'bi-us, *a.* Wavering in opinion, doubtful; uncertain.

duel, dū'el, *n.* A premeditated combat between two persons, single combat; contest.

duet, dū'et, *n.* A piece of music for two performers, vocal or instrumental.

dugout, dug-out, *n.* A rudely hollowed-out canoe from trunk of tree, an underground shelter from shells, an elderly officer recalled to duty from retirement.

dull, dul, *a.* Stupid, slow, blunt drowsy, cheerless, not bright or clear; tarnished; uninteresting.— *vt.* To make dull, to stupefy, to blunt, to make sad to sully.—*vi.* To become dull, blunt or stupid.

dulness, dullness, dul'nes, *n.* Stupidity; heaviness; slowness; dimness.

duly, dū'li, *adv.* Properly; fitly.

dumb, dum, *a.* Incapable of speech, mute, silent, not accompanied with speech.

dump, dump, *n.* A heap of refuse; a place where refuse is deposited, a large concentration of military stores especially of ammunition.

dumpling, dump'ling, *n.* A pudding of boiled suet paste, with or without fruit.

dumpy, dump'i, *a.* Short and thick.

dunce, duns, *n.* One slow at learning, a dullard, a dolt.

dune, dūn, *n.* A sand-hill on the sea-coast.

dung, dung, *n.* The excrement of animals.—*vt.* To manure; to immerse (calico) in cow-dung and water.—*vi.* To void excrement.

dungeon, dun'jon, *n.* A strong tower in the middle of a castle; a deep, dark place of confinement.

durable, dūr'a-bl, *a.* Having the quality of lasting long; permanent, firm.

dust, dust, *n.* Fine dry particles of earth, etc.; powder; earth as symbolic of mortality; a low condition.—*vt.* To free from dust, to sprinkle, as with dust.

Dutch, duch, *a.* Pertaining to Holland, or to its inhabitants.—*n.pl.* The people of Holland; sing. their language.

duty, dū'ti, *n.* That which a person is bound to perform; obligation; act of reverence or respect; business, service, or office; tax, impost or customs.

dwell, dwel, *vi.* (pret. and pp. dwelled). To live in a place; to reside; to hang on with fondness; to continue.

dwindle, dwin'dl, *vi.* (dwindling dwindled). To diminish gradually to shrink; to sink.

dye, dī, *vt.* (dyeing, dyed). To stain; to give a new and permanent color to.—*n.* A coloring liquid or matter; tinge.

dying, dī'ing, *a.* Mortal; destined to death uttered, given, etc., just before death, pertaining to death fading away.

dynamics, dī-nam'iks, *n.* The science which investigates the action of force

dynamite, din'a-mīt, *n.* An explosive substance consisting of some powdery matter impregnated with nitro-glycerine.

dynamo, dī'na-mō, *n.* A machine for producing an electric current by mechanical power.

dynasty, di'nas-ti, *n.* A race of kings of the same family.

dyne, dīn, *n.* A unit of force, being that force which, acting on a gram for one second, generates a velocity of a centimeter per second.

dysentery, dis'en-te-ri, *n.* A disorder of the intestines; a flux in which the stools consist chiefly of blood and mucus.

E

each, ēch, *a.* and *pron.* Every one of any number considered individually.

eager, ē'gér, *a.* Sharp; ardent; keenly desirous; impetuous; earnest, intense.

eagle, ē'gl, *n.* A large bird of prey, of great powers of flight and vision; a military standard.

ear, ēr, *n.* The organ of hearing power of distinguishing musical sounds; heed; regard; anything resembling an ear or ears; a spike, as of corn—*vi.* To form ears, as corn.—*vt.* To plow or till.

earnest, érn'est, *a.* Ardent in the pursuit of an object; eager; zealous, serious—*n.* Seriousness, a reality first-fruits, a part given beforehand as a pledge for the whole, indication, token.

earnest-money, érn'est-mun-i, *n.* Money paid as earnest, to bind a bargain, etc

Earth, érth, *n.* The globe we inhabit, the world; the fine mold on the surface of the globe; dry land; the ground, the hiding hole of a fox, etc.—*vt.* To cover with earth.— *vi.* To retire underground; to burrow.

east, ēst, *n.* That part of the heavens where the sun rises, the countries east of Europe.—*a.* In or toward the east, easterly.—*adv.* Eastwards.

Easter, ēs'tér, *n.* A festival of the Christian church in March or April, in commemoration of Christ's resurrection.

easy, ēz'i, *a.* Being at ease free from pain or anxiety; not difficult; gentle; complying; affluent; not stiff or formal.

ebony, eb'on-i, *n.* A hard, heavy dark wood admitting of a fine polish.

ebullient, ē-bul'yent, *a.* Boiling over, as a liquor; over enthusiastic.

eccentric, ek-sen'trik, *a.* Not having its axis in the center; not having the same center; deviating from usual practice, etc., anomalous; whimsical.—*n.* An eccentric person; mechanical contrivance for converting circular into reciprocating rectilinear motion.

echelon, esh'e-lon, *n.* The position of troops or ships in parallel lines each line being a little to the right or left of the preceding one.

eclectic, ek-lek'tik, *a.* Proceeding by the method of selection, applied to certain philosophers who selected from the principles of various schools what they thought sound.—*n.* One who follows an eclectic method in philosophy, etc.

economic, economical, ē-kon-om'ik, e-kon-om'ik-al, *a.* Pertaining to economy or economics; frugal; careful.

edify, ed'i-fī, *vt.* (edifying, edified). To build up, in a moral sense; to instruct or improve generally.

edition, ēdi'shon, *n.* A published book as characterized by form or editorial labors, the whole number of copies of a work published at once.

editorial, ed-i-tō'ri-al, *a.* Pertaining to or written by an editor.—*n.* A leading article in a newspaper.

educate, ed'ū-kāt, *vt.* (educating educated). To teach, to cultivate and train; to enlighten.

education, ed'ū-kā'shon, *n.* Act of educating; instruction and discipline; schooling.

efficiency, ef-fi'shen-si, *n.* The state or character of being efficient; effectual agency.

efficient, ef-fi'shent, *a.* Effecting; capable, qualified for duty.

effusion, ef-fū'zhon, *n.* Act of pouring out, that which is poured out; in *pathology,* the escape of fluid out of its proper vessel into another part; cordiality of manner; a literary production.

egotism, eg'ot-izm or ē', *n.* The practice of too frequently using the word I; an exaggerated love of self, self-exaltation.

egotist, eg'ot-ist or ē', *n.* One always talking of himself, one who magnifies his own achievements.

either, ē'THèr or ī'THèr, *a.* or *pron.* One or the other; one of two; each; *conj.* or *adv.* Used disjunctively as correlative to or.

elaborate, ē-lab'o-rāt, *vt.* (elaborating, elaborated). To produce with labor; to refine by successive operations.—*a.* Wrought with labor; studied, high-wrought.

elaboration, ē-lab'o-rā''shon, *n.* Refinement by successive operations, the process in animal and vegetable organs by which something is produced.

elastic, ē-las'tik, *a.* Having the power of returning to the form from which it is bent or distorted; rebounding.—*n.* Cord or ribbon made of cotton or silk, etc., with strands of rubber.

elate, ē-lāt', *a.* Elevated in mind; flushed, as with success.—*vt.* (elating, elated). To exalt; to puff up; to make proud.

elect, ē-lekt', *vt*. To pick or choose; to select for an office.—*a*. Chosen; chosen to an office, but not yet in office.—*n. sing.* or *pl.* One or several chosen, those favored by God.

election, ē-lek'shon, *n*. Act of choosing, choice, voluntary preference; divine choice; predestination.

electricity, ē-lek-tris'i-ti, *n*. The force that manifests itself in lightning and in many other phenomena; the science which deals with these phenomena.

electrify, ē-lek'tri-fī, *vt*. (electrifying, electrified). To communicate electricity to, to thrill.—*vi*. To become electric.

electrolyte, ē-lek'tro-līt, *n*. A compound decomposable by electricity.

electron, ē-lek'tron, *n*. One of the extremely small particles of negative electricity, which form essential constituents of atoms, and by which, according to the electron theory, heat and electricity are conducted.

eleemosynary, el-ē-mos'i-na-ri, *a*. Given in or relating to charity; founded to dispense some gratuity.—*n*. One who subsists on charity.

elegance, elegancy, el'ē-gans, el' ē-gan-si, *n*. Quality of being elegant; beauty resulting from propriety; refinement.

elegiac, el'ē-ji'ak, *a*. Belonging to elegy; plaintive.—*n*. Elegiac verse.

elegy, el'ē-ji, *n*. A poem or a song expressive of sorrow and lamentation.

element, el 'ē-ment, *n*. A fundamental part or principle, an ingredient; proper sphere; suitable state of things; *pl*. first principles of an art or science; data employed in a calculation; the bread and wine used in the Lord's supper.

elementary, el-ē-ment'ar-i, *a*. Primary; uncompounded; teaching first principles or rudiments.

elephant, el'ē-fant, *n*. A huge quadruped, having a long trunk and tusks.

elevate, el'ē-vāt, *vt*. (elevating, elevated). To raise; to refine or dignify, to elate, to cheer.

elevator, el'ē-vāt-ėr, *n*. One who or that which elevates; a hoist.

elicit, ē-lis'it, *vt*. To draw out by reasoning, discussion, etc.; to educe.

eligibility, el'i-ji'bil''i-ti, *n*. Worthiness or fitness to be chosen.

elongation, ē-long-gā'shon, *n*. Act of lengthening; state of being extended; continuation; apparent distance of a planet from the sun.

elope, ē-lōp', *vi*. (eloping, eloped). To escape privately; to run away with a lover.

eloquence, e'lō-kwens, *n*. The quality or faculty of being eloquent; oratory.

eloquent, e'lō-kwent, *a*. Having the power of fluent, elegant, or forcible speech; characterized by eloquence.

emaciate, ē-mā'shi-āt, *vi*. and *t*. (emaciating, emaciated). To become or make lean.

emaciation, ē-mā'shi-ā''shon, *n*. Act of emaciating, leanness.

emancipate, ē-man'si-pāt, *vt*. (emancipating, emancipated). To set free from slavery; to liberate.

emancipation, ē-man'si-pā''shon, *n*. Liberation; freedom; enfranchisement.

emasculate, ē-mas'kū-lāt, *vt*. To castrate; to render effeminate; to expurgate.

embark, em-bärk', *vt*. To put on board a ship, to engage in.—*vi*. To go on board of a ship; to engage in, to take a share.

embarrass, em-ba'ras, *vt*. To involve in difficulties; to entangle; to disconcert.

embarrassment, em-ba'ras-ment, *n*. Entanglement; trouble; abashment.

embezzlement, em-bez'l-ment, *n*. Act of fraudulently appropriating money, etc., intrusted to one's care.

embitter, em-bit'ėr, *vt*. To make bitter or more bitter, to exasperate.

emblem, em 'blem, *n*. A picture representing one thing and suggesting another; a symbol; type; device.

embower, em-bou'ėr, *vt*. To inclose in or cover with a bower; to shade.

embrace, em-brā s', *vt*. (embracing embraced). To take within the arms; to press to the bosom; to seize ardently, to include; to accept.—*vi*. To join in an embrace.— *n*. Clasp with the arms; a hug; conjugal endearment.

emerald, e'me-rald, *n*. A precious stone, akin to the beryl, usually green; a small printing type.—*a*. Of a bright-green color.

emerge, ē-merj', *vi*. (emerging, emerged). To rise out of a fluid or other substance; to issue; to rise into view; to reappear.

emeritus, ė'-mer'i-tus, *a*. Discharged from duty with honor on account of infirmity, age, or long service.

emersion, ē-mėr'shon, *n*. Act of rising out of a fluid or other substance, reappearance of a heavenly body after eclipse, etc.

emetic, ē-met'ik, *a*. Causing vomiting.— *n*. A medicine that provokes vomiting.

emigrant, em'i-grant, *a*. Emigrating; pertaining to emigration or emigrants.—*n.* One who emigrates.

emigrate, em'i-grāt, *vi.* (emigrating, emigrated). To remove from one country or state to another for the purpose of residence.

eminence, em'in-ens, *n.* A rising ground; elevation; top; distinction; fame; a title of honor given to cardinals, etc.

emotion, ē-mō'shon, *n.* Any agitation of mind, feeling.

empale, em-pāl', *vt.* (empaling, empaled). To put to death by fixing on a stake.

emperor, em'pėr-ėr, *n.* The sovereign of an empire.

emphasis, em'fa-sis, *n.* A stress laid on a word or clause to enforce a meaning; impressiveness; weight.

emphasize, em'fa-sīz, *vt.* (emphasizing, emphasized). To place emphasis on.

empire, em'pîr, *n.* Supreme power in governing; sway; dominion of an emperor; region over which dominion is extended.

employ, em-ploi', *vt.* To occupy; to engage in one's service, to keep at work, to make use of.—*n.* Business, occupation; engagement.

employee, em-ploi'ē, *n.* One who works for an employer.

employer, em-ploi'ė r, *n.* One who employs; one who keeps men in service.

emporium, em-pō'ri-um, *n.; pl.* -ia or -iums. A commercial center; a warehouse or shop.

empower, em-pou'ėr, *vt.* To give legal or moral power to; to authorize.

empress, em'pres, *n.* The consort of an emperor; a female invested with imperial power.

empty, em'ti, *a.* Containing nothing, or nothing but air; void; unsatisfactory; unburdened; hungry; vacant of head.—*vt.* (emptying, emptied). To make empty.—*vi.* lo become empty.—*n.* An empty packing case, etc.

enamel, en-am'el, *n.* A substance of the nature of glass, used as a coating; that which is enameled; a smooth glossy surface of various colors; the smooth substance on a tooth.—*vt.* (enameling, enameled). To lay enamel on, to paint in enamel; to form a surface like enamel; to adorn with different colors.—*vi.* To practice the art of enameling.

enamor, en-am'ėr, *vt.* To inspire with love, to charm; to fill with delight.

enceinte, äng-sangt, *n.* The rampart which surrounds a fortress; the area thus surrounded.—*a.* Pregnant, with child.

encompass, en-kum'pas, *vt.* To encircle; to hem in; to go or sail round.

encounter, en-koun'tėr, *n.* A meeting in contest; a conflict; a meeting, controversy, debate.—*vt.* To meet face to face; to meet suddenly; to strive against.—*vi.* To meet unexpectedly, to conflict.

encourage, en-ku'rā j, *vt.* (encouraging, encouraged). To give courage to; to stimulate; to embolden; to countenance.

encroach, en-krōch', *vi.* To trespass on the rights and Possessions of another; to intrude; to infringe, with on or *upon.*

encroachment, en-krōch-ment, *n.* Act of encroaching; invasion; inroad; that which is taken by encroaching.

encumber, en-kum'bėr, *vt.* To impede the motion of with a load, to embarrass; to load with debts or legal claims.

endanger, en-dān'jėr, *vt.* To bring into danger; to expose to loss or injury.

endear, en-der', *vt.* To make dear; to make more beloved

endeavor, en-dev'ėr, *n.* Effort, attempt; exertion; essay; aim.—*vi.* To try; to strive; to aim.—*vt.* To try to effect, to strive after.

endemic, endemical, en-dem'ik, en-dem'ik-al, *a.* Peculiar to a people or region, as a disease.—*n.* A disease of endemic nature.

endive, en'div, *n.* A plant allied to chicory; garden succory.

endless, end'les, *a.* Without end everlasting, infinite, incessant.

endogen, en'dō-jen, *n.* A plant whose stem grows by additions developed from the inside, as palms and grasses.

endogenous, en-doj'e-nus, *a.* Pertaining to endogens; developing from within.

endorse, en-dors', *vt.* (endorsing, endorsed). To write on the back of, as one's name on a bill; to assign by endorsement, to ratify

endorsement, en-dors'ment, *n.* The act of endorsing; a docket; signature of one who endorses; sanction or approval

enema, en'e-ma, *n.* A liquid or gaseous medicine injected into the rectum; a clyster.

enemy, en'e-mi, *n.* One who is unfriendly; an antagonist; a hostile army.

energetic, energetical, en-ėr-jet'ik, en-ėr-jet'ik-al *a.* Acting with energy; forcible; potent; active; vigorous.

energy, en'ėr-ji, *n.* Inherent power to operate or act; power exerted; force; vigor; strength of expression; emphasis, in physics, power to do work; it may be mechanical, electrical, thermal, chemical, etc.

enforcement, en-fōrs'ment, *n.* Act of enforcing; compulsion; a giving of force or effect to; a putting in execution, as law.

enfranchise, en-fran'chiz, *vt.* (en-franchising, enfranchised). To set free; to admit to the privileges of a citizen; to endow with the franchise.

engineer, en-ji-nēr', *n.* One who constructs or manages engines one who plans works for offense or defense; one who constructs roads, railways, etc.—*vt.* To direct the making of in the capacity of engineer.

English, ing'glish, *a.* Belonging to England, or to its inhabitants.—*n.* The people or language of England.—*vt.* To translate into English.

engulf, en-gulf', *vt.* To engulf; to swallow up.

enhance, en-hans', *vt.* (enhancing enhanced). To raise to a higher point; to increase; to aggravate. —*vi.* To grow larger.

enigma, ē-nig'ma, *n.* An obscure statement or question, riddle, anything inexplicable.

enjoin, en-join', *vt.* To order with urgency, to admonish, to prescribe.

enjoy, en-joi', *vt.* To feel gladness in to have, use, or perceive with pleasure.

enjoyment, en-joi'ment, *n.* State of enjoying; pleasure; satisfaction; fruition.

enlarge, en-lärj', *vt.* (enlarging, enlarged). To make large or larger; to set free.—*vi.* To grow large or larger; to expatiate.

enlargement, en-lärj'ment, *n.* Act of enlarging, state of being enlarged; expansion; release; addition.

enlighten, en-līt'en, *vt.* To make clear; to enable to see more clearly, to instruct.

enlist, en-list', *vt.* To enter on a list to engage in public service, especially military; to engage the services of—*vi.* To engage voluntarily in public service; to enter heartily into a cause.

enough, ē-nuf', *a.* That satisfies desire, that may answer the purpose.—*n.* A sufficiency, that which is equal to the powers or abilities.—*adv.* Sufficiently, tolerably.

enrage, en-rāj', *vt.* To excite rage in; to incense.

enrapture, en-rap'tūr, *vt.* To transport with rapture; to delight beyond measure.

enroll, enrol, en-rōl', *vt.* To write in a roll

or register, to record.

ensign, en'sīn, *n.* A mark of distinction; the flag of a company of soldiers or a vessel, formerly the lowest rank of commissioned officer in the infantry.

entail, en-tāl', *vt.* To cut off an estate from the heirs general; lo settle, as the descent of lands by gift to a man and to certain heirs, to devolve as a consequence or of necessity.—*n.* The act of entailing; an estate entailed, rule of descent settled for an estate.

entangle, en-tang'gl, *vt.* To knit or interweave confusedly; to involve; to hamper.

enter, en'tèr, *vt.* To go or come into; to begin; to set down in writing; to register; to take possession of.—*vi.* To go or come in; begin; engage in; be an ingredient in.

enterprise, en'tèr-prīz, *n.* That which is undertaken, a bold or hazardous attempt; adventurous spirit; hardihood.—*vt. To* undertake.

entertain, en-tèr-tān', *vt. To* receive as a guest; to cherish; to treat with conversation, to please; to admit with a view to consider.—*vi.* To give entertainments.

entire, en-tīr', *a.* Whole, unshared complete; sincere; hearty; in full strength.

entirely, entīr'li, *adv.* Wholly; fully.

entitle, en-tī'tl, *vt.* (entitling, entitled). To give a title to, to style, to characterize; to give a claim to; to qualify.

entrail, en'trāl, *n.* One of the intestines; generally in *pl.;* the bowels.

entrain, en-trān', *vt.* To put on board a railway train.—*vi.* To take places in a train.

entrance en'trans, *n.* Act or power of entering into a place, the door or avenue by which a place may be entered; beginning; act of taking possession.

entrance, en-trans', *vt.* To put in a trance or ecstasy; to enrapture; to transport.

enumerate, ē-nu'me-rāt, *vt.* (enumerating, enumerated). To count number by number; to reckon or mention a number of things, each separately.

enunciation, ē-nun'si-ā"shon, *n.* Act or manner of enunciating, expression; declaration; public attestation.

envelop, en-vel'op, *vt.* To cover by wrapping or folding; to lie around and conceal.

envelope, en'vel-ōp, *n.* That which infolds; a wrapper; a covering for a letter, etc.; an investing integument.

environ, en-vī'ron, *vt.* To encompass; to

encircle; to besiege; to invest.

environment, en-vī'ron-ment, *n.* Act of environing, state of being environed; that which environs conditions under which one lives.

envoy, en'voi, *n.* One sent on a mission; a person next in rank to an ambassador deputed to transact business with a foreign power.

epic, ep'ik, *a.* Composed in a lofty narrative style, heroic.—*n.* A poem of elevated character, describing the exploits of heroes.

epicure, ep 'i-kūr, *n.* One devoted to sensual enjoyments; a voluptuary.

epidemic, epidemical, ep-i-dem'ik ep-i-dem'ik-al, *a.* Affecting a whole community, as a disease prevalent.—**epidemic**, ep-i-dem' ik, *n.* A disease which attacks many people at the same period.

epigram, ep'i-gram, *n.* A short poem, usually keenly satirical; a pointed or antithetical saying.

epigraph, ep'i-graf, *n.* An inscription; quotation; motto.

epilepsy, ep'i-lep-si, *n.* The falling sickness, a disease characterized by spasms and loss of sense.

epilogue, ep'i-log, *n.* A speech or short poem spoken by an actor at the end of a play.

Epiphany, ē-pif'a-ni, *n.* A church festival on January 6th, celebrating the manifestation of Christ to the wise men of the East.

epitaph, ep'i-taf, *n.* That which is written on a tomb; an inscription, or a composition, in honor of the dead.

epithalamium, ep'i-tha-lā'mi-um, *n.*; pl. **-iums** or **-ia**. A nuptial song or poem.

epithet, ep'i-thet, *n.* Any word implying a quality attached to a person or thing.

epitome, e-pit'o-mi, *n.* A brief summary; abridgment; compendium.

epoch, ē'pok, *n.* A fixed point of time from which years are numbered; period; era; date.

equal, ē'kwal, *a.* The same in extent, number, degree, rank, etc., same in qualities, uniform, proportionate; adequate; just.—*n.* One not inferior or superior to another.—*vt.* (equalling, equalled). To make equal to; to become or be equal to.

equanimity, ē-kwa-nim'i-ti or ek-, *n.* Evenness of mind; steadiness of temper.

equate, ē-kwāt, *vt.* (equating equated). To make equal; to reduce to an equation; to reduce to mean time or motion.

equation, ē-kwā'shon, *n.* The act of equating; an expression asserting the equality of two quantities; a quantity to be taken into account in order to give a true result.

Equator, ē-kwā'tèr, *n.* The great circle of our globe which divides it into the northern and southern hemispheres; a circle in the heavens coinciding with the plane of the earth's equator

equilibrium, ē-kwi-li'bri-um or ek-, *n.* State of rest produced by the counteraction of forces; balance.

equinoctial, ē-kwi-nok'shal, or ek-, *a.* Pertaining to the equinoxes.—*n.* The celestial equator when the sun is on it, the days and nights are of equal length.

Equinox, ē'kwi-noks or ek', *n.* The time when the day and night are of equal length, about March 21st and September 23rd.

equip, ē-kwip', *vt.* (equipping, equipped). To fit out or furnish, as for war, to dress, to array.

equipment, ē-kwip'ment, *n.* Act of equipping; habiliments; warlike apparatus; necessary adjuncts.

equitable, ek'wit-a-bl, *a.* Distributing equal justice; just; upright; impartial.

equity, ek'wi-ti, *n.* The giving to each man his due; impartiality; uprightness; a system of supplementary law founded upon precedents and established principles.

equivalent, ē-kwiv'a-lent or ek-, *a.* Equal in excellence, worth, or weight, of the same import or meaning.—*n.* That which is equal in value, etc., compensation.

equivocate, ē-kwiv'ō-kāt, *vi.* To use ambiguous expressions to mislead to quibble.

erect, ē-rekt', *a.* Upright; bold; undismayed.—*vt.* To raise and set upright, to build, to found, to cheer.

erode, ē-rōd', *vt.* (eroding, eroded). To gnaw off or away, to corrode.

erotic, ē-rot'ik *a.* Pertaining to or prompted by love; treating of love.

err, er, *vi.* To wander; to stray; to depart from rectitude, to blunder.

errand, e'rand, *n.* A message; mandate, business to be transacted by a messenger.

erratic, e-rat'ik, *a.* Wandering; irregular eccentric.

erratum; e-rā'tum, *n.*; pl. **-ata**. An error or mistake in writing or printing.

error, e'rèr, *n.* A deviation from truth or what is right; a mistake; a blunder, fault;

offense.

escapade, es-ka-pād', *n.* A runaway adventure; a freak; a mad prank.

escape, es-kāp', *vt.* (escaping, escaped). To get out of the way of; to pass without harm, to pass unobserved; to avoid.—*vi.* To be free; to avoid, to regain one's liberty.—*n.* Flight, to shun danger; an evasion of legal restraint or custody.

escarpment, es-kärp'ment, *n.* A steep declivity, ground cut away nearly vertically

eschew, es-chö', *vt.* To shun; to avoid.

escort, es'kort, *n.* A guard attending an officer or baggage, etc.; persons attending as a mark of honor.—*vt.* es-kort'. To attend and guard.

espionage, es'pi-on-āj, *n.* Practice or employment of spies; practice of watching others without being suspected.

espousal, es-pouz'al, *n.* Betrothal; nuptials: in this sense generally in *pl;* the adopting of a cause.

espouse, es-pouz', *vt.* (espousing, espoused). To give or take in marriage; to betroth; to wed; to embrace or adopt, to uphold.

esprit, es-prē, *n.* Soul; spirit; mind; wit.

essential, es-sen'shal, *a.* Relating to or containing the essence; necessary to the existence of, indispensable, highly rectified, volatile diffusible (oils).—*n.* Something necessary; the chief point; constituent principle.

establish, es-tab'lish, *vt.* To make stable; to found permanently; to institute; to enact; to sanction; to confirm; to make good.

esteem, es-tēm', *vt.* To set a value on; to regard with respect; to prize.—*n.* Judgment of merit or demerit, estimation, great regard.

estimate, es'tim-āt, *vt.* (estimating, estimated). To form an opinion regarding, to calculate, to appraise to esteem,—*n.* Valuation; calculation of probable cost.

estrange, es-trā nj', *vt.* (estranging estranged). To alienate, as the affections.

estuary, es'tū-a-ri, *n.* The mouth of a river where the tide meets the current; a firth.

etching, ech'ing, *n.* The act or art of the etcher; a mode of engraving; the impression taken from an etched plate.

eternal, ē-tern'al, *a.* Everlasting without beginning or end of existence; unchangeable.—*n.* An appellation of God.

eternity, ē-tern'i-ti, *n.* Continuance with-

out beginning or end; duration without end, the state or time after death.

ethereal, ē-thē'rē-al, *a.* Formed of ether; heavenly; aerial; intangible.

ethic, ethical, eth'ik, eth'ik-al, *a.* Relating to morals; treating of morality; delivering precepts of morality.

ethics, eth'iks *n.* The doctrine of morals, moral philosophy, a system of moral principles.

ethnic, ethnical, eth'nik, eth'nik-al, *a.* Pertaining to the gentiles; pagan; ethnological.

etymology, et-i-mol'o-ji, *n.* that part of philology which traces the origin of words; the derivation or history of any word.

eulogy, ū'lo-ji, *n.* A speech or writing in commendation; praise; panegyric.

euphemism, ū'fem-izm, *n.* A mode of speaking by which a delicate word or expression is substituted for one which is offensive, a word or expression so substituted.

evade, ē-vād', *vt.* (evading, evaded). To avoid by dexterity; to slip away from; to elude; to baffle.—*vi.* To practice evasion.

evaluate, ō-val'ū-āt, *vt.* To value carefully; to ascertain the amount of.

evanesce, ev-a-nes', *vi.* To vanish.

evaporate, ē-va'per-āt, *vi.* (evaporating, evaporated). To pass off in vapor, to exhale, to be wasted.—*vt.* To convert into vapor; to disperse in vapors.

evasion, ē-vā'zhon, *n.* Act of evading; artifice to elude; shift; equivocation.

even, ē'vn, *a.* Level, smooth, equable; on an equality; just; settled; balanced; capable of being divided by 2 without a remainder.— *vt.* To make even or level, to equalize; to balance.—*adv.* Just, exactly; likewise; moreover.—*n.* The evening.

evening, ē'vn-ing, *n.* The close of the day; the decline of anything.— *a.* Being at the close of day.

ever, ev'ėr *adv.* At all times; at any time; continually; in any degree.

evergreen, ev'ėr-grēn, *n.* A plant that always retains its greenness.—*a.* Always green.

evict, ē-vikt', *vt.* To dispossess by judicial process, to expel from lands, etc., by law.

evidence, ev'i-dens, *n.* That which demonstrates that a fact is so, testimony; proof; witness.—*vt.* To make evident, to prove.

evince, ē-vins', *vt.* (evincing evinced). To show in a clear manner; to manifest.

evolve, ē-volv', *vt.* (evolving evolved). To unfold, to develop, to open and expand.—*vi.* To open or disclose itself.

exaggerate, egz-aj'e-rāt, *vt.* (exaggerating, exaggerated). To increase beyond due limits; to depict extravagantly.

exalt, egz-ält', *vt.* To raise high; to raise to power or dignity; to extol.

examination, egz-am'in-ā''shon, *n.* Act of examining; inquiry into facts, etc., by interrogation; scrutiny by study.

examine, egz-am'in, *vt.* (examining, examined). To inspect carefully; to inquire into, to interrogate, as a witness, a student, etc.; to discuss.

example, egz-am'pl, *n.* A sample; pattern; model; precedent; instance.

exasperate, egz-as'pé-rāt, *vt.* (exasperating, exasperated). To irritate; to enrage; to make worse; to aggravate.

excavate, eks'ka-vāt, *vt.* (excavating, excavated). To hollow out.

excel, ek-sel', *vt.* (excelling, excelled). To surpass; to transcend; to outdo.—*vi.* To be eminent or distinguished.

exception, ek-sep 'shon, *n.* Act of excepting; state of being excepted; that which is excepted; an objection; offense.

excerpt, ek-sérpt', *n.* An extract; a passage selected from an author.—*vt.* To pick out from a book etc.; to cite.

excess, ek-ses', *n.* That which exceeds, super-abundance; intemperate conduct; that by which one thing exceeds another.

exchange, eks-chānj', *vt.* To change one thing for another; to commute, to bargain.—*n.* Act of exchanging; interchange; barter; the thing interchanged; place where merchants, etc., of a city meet to transact business; a method of finding the equivalent to a given sum in the money of another country.

excise, ek-sīz', *n.* A tax on certain commodities of home production and consumption, as beer, etc.; also for licenses to deal in certain commodities.—*vt.* (excising, excised). To impose a duty on articles produced and consumed at home, to cut out.

exclamation, eks-klam-ā'shon, *n.* A loud outcry, a passionate sentence, a note by which emphatical utterance is marked, thus, !; an interjection.

exclude, eks-klūd', *vt.* (excluding, excluded). To shut out; to thrust out; to debar; to prohibit; to except.

excrement, eks'krē-ment, *n.* That which is separated from the nutriment by digestion, and discharged from the body; ordure; dung.

excrete, eks-krēt', *vt.* (excreting, excreted). To separate and discharge from the body by vital action.

excruciate, eks-krö'shi-āt, *vt.* To torture; to rack.

execrate, ek'sē-krāt, *vt.* (execrating, execrated). To curse; to abominate.

execute, ek'sē-kūt, *vt.* (executing executed). To effect to achieve, to inflict capital punishment on, to make valid, as by signing and sealing; to perform.—*vi.* To perform.

executioner, ek-sēkū''shon-èr, *n.* One who puts to death by law.

executive, egz-ek'ūt-iv, *a.* That executes; carrying laws into effect, or superintending their enforcement.—*n.* The person or persons who administer the government.

exempt, egz-emt', *vt.* To free from to privilege; to grant immunity from.—*a.* Free by privilege; not liable.

exemption, egz-em'shon, *n.* Act of exempting; state of being exempt; immunity.

exfoliate, eks-fō'li-āt, *vt.* and *i.* To scale off.

exhaust, egz-äst', *vt.* To drain off contents; to expend entirely; to treat thoroughly; to tire.

exhibit, egz-ib 'it, *vt.* To show, to display; to administer by way of remedy.—*n.* Anything exhibited.

exhibition, eks-i-bi'shon, *n.* Act of exhibiting; display; any public show, a benefaction for students in English universities.

exhilarate, egz-il'a-rāt, *vt.* (exhilarating, exhilarated). To make cheerful; to inspirit.

exist, egz-ist', *vi.* To be; to live; to endure.

existence, egz-ist'ens, *n.* State of being; life; continuation; anything that exists.

exit, eks'it, *n.* A going out; the departure of a player from the stage; death, a way out.

exonerate, egz-on'ē-rāt, *vt.* To exculpate; to acquit; to justify.

exorable, eks'ōr-a-bl, *a.* That can be persuaded; placable.

exorbitant, egz-or'bit-ant, *a.* Excessive; extravagant.

expand, ek-spand', *vt.* and *i.* To spread out; to enlarge; to distend; to dilate.

expect, ek-spekt', *vt.* To wait for; to look

E

for to happen, to anticipate.

expectance, expectancy, ek-spek' tans, ek-spek'tan-si, *n.* Act or state of expecting; expectation; hope.

expectation, ek-spek-tā'shon, *n.* Act or state of expecting; prospect of good to come; prospect of reaching a certain age.

expectorate, eks-pek'tō-rāt, *vt.* (expectorating, expectorated). To expel, as phlegm, by coughing; to spit out.

expeditious, eks-pē-di'shus, *a.* Speedy, prompt, nimble, active.

expend, ek-spend', *vt.* To spend; to use or consume, to waste.

expenditure, ek-spend'i-tūr, *n.* Act of expending; a laying out, as of money; money expended; expense.

expense, ek-spens', *n.* That which is expended; cost; charge; price.

experiment, eks-pe'ri ment, *n.* A trial; an operation designed to discover something unknown, or to establish it when discovered.—*vi.* To make trial or experiment.

expert, eks-pėrt', *a.* Skillful; dexterous, adroit.—*n.* eks'pert. An expert person; a scientific witness.

explanation, eks-pla-nā'shon, *n.* Act of explaining, interpretation clearing up of matters between parties at variance.

expletive, eks'plēt-iv, *a.* Serving to fill out; superfluous.—*n.* A word or syllable inserted to fill a vacancy or for ornament; an oath or interjection.

explicate, eks'pli-kāt, *vt.* To unfold the meaning of, to explain.

explode, eks-plō d', *vt.* (exploding, exploded). To drive out of use or belief, to cause to burst with violence and noise.—*vi.* To burst with noise; to burst into activity or passion.

exploit, eks-ploit', *n.* A deed; a heroic act; a deed of renown.—*vt.* To make use of; to work.

exploitation, eks-ploi-tā 'shon, *n.* Successful application of industry on any object, as land, mines, etc.

exploration, eks-plo-rā'shon, *n.* Act of exploring; strict or careful examination.

explore, eks-plōr', *vt.* (exploring, explored) To travel with the view of making discovery; to search; to examine closely.

explosion, eks-plō'zhon, *n.* Act of exploding; a bursting with noise; a violent outburst of feeling.

explosive, eks-plō'siv, *a.* Causing explosion; readily exploding.—*n.* Anything liable to explode, as gunpowder; a mute or non-continuous consonant, as k, t, b.

exponent, eks-pō'nent, *n.* One who explains or illustrates; that which indicates; the index of a power in algebra.

expound, eks-pound', *vt.* To explain; to interpret; to unfold.

express, eks-pres', *vt.* To press out to set forth in words; to declare; to make known by any means; (refl.) to say what one has got to say.—*a.* Clearly exhibited; given in direct terms, intended or sent for a particular purpose; traveling with special speed.—*n.* A messenger or vehicle sent on a particular occasion; a message specially sent, a specially fast railway train.—*adv.* For a particular purpose; with special haste.

expression, eks-pre'shon, *n.* Act of expressing; a phrase or mode of speech; manner of utterance; a natural and lively representation in painting and sculpture; musical tone, grace, or modulation; play of features; representation of a quantity in algebra.

expropriate, eks-prō'pri-ā t , *vt.* To take for public use, to dispossess.

extemporize, eks-tem'pō-rīz, *vi.* To speak without preparation.—*vt.* To make without forethought; to prepare in haste.

extend, eks-tend', *vt.* To stretch out; to spread; to prolong; to bestow on.—*vi.* To stretch; to reach; to become larger.

extenuate, eks-ten'ū-ā t, *vt.* To lessen; to weaken the force of; to palliate.

exterior, eks-tē'ri-ėr, *a.* External; on the outside; foreign.—*n.* The outward surface; that which is external.

extirpation, eks-tėrp-ā 'shon, *n.* Act of rooting out; eradication; total destruction.

extortion eks-tor'shon, *n.* Act of extorting; illegal or oppressive exaction.

extract, eks-trakt', *vt.* To draw out or forth; to select; to draw or copy out, to find the root of a number.— *n.* eks'trakt. That which is extracted; a quotation; an essence, tincture, etc.

extraction, eks-trak'shon, *n.* Act of extracting; lineage; operation of drawing essences, tinctures; etc.; operation of finding the roots of numbers.

extradite, eks'tra-dīt, *vt.* To deliver up (a criminal) to the authorities of the country from which he has come.

extradition, eks-traä-di'shon, *n.* The delivery, under a treaty, of a fugitive from justice by one government to another.

extreme, eks-trēm', *a.* Outermost; furthest; most violent, last; worst or best; most pressing.—*n.* The utmost point or verge of a thing; end; furthest or highest degree; *(pl.)* points at the greatest distance from each other.

extremist, eks-trēm'ist, *n.* A supporter of extreme doctrines or practice.

extremity, eks-trem'i-ti, *n.* That which is extreme, utmost point part, or degree; utmost distress or violence.

extricate, eks'tri-kā t, *vt.* (extricating, extricated). To disentangle; to set free.

extrinsic, extrinsical, eks-trin'sik, eks-trin'-sik-al, *a.* Being on the outside; extraneous; accessory.

extrusion, eks-trö'zhon, *n.* Act of extruding; a driving out; expulsion.

exude, eks-ūd, *vt.* (exuding, exuded). To discharge through the pores; to let ooze out.—*vi.* To flow through pores; to ooze out like sweat.

exult, egz-ult', *vi.* To rejoice exceedingly; to triumph.

exultation, egz-ult-ā'shon, *n.* Lively joy; triumph; rapture; ecstasy.

eyrie, eyry, ī'ri, *n.* An aerie; nest of a bird of prey.

F

fable, fā'bl, *n.* A fictitious narrative to instruct or amuse, often to enforce a precept; falsehood; an idle story, the plot in a poem or drama.—*vi.* (fabling, fabled). To tell fables or falsehoods. —*vt.* To feign, to invent.

fabric, fab'rik, *n.* Frame or structure of anything; a building; texture; cloth.

fabricate, fab'rik-āt, *vt.* (fabricating, fabricated). To make or fashion, to form by art or labor; to devise falsely.

fabulous, fa'bū-lus, *a.* Containing or abounding in fable; feigned; mythical, incredible.

facade, facade, fa-säd', fa-säd', *n.* Front view or elevation of an edifice.

face, fās, *n.* The front part of an animal's head, particularly of the human head; the visage, front, effrontery, assurance, dial of a watch, etc.—*vt.* (facing; faced). To meet in front; to stand opposite to; to oppose with firmness; to finish or protect with a thin external covering, to dress the face of (a stone etc.).—*vi.* To turn the face; to look.

facsimile, fak-sim'i-lē, *n.* An exact copy or likeness.

faction, fak'shon, *n.* A party in political society in opposition to the ruling power, a party unscrupulously promoting its private ends; discord, dissension.

factor, fak'tėr, *n.* An agent, particularly a mercantile agent; in Scotland, one appointed to manage an estate; one of two or more numbers or quantities, which, when multiplied together, form a product; one of several elements which contribute to a result.

factory, fak'to-ri, *n.* An establishment where factors in foreign countries reside to transact business for their employers; buildings appropriated to the manufacture of goods, a manufactory.

fairy, fā' ri, *n.* An imaginary being of human form, supposed to play a variety of pranks.—*a.* Belonging to fairies; given by fairies.

faith, fāth, *n.* Belief; trust, confidence, conviction in regard to religion; system of religious beliefs; strict adherence to duty and promises, word or honor pledged.

falcon, fä'kn, or fäl'kon, *n.* The name of various small or medium-sized raptorial birds, a hawk of any kind trained to sport.

fall, fäl, *vi.* (pret. fell, pp. fallen). To sink to a lower position, to drop down, to empty or disembogue; to sink into sin, weakness, or disgrace; to come to an end suddenly; to decrease; to assume an expression of dejection, etc., to happen to pass or be transferred; to belong or appertain; to be uttered carelessly.—*n.* Descent; tumble; death; ruin; cadence; a cascade or cataract; extent of descent; declivity, autumn. that which falls; a kind of ladies' veil; lapse or declension from innocence or goodness; *naut.* the part of a tackle to which the power is applied in hoisting.

false, fäls, *a.* Not true; forged; feigned, fraudulent; treacherous; inconstant; constructed for show or a subsidiary purpose.

falsehood, fäls'höd, *n.* Quality of being false; untruth; fiction; a lie.

falsetto, fäl-set'tō, *n.* A false or artificial voice; the tones above the natural compass of the voice.

familiar, fa-mil'i-ėr, *a.* Well acquainted; intimate; affable; well known, free, unconstrained.—*n.* An intimate; one long acquainted; a demon supposed to attend at call.

family, fam'i-li, *n.* Household; the parents and children alone, the children as distinguished from the parents; kindred; line of ancestors; honorable descent; a group or class of animals or plants.

famine, fam'in, *n.* Scarcity of food; dearth.

famish, fam'ish, *vt.* To kill or exhaust with hunger, to starve, to kill by denial of anything necessary.—*vi.* To die of hunger; to suffer extreme hunger or thirst.

fan, fan, *n.* An instrument for winnowing grain, an instrument to agitate the air and cool the face; something by which the air is moved a wing.—*vt.* (fanning fanned). To cool and refresh by moving the air with a fan; to winnow, to stimulate.

fanatic, fanatical, fa-nat'ik, fanat'ik-al, *a.* Wild in opinions, particularly in religious opinions, excessively enthusiastic.—**fanatic,** fa-nat'ik, *n.* A person affected by excessive enthusiasm, particularly on religious subjects; an enthusiast, a visionary.

fancy, fan'si, *n* A phase of the intellect of a lighter cast than the imagination;

thought due to this faculty; embodiment of such in words, opinion or notion, liking caprice; false notion.—*vi.* (fancying, fancied). To imagine; to suppose without proof.—*vt.* To imagine; to like; to be pleased with.—*a.* Fine, ornamental, adapted to please the fancy; beyond intrinsic value.

fantasy, fan'ta-si, *n.* Fancy, a vagary of the imagination; a fanciful artistic production.—*vt.* To picture in fancy.

farce, färs, *n.* A play full of extravagant drollery; absurdity; mere show.—*vt.* To stuff with forcemeat or mingled ingredients.

fare, fär, *vi.* (faring, fared). To go; to travel; to be in any stale, good o bad, to be entertained with food to happen well or ill.—*n.* Sun charged for conveying a person person conveyed; food; provisions of the table.

fascinate, fas'si nät, *vt.* (fascinating, fascinated). To bewitch, to charm; to captivate.

fashion, fa'shon, *n.* The make or form of anything; external appearance; form of a garment; prevailing mode, custom, genteel life.—*vt.* To give shape to; to mold; to adapt.

fast, fäst, *a.* Firmly fixed; closely adhering; steadfast; durable swift dissipated.—*adv.* Firmly rapidly; durably; near; with dissipation.—*vi.* To abstain from eating and drinking, or from particular kinds of food.—*n.* Abstinence from food; a religious mortification by abstinence; the time of fasting.

fasten, fäs'n, *vt.* To fix firmly closely, or tightly to hold together to affix.—*vi.* To become fixed; t seize and hold on.

fastidious, fas-tid'i-us. *a.* Squeamish; delicate to a fault; difficult to please

fat, fat, *a.* Fleshy; plump, unctuous heavy; stupid; rich; fertile.—*n.* solid oily substance found in parts of animal bodies; the best or rich est part of a thing.—*vt.* (fatting, fat ted). To make fat.

fatal, fät'al, *a.* Proceeding from fate; causing death; deadly; calamitous.

fate, fat, *n.* Destiny; inevitable necessity; death; doom; lot; *pl.* the three goddesses supposed to preside over the birth and life of men.

father, fä'THèr, *n.* A male parent; the first ancestor, the oldest member of a society or profession; the first to practice any art; a creator; a name given to God, a dignitary of the church; one of the early expounders of Christianity.—*vt.* To

become a father to, to adopt, to profess to be the author of; to ascribe to one as his offspring or production.

fathom, faTH'um, *n.* A measure of length containing six feet.—*vt.* To try the depth of; to sound; to master, to comprehend.

fatigue, fa-tēg', *vt.* (fatiguing, fatigued) To employ to weariness; to tire, to harass with toil or labor.—*n.* Weariness from bodily or mental exertion; exhaustion; toil; labors of soldiers distinct from the use of arms.

fatten, fat'n, *vt.* To make fat; to feed for slaughter; to make fertile.—*vi.* To grow fat.

fauna, fä'na, *n.* A collective term for the animals peculiar to a region or epoch.

faux-pas, fō-pä, *n.* A false step; a breach of manners or moral conduct.

fear, fär, *n.* Painful emotion excited by apprehension of impending danger; dread; the object of fear; filial regard mingled with awe; reverence.—*vt.* To feel fear, to apprehend; to dread; to reverence.— *vi.* To be in apprehension of evil, to be afraid.

feasibility, fēz-i-bil 'i-ti, *n.* Quality of being feasible; practicability.

feasible, fēz-i-bl, *a.* That may be done, practicable.

feast, fēst, *n.* A festal day, a sumptuous entertainment; a banquet; a festival, that which delights and entertains.—*vi.* To partake of a feast; to eat sumptuously; to be highly gratified.—*vt.* To entertain sumptuously.

feather, feTH'èr, *n.* One of the growths which form the covering of birds, a plume, projection on a board to fit into another board; kind of nature, birds collectively, a trifle.—*vt.* To cover or fit with feathers; to turn (an oar) horizontally over the water.

feature, fē'tur, *n.* The make or cast of any part of the face; any single lineament; a prominent part or characteristic.

federal, fed'èr-al, *a.* Pertaining to a league or contract; confederated; founded on alliance between states which unite for national purposes.—*n.* One who upholds federal government.

federation, fed-e' r-a'shon, *n.* Act of uniting in a league; confederacy.

fee, fē, *n.* A reward for services; recompense for professional services; a fief; a freehold estate held by one who is absolute owner.—*vt.* (feeing, feed). To pay a fee to; to engage in one's service by advancing a fee to.

feeble, fē'bl, *a.* Weak; impotent; deficient in vigor, as mental powers sound, light, etc.

feed, fēd, *vt.* (feeding, fed). To give food to; to furnish with anything of which there is constant consumption; to fatten.—*vi.* To take food, to eat; to prey, to graze, to grow fat.—*n.* That which is eaten; fodder; portion of provender given to a horse, cow, etc.

feel, fēl, *vt.* (feeling, felt). To perceive by the touch, to have the sense of; to be affected by; to examine by touching.—*vi.* To have perception by the touch; to have the sensibility moved; to have perception mentally.—*n.* Act of feeling; perception caused by the touch.

feign, fān, *vt.* To pretend, to counterfeit; to simulate.—*vi.* To represent falsely; to pretend.

felicitate, fē-lis'it-āt, *vt.* To congratulate.

felon, fe'lon, *n.* One who has committed felony, a culprit, a whitlow.—*a.* Fierce; malignant; malicious.

felony, fe'lon-i, *n.* Any crime which incurs the forfeiture of lands or goods, a heinous crime.

female, fē'māl, *n.* One of that sex which conceives and brings forth young. *a.* Belonging to the sex which produces young; feminine; weak.

feminine, fem'in-in, *a* Pertaining to females; womanly; effeminate; denoting the gender of words which signify females.

femur, fē'mėr, *n.* The thigh-bone.

fence, fens, *n.* That which defends or guards, a wall, railing, etc. forming a boundary, etc.—*vi.* To practice the swordsman's art; to parry arguments, to prevaricate.

fencing, fens'ing, *n.* The art of using a sword or foil in attack or defense, material used in making fences; that which fences.

fenestration, fen-es-trā'shon, *n.* The arrangement of windows in a building.

fennel, fen'el, *n.* A plant cultivated for the aromatic flavor of its seeds and for its leaves.

fermentation, fė r-ment-ā'shon, *n.* Decomposition or conversion of an organic substance into new compounds by a ferment, indicated by the development of heat, bubbles etc., process by which grape juice is converted into wine agitation; excitement.

ferocious, fē-rō'shus, *a.* Fierce; savage; cruel.

ferry, fe'ri, *vt.* (ferrying, ferried). To carry over a river or other water in a boat.—*n.* Place where boats pass over to convey passengers; regular conveyance provided at such a place; a boat that plies at a ferry.

fertile, fėr'til, *a.* Fruitful, prolific, inventive; able to produce abundantly.

fertility, fėr-til'i-ti, *n.* Fruitfulness; richness, fertile invention.

fertilize, fėr'til-īz, *vt.* To make fertile or fruitful; to enrich; to impregnate.

fervent, fėr'vent, *a.* Burning; vehement; ardent; earnest.

fever, fē'vėr, *n.* A disease characterized by an accelerated pulse, heat, thirst, and diminished strength, agitation; excitement.— *vt.* To put in a fever.—*vt.* To be seized with fever.

fiasco, fē-as'kō, *n.* An ignominious failure.

fiber, fī bėr, *n.* A thread; a fine, slender body which Constitutes a part of animals, plants, or minerals.

fiction, fik'shon, *n.* A feigned story; literature in the form of novels, tales, etc., a falsehood; fabrication.

fidelity, fi-del'i-ti, *n.* Faithfulness; trustiness; loyalty; integrity.

fiduciary, fi-dū'shi-a-ri, *a.* Held in trust; having the nature of a trust.—*n.* One who holds a thing in trust, a trustee.

field, fēld, *n.* A piece of land suitable for tillage or pasture; piece of enclosed land; place of battle, battle; open space for action; sphere; blank space on which figures are drawn, those taking part in a hunt or race.—*vi.* and *t.* To watch and catch the ball, as in cricket.

fiend, fēnd, *n.* A demon; the devil; a wicked or cruel person

fierce, fėrs, *a.* Wild; savage; outrageous; violent.

fight, fit, *vi.* (fighting, fought). To strive for victory; to contend in arms.—*vt.* To war against; to contend with in battle, to win by struggle.—*n.* A struggle for victory; a battle; an encounter.

fighter, fi t'ėr, *n.* One who fights; a combatant; a warrior; an aeroplane designed for aerial combat.

figment, fig'ment, *n.* A fiction; fabrication.

figure-head, fig'ūr-hed, *n.* The ornamental figure on a ship under the bowsprit.

filament, fil'a-ment, *n.* A slender thread, a fine fiber.

file, fīl, *n.* A line or wire on which papers are strung; the papers so strung, a row of soldiers one behind another, a steel instrument for cutting and smoothing iron wood, etc.—*vt.* (filing, filed). To arrange or place on or in a file; to bring before a court by presenting the proper papers; to rub or cut with a file; to polish.—*vi.* To march in a line one after the other.

fill, fil, *vt.* To make full; to occupy; to pervade; to satisfy; to surfeit; to supply with an occupant, to hold to possess and perform the duties of.—*vi.* To grow or become full.—*n.* As much as fills or supplies want.

fillet, fil'et, *n.* A little band to tie about the hair, the fleshy part of the thigh in veal, meat rolled together and tied round; something resembling a fillet or band.—*vt.* (filleting, filleted). To bind with a little band.

filter, fil'tèr, *n.* A strainer; any substance through which liquors are passed—*vt.* To purify by passing through a filter.—*vi.* To percolate to pass through a filter.

finance, fi-nans', *n.* The science of public revenue and expenditure; management of money matters; pl. public funds or resources of money, private income. — *vi.* (financing, financed). To conduct financial operations.—*vt.* To manage the financial affairs of.

finch, finsh, *n.* A small singing bird.

finding, find'ing, *n.* Discovery; act of discovering: that which is found, a verdict.

finery, fin'è-ri, *n.* Fine things, showy articles of dress; a furnace where cast-iron is converted into malleable iron.

finger, fing'gèr, *n.* One of the five members of the hand; something resembling a finger; skill in playing on a keyed instrument.—*vt.* To handle with the fingers; to touch lightly, to pilfer.—*vi.* To dispose the fingers aptly in playing on an instrument.

finis, fi'nis, *n.* An end, conclusion.

finish, fin'ish, *vt.* To bring to an end; to perfect; to polish to a high degree.—*vi.* To come to an end; to expire.—*n.* Completion; the last touch to a work, polish.

finite, fi'nit, *a.* Limited; bounded; circumscribed, not infinite.

fire, fir, *n.* Heat and light emanating from a body; fuel burning; a conflagration; discharge of firearms; splendor; violence of passion; vigor of fancy animation; ardent affection: affliction.—*vt.* (firing, fired). To set on fire; to irritate; to animate; to bake, to cause to explode, to discharge (firearms).—*vi.* To take

fire; to be inflamed with passion, to discharge firearms.

firmament, fèrm'a-ment, *n.* The sky or heavens; region of the air; an expanse.

first, fèrst, *a.* Foremost in time, place, rank, value, etc., chief, highest; the ordinal of one.—*adv.* Before all others in time, place, etc.

fiscal, fis'kal, *a.* Pertaining to the public treasury.—*n.* A treasurer; a public prosecutor, as in Scotland.

fisherman, fish'èr-man, *n.* One whose occupation is to catch fish.

fistular, fis'tū-lèr, *a.* Hollow like a pipe.

fixation, fiks-ā'shon, *n.* Act of fixing; state in which a body resists evaporation.

fixture, fiks'tūr, *n.* That which is fixed; that which is permanently attached, an appendage.

flabby, flab'i, *a.* Soft; yielding to the touch; languid; feeble.

flaccid, flak 'sid, *a.* Flabby; soft and weak, drooping, limber.

flake, flāk, *n.* A loose, filmy mass of anything, a scale; a fleecy or feathery particle, as of snow; a flock, as of wool.—*vt.* (flaking flaked). To form into flakes.—*vi.* To break in layers; to peel off.

flamboyant, flam-boi'ant, *a.* Noting that style of gothic architecture characterized by wavy tracery in the windows; florid.

flame, flām, *n.* Light emitted from fire, a blaze, fire, heat of passion; ardor of temper or imagination; ardent love; rage; one beloved.—*vi.* (flaming, flamed). To blaze; to glow; to rage.

flamingo, fla-ming'gō, *n.* A webfooted, long-necked bird about 5 to 6 feet high.

flank, flangk, *n.* The part of the side of an animal, between the ribs and the hip, the side of an army; the extreme right or left; the side of any building.—*vt.* To be situated at the side of; to place troops so as to command or attack the flank, to pass round the side of

flannel, flan'el, *n.* A soft, nappy, woolen cloth of loose texture; garment made of flannel.

flask flask, *n.* A kind of bottle; a bottle for the pocket; a vessel for powder.

flatter, flat'èr, *vt.* To gratify by praise; to compliment; to praise falsely.

flattery, flat'é-ri, *n.* False praise; sycophancy, cajolery.

flaunt, flänt, *vi.* and *t.* To display ostentatiously.—*n.* Bold or impudent parade.

flavor, flā'vèr, *n.* The quality of a substance which affects the smell or taste;

relish; zest.—*vt.* To give a flavor to.

flawless, flä'les, *a.* Without defect; perfect.

flesh, flesh, *n.* The muscular part of an animal; animal food; beasts and birds used as food; the body, as distinguished from the soul mankind, corporeal appetites kindred, family.—*vt.* To feed with flesh; to initiate to the taste of flesh.

fleshly, flesh'li, *a.* Carnal, worldly lascivious; human; not spiritual.

flicker, flik'e'r, *vi.* To flutter; to waver, as an unsteady flame.—*n.* A wavering gleam.

flight, flît, *n.* Act of fleeing or flying; power or manner of flying; a flock of birds; a volley, as of arrows; pace passed by flying; a soaring; lofty elevation, as of fancy; extravagant sally; a series of steps or stairs.

flimsy, flim'zi, *a.* Thin; slight; weak; without force, shallow.

flinch, flinsh, *vi.* to shrink; to withdraw, to wince, to fail.

fling, fling, *vi.* (flinging, flung). To cause to fly from the hand; to hurl; to scatter, to throw to the ground.—*vi.* To fly into violent and irregular motions; to flounce; to rush away angrily.—*n.* A throw; a gibe; a lively Scottish dance.

flint, flint, *n.* A very hard siliceous stone, which strikes fire with steel anything proverbially hard.

flirt, flė rt, *vt.* To throw with a jerk to make coquettish motions with (a fan). *vi.* To run and dart about; to coquette, to play at courtship.—*n.* A sudden jerk; one who plays at courtship; a coquette.

float, flôt, *n.* That which is borne on water or any fluid; a raft.—*vi.* To be borne on the surface of a fluid; to be buoyed up, to move with a light, irregular course.—*vt.* To cause to be conveyed on water; to flood; to get (a company, scheme, etc.) started.

flock, flok, *n.* A lock of wool or hair; stuffing for mattresses, etc., a company, as of sheep, birds, etc; a Christian congregation in relation to their pastor.—*vi.* To gather in companies; to crowd; to move in crowds.

flood, flud, *n.* A great flow of water a deluge; a river; the flowing of the tide; a great quantity; abundance.—*vt.* To overflow; to deluge; to overwhelm.

floor, flôr, *n.* That part of a building on which we walk, bottom of a room; story in a building; a flat, hard surface of loam, lime, etc. used in some kinds of business, as in malting.—*vt.* To lay a floor upon; to strike down.

flounder, floun'dèr, *n.* A flat fish found in the sea near the mouths of rivers.—*vi.* To struggle, as in mire, to roll, toss, and tumble.

flour, flour, *n.* Finely ground meal of wheat or other grain; fine powder of any substance.—*vt.* To convert into flour; to sprinkle with flour.

flourish, flu'rish, *vi.* To grow luxuriantly, to thrive; to live; to use florid language, to make ornamental strokes in writing, etc.; to move in bold and irregular figures.—*vt.* To adorn with flowers or figures, to ornament with anything showy, to brandish.—*n.* Showy splendor, parade of words and figures; fanciful stroke of the pen; decorative notes in music; brandishing.

flow, flō, *vi.* To move, as water; to issue; to abound; to glide smoothly; to hang loose and waving; to rise, as the tide; to circulate, as blood.—*vt.* To flow over, to flood.—*n.* A moving along, as of water; stream; current; rise of water; fullness; free expression, feeling.

flower, flou'è r, *n.* The delicate and gaily-colored leaves or petals on a plant, a bloom or blossom; youth; the prime; the best part; one most distinguished, an ornamental expression; *pl.* a powdery substance.—*vi.* To blossom, to bloom.—*vt.* To embellish with figures of flowers.

flowing, flō'ing, *p.a.* Moving as a steam; abounding; fluent; undulating.

fluctuate, fluk'tū-āt, *vi.* To move as a wave, to waver, to hesitate; to experience vicissitudes.

fluctuation, fluk-tū-ā'shon, *n.* A rising and falling; change, vicissitude.

fluff, fluf, *n.* Light down or nap such as rises from beds, cotton, etc

fluid, flü'id, *a.* Capable of flowing; liquid or gaseous.—*n.* Any substance whose parts easily move and change their relative position without separation; a liquid.

flurry, flu'ri, *n.* Bustle, hurry, a gust of wind; light things carried by the wind.—*vt.* (flurrying, flurried). To agitate or alarm.

fluster, flus'tèr, *vt.* To agitate; to make hot with drink.—*n.* Agitation, confusion, heat.

flute, flöt, *n.* A small wind-instrument with holes and keys, a channel cut along the shaft of a column; a similar channel.—*vi*. (fluting, fluted). To play on a flute.—*vt*. To play or sing in notes like those of a flute; to form flutes or channels in.

flutist, flöt'ist, *n*. A performer on the flute.

flutter, flut'ėr, *vi*. To move or flap the wings rapidly; to be in agitation; to fluctuate.—*vt*. To agitate; to throw into confusion.—*n*. Quick confused motion; agitation; disorder.

flux, fluks, *n*. Act of flowing, any flow of matter; dysentery; flow of the tide; anything used to promote fusion; fusion; liquid state from the operation of heat.—*vt*. To melt; to fuse.

fly, flī', *vi*. (flying, pret. flew, pp. flown). To move through air by wings, to move in air by the force of wind, etc., to rise in air, to move rapidly; to pass away; to depart suddenly; to spring; to flutter.—*vt*. To flee from; to cause to float in the air.—*n*. A winged insect; a revolving mechanism to regulate the motion of machinery; a light carriage, a cab.

foal, fōl, *n*. The young of a mare she-ass etc.; a colt or filly.—*vt*. To bring forth, as a colt or filly.—*vi*. To bring forth a foal.

foam, fōm, *n*. Froth; spume.—*vt*. To froth, to show froth at the mouth to rage.—*vt*. To cause to give out foam; to throw out with rage or violence.

fob, fob, *n*. A little pocket for a watch in the waistband of the breeches.

focus, fō'kus, *n*.; pl. **-cuses** or **-ci**. A point in which rays of light meet after being reflected or refracted point of concentration.—*vt*. To bring to a focus.

fodder, fod'ėr, *n*. Food for cattle, etc.—*vt*. To furnish with fodder.

foe, fō, *n*. An enemy; an opposing army; one who opposes anything.

fog, fog, *n*. A dense vapor near the surface of the land or water, mental confusion; dimness; second growth of grass; long grass that remains in pastures till winter.

fogey, fogy, fō'gi, *n*.; pl. **-eys, -ies,** A stupid fellow; an old-fashioned person.

foible, foi'bl, *n*. A weak point in character; a failing; the weak part of a sword.

folio, fō'li-ō, *n*. A book of the largest size, formed by sheets of paper once doubled; a page; number appended to each page; a written page of a certain number of words.

follicle, fol'li-kl, *n*. A little bag or vesicle in animals or plants.

follow, fol'ō, *vt*. To go or come after; to chase, to accompany, to succeed; to result from; to understand; to copy; to practice; to be occupied with, to be guided by.—*vi*. To come after another; to ensure, to result.

folly, fol'i, *n*. Foolishness; imbecility; a weak or foolish act; criminal weakness.

foment, fō-ment', *vt*. To apply warm lotions to; to abet; to stir up (in a bad sense).

fondle, fon'dl, *vt*. (fondling, fondled). To treat with fondness; to caress.

foolish, föl'ish, *a*. Void of understanding; acting without judgment or discretion; silly; ridiculous; unwise.

football, füt'bäl, *n*. An inflated leather ball to be driven by the foot; a game played with such a ball.

footstep, füt'step, *n*. A track, the mark of the foot; vestige; *pl*. example; course.

forbear, for-bār', *vi*. To keep away; to cease; to delay; to refrain.—*vt*. To abstain from; to avoid doing.

forbid, for-bid', *vt*. To prohibit; to oppose; to obstruct.—*vi*. To utter a prohibition.

forcible, fōrs'i-bl, *a*. Efficacious, *potent*, cogent; done by force; suffered by force.

forcing, fōrs'ing, *n*. Art of raising plants or fruits, at an earlier season than the natural one, by artificial heat.

foreign, fo'rin, *a*. Belonging to another nation or country; alien; not to the purpose; irrelevant.

forensic, fō-ren'sik *a*. Belonging to courts of justice, or to public debate; used in courts or legal proceedings.

forest, fo'rest, *n*. An extensive wood; a district devoted to the purposes of the chase; a tract once a royal forest.—*a*. Relating to a forest; sylvan; rustic.—*vt*. To convert into a forest.

forever, for-ev'ėr, *adv*. At all times; through endless ages, eternally.

forewarn, fōr-warn', *vt*. To warn beforehand, to give previous notice to.

foreword, for'wėrd, *n*. A preface.

forfeiture, for'fit-ūr, *n*. Act of forfeiting, loss of some right, estate, honor, etc., by a crime or fault; fine; penalty.

forgery, fōrj'ė-ri, *n*. The crime of counterfeiting, that which is forged or counterfeited.

forget, for-get', *vt*. (forgetting, pret. forgot, pp. forgot, forgotten). To lose the remembrance of; to slight; to neglect.

forlorn, for-lorn', *a*. Deserted; abandoned; miserable.—**Forlorn hope,** a

F

body of men appointed to perform some specially perilous service.

former, form'ér, *n.* He who forms. — *a comp. deg.* Before in time; long past; mentioned before another.

formidable, for'mid-a-bl, *a.* Exciting fear or apprehension; difficult to deal with or undertake.

formula, for'mū la, *n.*, pl. -lae. A prescribed form; a confession of faith, expression for resolving certain problems in mathematics; expression of chemical composition.

formulate, for'mū-lāt, *vt.* To express in a formula; to put into a precise and comprehensive statement.

fornicate, for'ni-kāt, *vi.* To have unlawful sexual intercourse.

forthcoming, fôrth-kum'ing, *a.* Coming forth; making appearance, ready to appear.

fortification, for'ti-fi-kā''shon, *n.* The art or science of fortifying places; the works erected in defense; a fortified place; additional strength.

fortify, for'ti-fī, *vt.* (fortifying, fortified). To make strong; to strengthen by forts, batteries, etc.; to invigorate, to increase the strength of.

fortunate, for'tu-nāt, *a.* Having good fortune; successful, coming by good luck.

fortune, for'tūn, *n.* Chance, luck the good or ill that befalls man means of living; estate; great wealth; destiny, the power regarded as determining the lots of life.

forum, fō'rum, *n.* A public place in ancient Rome, where causes were tried; a tribunal; jurisdiction.

forward, for'wérd, *adv.* Toward a place in front, onward.—*a.* Near or towards the forepart; in advance of something; ready; bold; pert; advanced beyond the usual degree; too ready.—*vt.* To help onward, to hasten, to send forward to transmit.—*n.* In football hockey, etc., one of the players in the front line.

found, found, *vt.* To lay the base of; to establish, to institute, to form by melting metal and pouring it into a mold, to cast.—*vi.* To rest or rely (with on or *upon*). Pret. and pp. of *find.*

foundation, found-ā'shon, *n.* Act of founding; base of an edifice, base; endowment; endowed institution.

founder, found'ér, *n.* One who lays a foundation; an originator, an endower, one who casts metal.—*vi.* To fill with water and sink, to miscarry; to go lame, as a horse.

foundry, found'ri, *n.* An establishment for casting metals.

fountain, fount'ān, *n.* A spring or source of water, an artificial jet or shower; head of a river; original; source.

fraction, frak'shon, *n.* A fragment a very small part, one or more of the equal parts into which a unit of number is divided.

fracture, frak'tūr, *n.* A breach or break, breaking of a bone, manner in which a mineral breaks.—*vt.* (fracturing, fractured). To break.

fragility, fra-jil'i-ti, *n.* Quality of being fragile; delicacy of substance.

fragment, frag'ment, *n.* A part broken off; an imperfect thing.

fragrant, frā'grant, *a.* Sweet-smelling; spicy; balmy; aromatic.

frail, frāl, *a.* Easily broken; weak; liable to fail and decay.—*n.* A kind of basket.

frame, frām, *vt.* (framing, framed). To make, to construct, to devise, to adjust; to shape; to place in a frame.—*n.* Anything composed of parts fitted together; structure; bodily structure; framework; particular state, as of the mind; mood or disposition.

framing, frām'ing, *n.* Act of constructing a frame frame thus constructed; rough timber-work of a house.

fratricide, fra'tri-sīd, *n.* Murder of a brother; one who murders a brother.

fraud, frād, *n.* Artifice by which the right or interest of another is injured, deception.

freak, frēk, *n.* A sudden causeless turn of the mind; a caprice; a sport.—*vt.* To variegate.

freckle, frek'l, *n.* A yellowish spot in the skin any small snot or discoloration.—*vt.* or *i.* (freckling, freckled). To give or acquire freckles.

free, frē, *a.* Being at liberty; instituted by a free people; not arbitrary or despotic; open; clear; disjoined; licentious; candid; generous, gratuitous; guiltless.—*vt.* (freeing, freed). To set free; to liberate; to disentangle; to exempt; to absolve from some charge.

freedom, frē'dum, *n.* State of being free, liberty, particular privilege: facility of doing anything: frankness, undue familiarity.

free-will, frē'wil, *n.* The power of directing our own actions, without restraint by necessity or fate.—*a.* Spontaneous.

freeze, frēz, *vi.* (freezing,pret. froze, pp. frozen or froze). To be congealed by cold; to be hardened into ice; to be of that degree of cold at which water congeals; to stagnate; to shiver or stiffen with cold.—*vt.* To congeal; to chill; to make credits, etc., temporarily unrealizable.

freight, frāt, *n.* The cargo of a ship lading; hire of a ship; charge for the transportation of goods.—*vt.* To load with goods; to hire for carrying goods.

frenzy, fren'zi, *n.* Madness, distraction; violent agitation of the mind.

fresh, fresh, *a.* Full of health and strength, vigorous; brisk; bright; not faded; in good condition; not stale; cool and agreeable; clearly remembered, new, not salt; unpracticed; unused.

friction, frik'shon, *n.* A rubbing effect of rubbing; resistance which a moving body meets with from the surface on which it moves.

Friday, frī'dā, *n.* The sixth day of the week.—**Good Friday**, the Friday preceding Easter, sacred as the day of Christ's crucifixion.

frighten, frīt'n, *vt.* To strike with fright or fear; to terrify; to scare; to alarm.

frigid, fri'jid, *a.* Cold; wanting spirit or zeal, stiff, formal lifeless.

frigidity, fri-jid'i-ti, *n.* Coldness coldness of affection; dullness.

frill, fril, *n.* A crisp or plaited edging on an article of dress a ruffle.—*vt.* To decorate with frills.

frolic, fro'lik, *a.* Joyous; merry; frisky; poetic.—*n.* A merry prank merry-making.—*vi.* To play merry pranks, to gambol.

frond, frond, *n.* The leaf of a fern or other cryptogamic plant.

front, frunt, *n.* The forehead; the whole face; the fore part, boldness impudence; the area of military operations.—*a.* Relating to the front or face.—*vt.* To stand with the front opposed to; to oppose; to face; to supply with a front.—*vi.* To face; to look.

frontage frunt'āj, *n.* The front part of an edifice, quay, etc.

frontal, frunt'al, *a.* Belonging to the forehead.—*n.* An ornament for the forehead; a frontlet; a small pediment.

frontier, fron'tēr, *n.* That part of a country which fronts another country, extreme part of a country.—*a.* Bordering; conterminous.

frontispiece, fron'tis-pēs, *n.* The principal face of a building, an illustration facing the title page of a book.

froward, frō'wėrd, *a.* Perverse; ungovernable; disobedient. peevish.

frown, froun, *vi.* To express displeasure by contracting the brow; to look stern; to scowl.—*n.* A wrinkling of the brow; a sour or stern look; any expression of displeasure.

fruit, fröt, *n.* Whatever of a vegetable nature is of use to man or animals; the reproductive produce of a plant; such products collectively; the seed or matured ovary that which is produced; offspring, effect; outcome.—*vi.* To produce fruit.

frustrate, frus'trāt, *vt.* (frustrating, frustrated). To balk, to foil, to bring to nothing; to render of no effect.

frustration, frus-trā'shon, *n.* Disappointment; defeat.

fry, frī, *vt.* (frying, fried). To cook by roasting over a fire.—*vi.* To be cooked as above; to simmer; to be in agitation.—*n.* A dish of anything fried; state of mental ferment; young fishes at an early stage, swarm of small fishes, etc. insignificant objects.

fuchsia, fū'shi-a, *n.* A beautiful flowering shrub.

fuddle, fud'l, *vt.* (fuddling, fuddled). To make stupid by drink, to spend in drinking.—*vi.* To drink to excess.

fugitive, fū-jit-iv, *a.* Apt to flee away; volatile; fleeting; vagabond; temporary.—*n.* One who flees from duty or danger, refugee.

full, fül, *a.* Having all it can contain; abounding; crowded; entire; strong, loud, clear, mature, perfect; ample.—*n.* Complete measure, the highest state or degree (usually with the).—*adv.* Quite, altogether; exactly; directly.—*vt.* To scour and thicken, as woolen cloth, in a mill.

fumble, fum'bl, *vi.* (fumbling, fumbled). To grope about awkwardly to attempt or handle something bunglingly.

fumigate, fūm'i-gāt, *vt.* (fumigating, fumigated). To smoke, to purify from infection, etc.

function, fungk'shon, *n.* Performance; office; duty; proper office of any organ in animals or vegetables; a ceremonial; a mathematical quantity connected with and varying with another.

fundamental, fun-da-ment'al, *a.* Pertaining to the foundation; essential, primary.—*n.* A leading principle which serves as the groundwork of a system; an essential.

funeral, fū'nė-ral, *n.* Burial; ceremony of burying a dead body.—*a.* Used at the interment of the dead.

funereal, fū-ne're̅-al, *a.* Suiting a funeral; dark; dismal; mournful.

funny, fun'i, *a.* Making fun; droll; comical.

furnace, fėr'nas, *n.* A structure in which a vehement fire may be maintained for melting ores, heating water, etc.; place or occasion Or torture or trial.

furniture, fėr'ni-tūr, *n.* That with which anything is furnished equipment; outfit; movable wooden articles in a house.

furrow, fu'rō, *n.* A trench made by a plow, a groove, a wrinkle.—*vt.* To make furrows in; to groove; to wrinkle.

further, fėr'THėr, *adv.* More in advance; besides; farther.—*a.* More distant, farther.—*vt.* To help forward; to advance.

furtive, fėr'tiv, *a.* Stolen; sly; stealthy.

fusion, fū'zhon, *n.* Act or operation of fusing; state of being melted or blended; complete union.

futile, fū'til *a.* Serving no useful end, trivial, worthless.

futility, fū-til'i-ti, *n.* Quality of being futile; worthlessness; unimportance.

future, fū'tūr, *a.* That is to be, pertaining to time to come.—*n.* The time to come, all that is to happen the future tense.

G

gab, gab, *vi.* (gabbling, gabbed). To talk much: to chatter.—*n.* Idle talk.

gabble, gab'l, *vi.* (gabbling, gabbled). To talk fast, or without meaning.—*n.* Rapid talk without meaning; inarticulate sounds rapidly uttered.

gadget, gad'jet, *n.* A tool, appliance, or contrivance.

gain, gān, *vt.* To obtain; to get, as profit or advantage; to receive, as honor, to win to one's side, to conciliate; to reach, arrive at.—*vi.* To reap advantage or profit; to make progress.—*n.* Something obtained as an advantage; profit; benefit.

gall, gäl, *n.* A bitter fluid secreted in the liver; bile; rancor; malignity; an excrescence produced by the egg of an insect on a plant, especially the oak; a sore place in the skin from rubbing.—*vt.* To make a sore in the skin of by rubbing; to fret, to vex; to harass.

gallant, gal'ant, *a.* Gay in attire; handsome; brave, showing politeness and attention to ladies (in this sense also pron. ga-lant').—*n.* A gay sprightly man; a daring spirit; (pron. also ga-lant') a man attentive to ladies, suitor paramour.—*vt.* ga-lant'. To act the gallant towards; to be very attentive to (a lady).

gallantry, gal'ant-ri, *n.* Show; bravery; intrepidity; polite attentions to ladies, vicious love or pretentions to love.

gallery, gal'ė-ri, *n.* A long apartment serving as a passage of communication, or for the reception of pictures, etc.; upper floor of a church, theatre, etc.; a covered passage; frame like a balcony projected from a ship.

gallop, gal'up, *vi.* To move or run with leaps; to ride at this pace; to move very fast.—*n.* The pace of a horse, by springs or leaps.

gallows, gal'ōz, *n. sing* or *pl.;* also **gallowses**, gal'oz-ez, in *pl.* A structure for the hanging of criminals; one of a pair of braces for the trousers.

gambit, gam'bit, *n.* An opening in chess incurring the sacrifice of a pawn.

gamble, gam'bl, *vi.* (gambling, gambled). To play for money.

gambling, gam'bl-ing, *n.* The act or practice of gaming for money or anything valuable.

gambol, gam'bol, *vi.* (gamboling, gamboled). To skip about in sport; to frisk; to frolic.—*n.* A skipping about in frolic, a prank.

game, gām, *n.* Sport of any kind; exercise for amusement, testing skill, etc., scheme pursued, fieldsports, animals hunted.—*vi.* (gaming, gamed). To play at any sport; to play for a stake or prize, to practice gaming. To die game. to maintain a bold spirit to the last.

gamester, gām'ster, *n.* A person addicted to gaming; a gambler.

gamin, gam'in, *n.* A street arab; a neglected street-boy.

gaming, gām'ing, *n.* The act or practice of gambling.

gangrene, gang'grēn, *n.* An eating away of the flesh; first stage of mortification.—*vt.* (gangrening, gangrened). To mortify.—*vi.* To become mortified.

gangster, gang'stėr, *n.* A member of a criminal organization.

gap, gap, *n.* An opening; breach; hiatus; chasm.

gape, gāp, *vi.* (gaping, gaped). To open the mouth wide, to yawn, to open in fissures; to stand open.— *n.* A gaping; the width of the mouth when opened, as of a bird fish, etc.

garage, gar'aj, *n.* A place for housing or repairing motor-cars.

garb, gärb, *n.* Dress; clothes; mode of dress.—*vt.* To dress.

garbage, gärb'āj, *n.* Waste matter; offal; vegetable refuse.

garlic, gär'lik, *n.* A plant allied to the onion, with a pungent taste and strong odor.

garment, gär'ment, *n.* An article of clothing, as a coat, a gown, etc.

garner, gär'nėr, *n.* A granary; a store.—*vt.* To store in a granary; to store up.

garnet, gär'net, *n.* A precious stone, generally of a red color.

garnish, gär'nish, *vt.* To adorn; to embellish (a dish) with something laid round.—*n.* Ornament; an embellishment round a dish.

garret, ga'ret, *n.* A room in a house on the uppermost floor, immediately under the roof

garrison, ga'ri-sn, *n.* A body of troops stationed in a fort or town.—*vt.* To place a garrison in.

garrotte, ga-rot', *vt.* To rob by seizing a person and compressing his windpipe till he become helpless.

garrulity, ga-rū'li-ti, *n.* Loquacity; practice or habit to talking much.

garter, gär'tèr, *n.* A band to hold up a stocking; the badge of the highest order or knighthood in Great Britain, the order itself.—*vt.* To bind with a garter.

gasteropod, gastropod, gas'tèr-opod, gas'trŏ-pod, *n.* A mollusk such as snails, having a broad muscular foot attached to the ventral surface.

gastric, gas'trik, *a.* Belonging to the stomach.

Gastronomy, gas-tron'o-mi, *n.* The art or science of good eating; epicurism.

gate, gāt, *n.* A large door or entrance; a frame of timber, iron, etc., closing an entrance, etc., a way or passage; the frame which stops the passage of water through a dam, lock, etc.

gate-crasher, gāt-krash'èr, *n.* An uninvited guest, one who obtains admission to a public entertainment without a ticket.

gateway, gāt'wā, *n.* A way through the gate of some enclosure; the gate itself.

gazette, ga-zet', *n.* A newspaper, especially an official newspaper.—*vt.* (gazetting, gazetted). To insert in a gazette, to announce or public officially.

gazetteer, ga-zet-tēr', *n.* A writer or publisher of news, a dictionary of geographical information.

gear, gēr, *n.* Dress; ornaments; apparatus, harness, tackle, a train of toothed wheels.—*vt.* To put gear on to harness.

gelatine, jel'a-tin, *n.* A concrete transparent substance obtained by boiling from certain parts of animals; the principle of jelly; glue.

geld, geld, *vt.* To castrate; to emasculate.

gelid, je'lid, *a.* Icy cold; frosty or icy.

gem, jem, *n.* A precious stone of any kind; a jewel; anything remarkable for beauty or rarity.—*vt.* (gemming, gemmed). To adorn, as with gems; to bespangle; to embellish.

Gemini, jem'i-nî, *n.pl.* The twins, a sign of the zodiac, containing the two stars Castor and Pollux.

general, jen'è-ral, *a.* Of or belonging to a genus; not special; public; common; extensive, though not universal; usual; taken as a whole.—*n.* The whole a comprehensive notion; a military officer of the highest rank.

generous, jen'è-rus, *a.* Noble, bountiful; liberal; full of spirit, as wine; courageous, as a steed.

genetic, genetical, jen-net'ik, jenet'ik-al, *a.* Relating to origin or production.

genial, jē'ni-al, *a.* Cordial kindly; contributing to life and cheerfulness.

genitals, jen'it-alz, *n.pl.* the parts of generation, sexual organs.

genitive, jen'it-iv, *a.* and *n.* Applied to a case of nouns, pronouns, etc., in English called the possessive.

genre, zhäng-r, *n.* A term applied to the department of painting which depicts scenes of ordinary life.

genteel, jen-tēl, *a.* Having the manners of well-bred people; refined; elegant.

gentle, jen'tl, *a.* Well-born; refined in manners, mild placid not rough, violent, or wild; soothing.— *n.* A person of good birth.

gentleman, jen'tl-man, *n.* A man of good social position; technically any man above the rank of yeoman, comprehending noblemen; a man of good breeding or of high honor; a polite equivalent for 'man'

genuflection, jen-ū-flek'shon, *n.* The act of bending the knee, particularly in worship.

genuine, jen'ū-in, *a.* Belonging to the original stock, real, pure true.

genus, jē'nus, *n.; pl.* **genera,** jen'è-ra. A kind, class, or sort; an assemblage of species having distinctive characteristics in common.

Geometry, jē-om'e-tri, *n.* The science of magnitude; that branch of mathematics which treats of the properties and relations of lines, angles, surfaces, and solids.

gerrymander, ge'ri-man-dèr, *vt.* To arrange so as to get an unfair result from the distribution of voters in political elections.

gerund, je'rund, *n.* A kind of verbal noun in Latin; a verbal noun, such as 'teaching' in 'fit for teaching boys.'

gestation, jest-ā'shon, *n.* The carrying of young in the womb from conception to delivery; pregnancy.

gesture, jes'tūr, *n.* A posture or motion of the body of limbs; action intended to express an idea or feeling; or to enforce an argument.

get, get, *vt.* (getting, pret, got, pp. got, gotten). To obtain; to gain; to reach, to beget, to learn; to induce.—*vi.* To arrive at any place or state by degrees; to become; to make gain.

geyser, gî'zèr, *n.* A hot-water spring, the water rising in a column.

ghastly, gast'li, *a.* Deathlike in looks; hideous; frightful, as wounds.

giant, jî'ant, *n.* A man of extraordinary

stature, a person of extraordinary powers, bodily or intellectual.—*a*. Like a giant; extraordinary in size.

gibberish, gib'bēr-ish, *n*. Rapid and inarticulate talk; unmeaning words.

gibbet, jib'bet, *n*. A gallows; the projecting beam of a crane. on which the pulley is fixed.—*vt*. To hang on a gibbet; to expose to scorn infamy, etc.

gift, gift, *n*. Anything given; act of giving; power of giving; talent or faculty.—*vt*. To endow with any power or faculty.

giggle, gig'l, *n*. A kind of laugh, with short catches of the voice or breath.—*vi*.(giggling, giggled). To laugh with short catches of the breath; to titter.

gigot, jig'ot, *n*. A leg of mutton.

gild, gild, *vt*. (pret. and pp. gilded or gilt). To overlay with gold in leaf or powder; to illuminate; to give a fair and agreeable appearance to.

gill, gil, *n*. The organ of respiration in fishes the flap below the beak of a fowl, the flesh on the lower part of the cheeks.

gin, jin. *n*. A distilled spirit flavored with juniper berries; a machine for driving piles, raising great weights, etc.; a machine for separating the seeds from cotton; a trap, snare.—*vt*. (ginning, ginned). To clear of seeds by a cotton-gin; to catch in a trap.

ginger, jin'jēr, *n*. A tropical plant, the root of which has a hot, spicy quality.

giraffe, ji-raf', *n*. The camelopard, the tallest of animals.

gird, gērd, *vt*. (pp. girded or girt). To bind; to make fast by binding, to invest; to encompass.—*vi*. To gibe; to sneer.—*n*. A stroke with a whip; a twitch; a sneer.

girder, gērd'ēr, *n*. One who girds; a main beam supporting a superstructure.

girdle, gēr'dl, *n*. That which girds; a band or belt, something drawn round the waist and tied or buckled.—*vt*. (girdling, girdled). To bind with a girdle; belt, or sash; to gird.

girl, gērl, *n*. A female child; young woman.

girth, gērth, *n*. That which girds; band fastening a saddle on a horse's back, measure round a person's body or anything cylindrical.

gist, jist, *n*. The main point of a question; substance or pith of a matter.

give, giv, *vt*. (giving, pret, gave, pp. given). To bestow; to deliver; to impart; to yield to afford; to utter; to show; to send forth; to devote (oneself); to pledge; to allow; to ascribe.—*vi*. To

make gifts; to yield to pressure; to recede.

gizzard, giz'ērd, *n*. The muscular stomach of a bird.

glacier, glä'shi-ēr, *n*. An immense mass of ice formed in valleys above the snow-line, and having a slow movement downwards.

glad, glad, *a*. Affected with pleasure; pleased; cheerful; imparting pleasure.— *vt*. (gladding, gladded). To make glad, to gladden.

glance, gläns, *n*. A sudden shoot of light or splendor; a glimpse or sudden look.— *vi*. (glancing, glanced). To shine; to gleam; to dart aside; to look with a sudden rapid cast of the eye; to move quickly, to hint.—*vt*. To shoot or dart suddenly or obliquely, to cast for a moment.

gland, gland, *n*. An acorn, any acorn-shaped fruit; a roundish organ in many parts of the body secreting some fluid; a secreting organ in plants.

glare, glär, *n*. A bright dazzling light, a fierce piercing look.—*vi*. (glaring, glared). To shine with excessive luster; to look with fierce piercing eyes.

glass, gläs, *n*. A hard transparent substance; a small drinking vessel of glass; a mirror; quantity of liquor that a glass vessel contains; a lens; a telescope; a barometer pl. spectacles.—*a*. Made of glass, vitreous.

glazier, glä'zhēr, *n*. One whose business is to set window-glass.

gleam, glēm, *n*. A small stream of light; brightness.—*vi*. To shoot or dart, as rays of light; to shine; to flash.

glider, glīd'ēr, *n*. A modification of the airplane, which can travel through the air for a certain time without engine power.

glimmer, glim'ēr, *vi*. To shine faintly, and with frequent intermissions; to flicker.— *n*. A faint light; a twinkle.

glimpse, glimps, *n*. A gleam or flash of light, short transitory view; faint resemblance, slight tinge.—*vi*. To appear by glimpses.

globe, glōb, *n*. A round solid body; a sphere; the earth; an artificial sphere on whose surface is drawn a map of the earth or heavens.—*vt*. To gather into a round mass.

globule, glob'ūl, *n*. A little globe a small spherical particle, one of the red particles of the blood

globulin, glob'ū-lin, *n*. The main ingredient of blood globules and resembling albumen.

gloom, glöm, *n.* Obscurity, thick shade; sadness; aspect of sorrow darkness of prospect or aspect.— *vi.* To shine obscurely, to be cloudy or dark; to be sullen or sad.

glorify, glō'ri-fī, *vt.* (glorifying, glorified). to make glorious, to ascribe glory or honor to; to extol.

glorious, glō'ri-us, *a.* Full of glory; renowned; celebrated; grand; brilliant.

glory, glō'ri, *n.* Praise, honor, admiration, or distinction, renown magnificence, celestial bliss; the divine presence; the divine perfections, that of which one may be proud.— *vi.* (glorying, gloried). To boast; to rejoice; to be proud with regard to something.

gloss, glos, *n.* Brightness from a smooth surface; sheen; specious appearance, an interpretation comment.— *vt.* To give superficial luster to; to give a specious appearance to; to render plausible to comment; to annotate.

glossary glos'a-ri, *n.* A vocabulary explaining antiquated or difficult words or phrases.

glow, glō, *vi.* To burn with intense heat, especially without flame; to feel great heat of body; to be flushed; to be ardent to rage.— *n.* White heat; brightness of color; animation.

glowworm, glō'wèrm, *n.* A wingless female beetle which emits a greenish light.

glucose, glö'kō s, *n.* Grape-sugar, a sugar produced from grapes, starch, etc.

glue, glö, *n.* A tenacious, viscid matter which serves as a cement.— *vt.* (gluing, glued). To join with glue; to unite.

glum, glum, *a.* Sullen; moody; dejected.

glycerine, glis'ēr-in, *n.* A transparent, colorless, sweet liquid obtained from fats.

glyphic, glif'ik, *a.* Of or pertaining to carving or sculpture.

glyptic, glip'tik, *a.* Pertaining to the art of engraving on precious stones.

gnarl, närl, *n.* A protuberance on the outside of a tree a knot.

gnash, nash, *vt.* To strike together, as the teeth.— *vi.* To strike or dash the teeth together, as in rage or pain.

gnat, nat, *n.* A small two-winged fly, the female of which bites.

gnaw, nä, *vt.* To bite by little and little; to bite in agony or rage; to fret; to corrode.— *vi.* To use the teeth in biting; to cause steady annoying pain.

gneiss, nīs, *n.* A species of rock composed of quartz, feldspar, and mica, and having a slaty structure.

gnome, nōm, *n.* A sprite supposed to inhabit the inner parts of the earth; a dwarf; a maxim, aphorism.

go, gō, *vi.* (going, pret, went, pp. gone). To move; to proceed, to depart; to be about to do; to circulate, to tend, to be guided, to be alienated or sold; to reach; to avail; to conduce; to die; to fare; to become.

goad, gōd, *n.* A pointed instrument to make a beast move faster; anything that stirs into action.— *vt.* To drive with a goad; to instigate.

goal, gōl, *n.* The point set to bound a race; a mark that players in some outdoor sport must attain; a success scored by reaching this; final purpose; end.

goat, gōt, *n.* A ruminant quadruped with long hair and horns.

gobble, gob'l, *vt.* (gobbling, gobbled). To swallow in large pieces or hastily.— *vi.* To make a noise in the throat, as a turkey.

goggle, gog'l, *vi.* (goggling, goggled). To roll or strain the eyes.— *a.* Prominent, rolling, or staring *(eyes)*.— *n.* A strained or affected rolling of the eye; *pl.* a kind of spectacles to protect the eyes or cure squinting.

going, gō'ing, *n.* Act of one who goes; departure; way; state of roads.— **goings-on**, actions; behavior

goiter, goi'tèr, *n.* A morbid enlargement of the thyroid gland, forming a mass on the front of the neck.

gold, gōld, *n.* A precious metal of a bright yellow color; money; something pleasing or valuable, a bright yellow color— *a.* Made or consisting of gold.

golden, gōld'n, *a.* Made of gold; like gold; splendid; most valuable; auspicious.

gong, gong, *n.* A kind of metallic drum; a similar article used instead of a bell.

good, güd, *a.* The opposite of bad; wholesome. useful, fit, virtuous valuable; benevolent, clever, adequate; valid; able to fulfill engagements, considerable, full or complete; immaculate.— *n.* What is good or desirable; advantage; welfare; virtue *pl.* commodities, chattels, movables.— **For good,** to close the whole business, finally.— *interj.* Well; right.

goose, gös, *n.*; pl. **geese**, gēs. A swimming bird larger than the duck; a tailor's smoothing-iron; a silly person.

gooseberry, gös'be-ri, *n.* The fruit of a prickly shrub, and the shrub itself.

gopher, gō'fė r, *n.* The name given in America to several burrowing animals.

gordian knot, gor'di-an not. An inextricable difficulty, *to cut the gordian knot,* to remove a difficulty by bold measures.

gore, gōr, *n.* Blood that is shed thick or clotted blood; a wedgeshaped piece of land or cloth; a gusset.—*vt.* (goring, gored). To cut in a triangular form; to pierce with a pointed instrument, or an animal s horns.

gorge, gorj, *n.* The throat; the gullet a narrow passage between hills or mountains; entrance into a bastion.—*vt.* and *i.* (gorging, gorged). To swallow with greediness; to glut; to satiate.

gory, gō'ri, *a.* Covered with gore; bloody; murderous.

gosling, goz'ling, *n.* A young goose.

Gospel, gos'pel, *n.* The history of Jesus Christ any of the four records of Christ's life by his apostles; scheme of salvation as taught by Christ, any general doctrine.— *a.* Relating to the gospel; accordant with the gospel.

gossamer, gos'a-mėr, *n.* A fine filmy substance, like cobwebs, floating in the air in calm, sunny weather, a thin fabric.

gossip, gos'ip, *n.* An idle tattler; idle talk. vi. To prate; to run about and tattle.

gourd, görd, *n.* The popular name of the family of plants represented by the melon, cucumber, etc.; a cup made from the rind of a gourd.

gourmet, gör-mā or gör'met, *n.* A connoisseur in wines and meats, a nice feeder.

gout, gout, *n.* A painful disease, affecting generally the small joints a drop; a clot or coagulation.

govern, gu'vėrn, *vt.* To direct and control; to regulate; to steer; to affect so as to determine the case etc., in grammar.— *vi.* To exercise authority; to administer the laws.

governess, gu'vėrn-es, *n.* A female who governs or instructs.

government, gu'vėrn-ment, *n.* Rule, control, administration of public affairs; system of polity in a state; territory ruled by a governor, executive power, the influence of a word in grammar in regard to construction.

governor, gu'vėrn-ėr, *n.* One who governs; one invested with supreme authority, a tutor, a contrivance in machinery for maintaining a uniform velocity.

gown, goun, *n.* A woman's outer garment; a long, loose garment worn by professional men, as divines.—*vt.* To put on a gown.

grab, grab, *vt.* (grabbing, grabbed). To seize; to snatch.—*n.* A sudden grasp; implement for clutching objects.

grace, grās, *n.* Favor, kindness love and favor of God; state of reconciliation to God, pardon, license or privilege; expression of thanks before or after meals; title of a duke or archbishop, elegance with appropriate dignity; an embellishment, one of three ancient goddesses in whose gift were grace and beauty; in music, a trill, shake, etc.—*vt.* (gracing, graced). To lend grace to; to adorn; to favor.

gracious, grā'shus, *a.* Full of grace, favorable, disposed to forgive offenses and impart blessings; benignant; condescending.

gradation, gra-dā'shon, *n.* Arrange-ment by grades; regular advance step by step; rank; series; regular process by degrees.

grade, grād, *n.* A step; degree; rank; gradient.—*vt.* (grading, graded). To arrange in order of rank, etc.; to reduce to a suitable slope.

gradient, grā'di-ent, *a.* Moving by steps; rising or descending by regular degrees.—*n.* The degree of ascent or descent in a road, etc.; part of a road which slopes.

graduate, grad'ū-āt, *vt.* (graduating, graduated). To divide into regular intervals or degrees, to mark with such; to arrange by grades; to confer a university degree on; to reduce to a certain consistency by evaporation.—*vi.* To receive a university degree; to change gradually.—*n.* One who has received a degree of a university, etc.

graft, graft, *n.* A small scion of a tree inserted in another tree which is to support and nourish the scion, corrupt gains or practices in politics.—*vt.* To insert a graft on; to propagate by a graft; to join on as if organically; a part.

Grail, Graal, grāl, *n.* The holy vessel containing the last drops of Christ's blood, brought to England by Joseph of Arimathea, and, being afterwards lost, eagerly sought for by King Arthur's knights.

grain, grān, *n.* A single seed of a plant; corn in general; a minute particle, a small weight, fibers of wood with regard to their arrangement substance of a thing with respect to the size, form, or direction of the constituent particles; texture;

dye.—*vt.* To paint in imitation of fibers; to granulate.

gram, gram, *n.* The French unit of weight, equal to 15.43 grains troy.

grammar, gram'ér, *n.* A system of principles and rules for speaking or writing a language; propriety of speech; an outline of any subject.

grammatical, grammatic, gram-mat'ik-al, gram-mat'ik, *a.* Belong-ing to grammar; according to the rules of grammar.

granary, gra'na-ri, *n.* A storehouse for grain after it is thrashed.

grand, grand, *a.* Great, figuratively majestic; magnificent; noble.

grandchild, grand'chïld, *n.* A son's or daughter's child.

granddaughter, grand'dä-tér, *n.* The daughter of a son or daughter.

grandeur, grand'yür, *n.* Greatness sublimity; splendor; magnificence.

granulate, gran'ū-lät, *vt.* and *i.* (granulating, granulated). To form into grains, to make or become rough on the surface.

granulation, gran-ū-lā'shon, *n.* Act of forming into grains; a process by which minute fleshy bodies are formed on wounds during healing, the fleshy grains themselves

grasp, gräsp, *vt.* To seize and hold by the fingers or arms, to take possession of, to comprehend.—*vi.* To make a clutch or catch.—*n.* Gripe of the hand, reach of the arms; power of seizing or comprehending.

grass, gräs *n.* Herbage; any plant of the family to which belong the grain-yielding and pasture plants.—*vt.* To cover with grass; to bleach on the grass.

grasshopper, gräs'hop-ér, *n.* An insect that hops among grass, allied to the locusts.

grate, grät, *n.* A frame composed of parallel or cross-bars; grating; iron frame for holding coals used as fuel.—*vt.* (grating, grated). To furnish or make fast with crossbars to wear away in small particles by rubbing; to offend. as by a discordant sound.—*vi.* To rub roughly on; to have an annoying effect; to sound harshly.

grateful, grät'fül, *a.* Pleasing, gratifying; feeling or expressing gratitude.

grave, gräv, *vt.* (graving, pret. graved, pp. graven, graved). To make incisions on, to engrave, to impress deeply, as on the mind; to clean, as a ship's bottom, and cover with pitch.—*n.* A pit for the dead, a tomb.—*a.* Weighty; serious; staid;

thoughtful; not gay; not tawdry, in music, low.

gravel, gra'vel, *n.* Small pebbles; a disease produced by small concretions in the kidneys and bladder.—*vt.* (gravelling, gravelled). To cover with gravel, to cause to stick in the sand or gravel; to puzzle.

gravely, gräv'li, *adv.* In a grave, solemn manner; soberly; seriously.

gravid, grav'id, *a.* Being with young; pregnant.

gravitation, grav-i-tā'shon, *n.* The force by which bodies are drawn towards the center of the earth tendency of all matter toward all other matter.

gravity, grav'i-ti, *n.* The tendency of matter toward some attracting body, particularly toward the center of the earth, state or character of being grave; weight; enormity.

gravy, grā'vi, *n.* The juice that comes from flesh in cooking.

gray, grā, *a.* Of the color of hair whitened by age, white with a mixture of black; having gray hairs.—*n.* A gray color; a gray animal, as a horse, early morning twilight

graze, grāz, *vt.* (grazing, grazed). To rub or touch lightly in passing; to feed with growing grass, as cattle to feed on.—*vi.* to pass so as to rub lightly; to eat grass; to supply grass.—*n.* A slight rub or brush.

grease, grēs, *n.* Animal fat in a soft state; oily matter.—*vt.* (greasing, greased). To smear with grease.

great, grāt, *a.* Large in bulk or number; long-continued; of vast power and excellence, eminent majestic; pregnant; distant by one more generation, as great-grandfather, etc.

greet, grēt, *vt.* To salute; to meet and address with kindness.—*vi.* To meet and salute.

grenade, gre-nād', *n.* A small bomb, thrown by hand or fired from a rifle.

greyhound, grā'hound, *n.* A tall, slender, fleet dog kept for the chase.

griddle, grid'l, *n.* A circular plate of iron, or a shallow pan, for baking cakes.

grief, grēf, *n.* Pain of mind produced by loss, misfortune, etc.; sorrow; cause of sorrow; trouble.

grievance, grēv'ans, *n.* A wrong suffered; cause of complaint; trouble.

grieve, grēv, *vt.* (grieving, grieved). To cause grief to; to deplore.—*vi.* To feel grief; to sorrow; to lament.

grim, grim, *a.* of a forbidding or fear-inspiring aspect; stern; sullen; surly; ugly.

grimace, gri-mās', *n.* A distortion of the countenance; air of affectation.—*vi.* To make grimaces.

grime, grîm, *n.* Foul matter.—*vt.* (griming, grimed). To sully or soil deeply.

grin, grin, *vi.* (grinning, grinned). To show the teeth, as in laughter, scorn, or anguish—*n.* Act of showing the teeth; a forced smile or restrained laugh.

grind, grīnd, *vt.* (grinding, ground). To reduce to fine particles; to sharpen or polish by friction, to rub together; to oppress; to crush in pieces.—*vi.* To turn a mill, to be moved or rubbed together, to be pulverized by friction; to study hard.—*n.* Act of one who grinds; a laborious spell of work.

grindstone, grīnd'stōn, *n.* A circular stone, made to revolve, to sharpen tools.

groan, grōn, *vi.* To utter a mournful voice, as in pain or sorrow, to moan.—*n.* A deep, mournful sound, uttered in pain, sorrow, or disapprobation; any low rumbling sound.

groin, groin, *n.* The part of the human body between the belly and thigh in front; the angular projecting curve made by the intersection of simple vaults at any angle.

gross, grōs, *a.* Thick; coarse; obscene; palpable; dense; shameful; dull, whole.—*n.* Main body, bulk the number of twelve dozen.

grotesque, grō-tesk', *a.* Wildly formed; extravagant, fantastic.—*n.* Whimsical figures or scenery.

grotto, grot'tō, *n.* A natural cave an artificial ornamented cave.

ground, ground, *n.* Surface of the earth, soil, land, basis, reason, foil or background; predominating color; *pl.* dregs, sediment; ornamental land about a mansion—*vt.* To set on the ground; to found; to fix firmly; to instruct in first principles.—*vi.* To strike the bottom and remain fixed, as a ship.

grove, grōv, *n.* A shady cluster of trees; a small wood.

grovel, gro'vel, *vi.* (grovelling, grovelled). To lie prone, or creep on the earth; to be low or mean.

grow, grō, *vi.* (pret. grew, pp. grown). To be augmented by natural process; to increase; to make progress, to become; to accrue, to swell.—*vt.* To raise from the soil, to produce.

growl, groul, *vi.* To murmur or snarl, as a dog; to utter an angry, grumbling sound.—*vt.* to express by growling.—*n.* Angry sound of a dog; grumbling murmur.

grown, grōn, *p.a.* Increased in growth; having arrived at full size or stature.

growth, grōth, *n.* Act or process of growing; product; increase; advancement.

grub, grub, *vi.* (grubbing, grubbed). To dig; to be employed meanly.— *vt.* To dig, to root out by digging.— *n.* The larva of an insect; caterpillar; maggot.

gruel, grü'el, *n.* A light food made by boiling meal in water.

gruesome, grö'sum, *a.* Causing one to shudder; frightful, horrible; repulsive.

guarantee, ga-ran-tē', *n.* An undertaking by a third person that a covenant shall be observed by the contracting parties or by one of them; one who binds himself to see the stipulations of another performed.—*vt.* (guaranteeing, guaranteed). To warrant; to pledge oneself for.

guard, gärd, *vt.* To keep watch over; to secure against injury, loss, or attack.— *vi.* To watch, by way of caution or defense; to be in a state of caution or defense.—*n.* Defense; protector; sentinel; escort; attention; caution; posture of defense. Conjecture; surmise.

guest, gest, *n.* A visitor or friend entertained in the house or at the table of another.

guffaw, guf-fä', *n.* A loud burst of laughter.—*vi.* To burst into a loud laugh.

guidance, gīd'ans, *n.* The act of guiding; direction; government; a leading.

guide, gīd, *vt.* (guiding, guided). To lead; to direct; to influence; to regulate.— *n.* A person who guides a director; a regulator; a guidebook.

guise, gīz, *n.* External appearance dress; mien; cast of behavior.

guitar, gi-tär', *n.* A musical instrument having six strings.

gulch, gulch, *n.* A gully; dry bed of a torrent.

gull, gul, *vt.* To cheat.—*n.* One easily cheated; a simpleton, a marine swimming bird.

gullet, gul'et, *n.* The passage in the neck of an animal by which food and liquor are taken into the stomach.

gully, gul'i, *n.* A channel worn by water; a ravine.—*vt.* To wear into a gully.

gulp, gulp, *vt.* To swallow eagerly. —*n.* Act of taking a large swallow.

gum, gum, *n.* The fleshy substance of the

jaws round the teeth: a juice which exudes from trees, etc., and thickens; a viscous substance.— vt. (gumming, gummed). To smear with or unite by a viscous substance.

gunshot, gun'shot, n. Range of a cannonshot, firing of a gun.—a. Made by the shot of a gun.

gunwale, gunnel, gun'wāl, gun'el, n. The upper edge of a ship's side.

gurgle, gėr'gl, vi. (gurgling, gurgled). To run or flow in a broken noisy current.— n. Sound produced by a liquid flowing from or through a narrow opening.

gush, gush, vi. To issue with violence and rapidity, as a fluid; to be effusively sentimental.—n. A sudden and violent issue of a fluid, the fluid thus emitted; effusive display of sentiment.

gutter, gut'ėr, n. A channel at the side of a road, etc., for water.—vt. To cut or form gutters in.—vi. To become channeled.

guttural, gut'tėr-al, a. Pertaining to the throat; formed in the throat.—n. A letter pronounced in the throat; any guttural sound.

guzzle, guz'l, v. and t. (guzzling, guzzled). To swallow greedily or frequently.—n. A debauch.

gymnasium jim-nā'zi-um, n., pl. -ia or -iums. A place for athletic exercises; a school for the higher branches of education.

gymnast, jim'nast, n. One who teaches or practices gymnastic exercises.

H

haberdasher, ha'bér-dash-ér, *n.* A dealer in drapery goods, as woollens, silks, ribbons, etc.

habilitate, ha-bil'i-tat, *vi.* To qualify.

habitat, ha'bit-āt, *n.* The natural abode or locality of a plant or animal.

habitation, ha-bit-ā'shon, *n.* Occupancy; abode; residence.

Hades, ha'dez, *n.* The abode of the dead, state of departed souls.

haft, haft, *n.* A handle; that part of an instrument which is taken into the hand.—*vt.* To set in a haft.

hag, hag, *n.* An ugly old woman; a witch; an eel-shaped fish that eats into other fishes.

haggard, hag'ärd, *a.* Wild; intractable, having the face worn and pale; gaunt.— *n.* An untrained or refractory hawk.

haggle, hag'l, *vt.* (haggling, haggled). To cut into small pieces; to mangle.—*vi.* To be difficult in bargaining; to stick at small matters; to chaffer.

hail, hāl *n.* Frozen drops of rain; a wish of health, a call.—*vi.* To pour down hail; to have as one's residence, or belong to (with *from*).—*vt.* To pour down in the manner of hail; to salute; to call to; to designate as.—*interj.* A salutation expressive of well-wishing.

hailstone, hāl'stōn, *n.* A single pellet of hail falling from a cloud.

hair, hār, *n.* A small filament issuing from the skin of an animal, the mass of filaments growing from the skin of an animal; anything similar a very small distance.

hale, hāl, *a.* Sound; healthy; robust.—*n.* A violent pull.—*vt.* (haling, haled). To take, pull, or drag by force.

hall, häl, *n.* A large room, especially a large public room; a large room at the entrance of a house, a manor-house; The name of certain colleges at Oxford and Cambridge.

Halleluiah, Hallelujah, hal-lē-lü'ya, *n.* and *interj.* A word used in sacred songs of praise, signifying *praise ye, Jehovah.*

Halloween, Hallow-even, hal'ō-ēn, hal'o-ē-vn, *n.* The eve or vigil of All-Hallows' or All-Saints' Day.

hallucination, hal-lü'si-nā''shon *n.* A mistaken notion; mere dream or fancy; morbid condition in which objects are believed to be seen and sensations experienced object or sensation thus erroneously perceived.

halo, hā'lō, *n.* A luminous ring round the sun or moon; any circle of light, as the glory round the head of saints; an ideal glory investing an object.—*vi.* To form itself into a halo.—*vt.* To surround with a halo.

halt, hält, *vi.* To limp; to be lame; to hesitate; to cease marching.—*vt.* To stop; to cause to cease marching.—*a.* Lame: limping.—*n.* A limp; a stopping; stoppage on march.

hammer, ham'ér, *n.* An instrument for driving nails, beating metals, and the like.—*vt.* To beat or forge with a hammer, to contrive by intellectual labor.— *vi.* To work with a hammer; to labor in contrivance.

hammock, ham'ok, *n.* A kind of hanging bed.

hamstring, ham'string, *n.* One of the tendons of the ham.—*vt.* (pp. hamstrung or hamstringed). To cut the tendons of the ham, and thus to lame or disable.

handcuff, hand'kuf, *n.* A fetter for the hands or wrists.—*vt.* To manacle with handcuffs.

handful, hand'fül, *n* As much as the hand will grasp or hold, a small quantity or number.

handicap, hand'i-kap, *n.* In racing, games, etc., an allowance to bring superior competitors to an equality with the others, a race or contest so arranged.—*vt.* To put a handicap on; to equalize by a handicap.

handle, hand'dl, *vt.* (handling, handled). To feel, use, or hold with the hand; to discuss; to deal with to treat or use well or ill.—*n.* That part of an instrument, etc., held in the hand; instrument for effecting a purpose.

hangar, hang'ar, *n.* A shed for housing airplanes.

hanging, hang'ing, *n.* Act of suspending; death by the halter; *pl.* linings for rooms, of tapestry, paper, etc.

happy, hap'i, *a.* Being in the enjoyment of agreeable sensations from the possession of good, fortunate, propitious; well suited, apt.

harangue, ha-rang', *n.* A noisy or pompous address, a declamatory public address; a tirade—*vi.* (haranguing, harangued). To make a harangue.—*vt.* To address by a harangue.

harass, ha'ras, *vt.* To vex, to tire with

labor; to fatigue with importunity.

harbinger, här'bin-jėr, *n.* A forerunner, that which precedes and gives notice of something else.—*vt.* To precede as harbinger

harbor, här'bėr, *n.* A shelter, a haven for ships; an asylum.—*vt.* To shelter, to entertain in the mind.— *vi.* To take shelter; to lodge or abide for a time.

hard, härd. *a.* Not easily penetrated or separated; firm; difficult to understand; arduous; unfeeling; severe; unjust; harsh; stiff; grasping applied to certain sounds, as sibilants contrasted with gutturals applied to water not suitable for washing, from holding minerals.—*adv.* Close, diligently; with difficulty; fast; copiously; with force.

hardy, härd'i, *a.* Bold; intrepid; full of assurance; inured to fatigue, capable of bearing exposure.

harm, härm, *n* Injury; hurt; evil.— *vt.* To hurt; to damage; to impair.

harmless, härm'les, *a.* Free from harm; not causing harm; inoffensive; uninjured.

harmonic, harmonical, här-mon' ik, här-mon'ik-al, a Pertaining to harmony; concordant; musical.— **harmonic,** här-mon'ik, *n.* A less distinct tone accompanying a principal tone.

harmony, här'mo-ni, *n.* The just adaptation of parts to each other musical concord; agreement, peace and friendship.

harness, här'nes, *n.* Armor; furniture of a carriage or draft horse.— *vt.* To dress in armor; to put harness on.

harp, harp, *n.* A stringed musical instrument of triangular form played with the fingers.—*vi.* To play on the harp; to dwell on tediously.

harpoon, här-pön', *n.* A spear or javelin, used to strike whales etc.—*vt.* To strike, catch, or kill with a harpoon.

harpy, här'pi, *n.* A fabulous winged monster with the face of a woman, any rapacious animal, an extortioner

harridan, ha'ri-dan, *n.* A hag; an odious old woman, a vixenish woman; a trollop.

harrow, ha'rō, *n.* A frame set with spikes, to prepare plowed land for seed or to cover the seed.—*vt.* To draw a harrow over; to lacerate; to torment.

harrowing, ha'rō-ing, *p.a.* Causing acute distress to the mind.

hasp, hasp, *n.* A clasp that passes over a staple to be fastened by a padlock.—*vt.* To fasten with a hasp.

hassock, has'ok, *n.* A thick mat or cushion used for kneeling on, etc.

haste, hā st, *n.* Speed, hurry, sudden excitement of passion; precipitance.—*vt.* (hasting, hasted). To drive or urge forward, to hurry.— *vi.* To move with celerity; to be speedy.

hate, hāt, *vt.* (hating, hated). To detest, to loathe to abhor.—*n.* Great dislike hatred.

haughty, hät'i, *a.* Proud and disdainful; lofty and arrogant.

haul, hāl, *vt.* To pull or draw with force; to drag; to compel to go.—*n.* A violent pull; draught of fish in a net; that which is taken or gained at once.

have, hav, *vt.* (having, had). To possess; to accept; to enjoy; to hold in opinion; to be under necessity, or impelled by duty; to procure; to bring forth.

haven, hā'vn, *n.* A harbor; port; shelter.

haversack, hav'ėr-sak, *n.* A soldier's bag for provisions on the march.

having, hav'ing, *n.* What one has; possession, goods.

havoc, hav'ok, *n.* Devastation; wide and general destruction, slaughter.

hawk, häk, *n.* A rapacious bird of the falcon family.—*vi.* To catch birds by means of hawks, to practice falconry, to take prey on the wing; to force up phlegm with noise.—*vt.* To carry about for sale from place to place.

hazel, hā'zl, *n.* A small tree of the oak family that bears edible nuts.—*a.* Pertaining to the hazel of a light-brown color.

hazy, hā z'i, *a.* Thick with haze mentally obscure or confused.

he, hē, *pron.* of the third person, nominative. A substitute for the third person masculine, representing the man or male named before, prefixed to names of animals to specify the male.

head, hed, *n.* The anterior part of animals; uppermost part of the human body; seat of the brain; etc., intellect; an individual; a chief; first place; top; chief part; principal source; crisis; height; promontory, division of discourse headway.—*vt.* To form a head to; to behead; to lead; to go in front of in order to stop; to oppose.— *vi.* To form a head; to be directed, as a ship.

heading, hed'ing, *n.* That which stands at the head, title of a section; passage excavated in the line of an intended tunnel.

heal, hēl, *vi.* To make hale or sound; to cure; to reconcile.—*vt.* To grow whole or sound, to recover.

health, helth, *n.* A sound state of body or mind, freedom from disease; bodily conditions; wish of health and happiness (used in drinking).

healthy, helth'i, *a.* Being in health; sound; hale; salubrious; wholesome.

heap, hēp, *n.* A mass, large quantity; pile.—*vt.* To raise in a heap; to amass, to pile.

hearing, hėr'ing, *n.* The faculty or sense by which sound is perceived; audience opportunity to be heard; judicial trial; reach of the ear

hearsay, hēr'sā, *n.* Report; rumor—*a.* Given at second hand.

hearse, hėrs *n.* A carriage for conveying the dead to the grave; bier.

heart, härt, *n.* The primary organ of the blood's motion, the inner, vital, or most essential part; seat of the affections, will, etc., disposition of mind, conscience, courage spirit; what represents a heart, one of a suit of playing cards marked with such a figure.

hearty, härt'i, *a.* Warm; cordial; healthy; having a keen appetite; large to satisfaction.

heat, hēt, *n.* The sensation produced by bodies that are hot, hot air; hot weather; high temperature; degree of temperature; a single effort; a course at a race, animal excitement; rage; ardor, animation in thought or discourse fermentation.—*vt.* To make hot, to warm with passion or desire, to rouse into action.—*vi.* To grow warm or hot.

heath, hēth, *n.* A small flowering shrub growing on waste or wild places; a place overgrown with heath; waste tract.

heather, heTH'ér, *n.* Common heath, a low shrub with clusters of rose-colored flowers.

heave, hēv, *vt.* (heaving, pret. and pp. heaved, hove). To lift to move upward; to cause to swell; to raise or force from the breast, as a groan; to throw; to turn in some direction.—*vi.* To rise; to swell, as the sea, to pant to retch, *to heave in sight,* to appear, as a ship.—*n.* A rising or swell, an effort upward, a throw; a swelling, as of the breast.

Heaven, hev'n, *n.* The blue expanse surrounding the earth, the sky; the abode of God and of his angels, God or Providence, supreme felicity; bliss.

heavenly, hev'n-li, *a.* Pertaining to heaven, divine, inhabiting heaven enchanting.—*adv.* In a heavenly manner.

heavy, he'vi, *a.* That is heaved or lifted with difficulty; weighty; sad; grievous; burdensome; drowsy; wearisome, not easily digested; soft and miry; difficult; large in amount; dense; abundant; forcible.

hedge, hej, *n.* A fence consisting of thorns or shrubs.—*vt.* (hedging hedged). To enclose with a hedge to surround or restrain.—*vi.* To hide oneself, to bet on both sides to skulk, to dodge or trim.—*a.* Pertaining to a hedge; mean; rustic.

Hedonism, hē'don-izm. *n.* The doctrine that the chief good of man lies in pursuit of pleasure.

Hedonist, hē'don-ist, *n.* One who professes hedonism.

heed, hēd, *vt.* To look to or after, to regard with care, to notice.—*vi.* To mind; to consider—*n.* Care; attention, regard.

heel, hēl, *n.* The hind part of the foot; a cant.—*vt.* To add a heel to; to furnish with heels, as shoes.— *vi.* To cant over from a vertical position.

height, hīt, *n.* The condition of being high; distance of anything above its base or above the earth eminence; any elevated ground, extent, degree, utmost degree.

heighten, hī t'n, *vt.* To raise higher; to improve; to increase.

heir, är, *n.* One who succeeds or is to succeed another in the possession of property.

helium, hē'li-um, *n.* An inert gas present in the air in small quantities, the lightest element next to hydrogen.

helix, hē'liks, *n;* pl. helices, hel'isez. A spiral line, as of wire in a coil; something that is spiral.

Hell, hel, *n.* The place or state of punishment for the wicked after death; the abode of the devil and his angels; the infernal powers; a gambling-house.

help, help, *vt.* To lend strength or means towards effecting a purpose, to aid, to relieve, to remedy; to prevent; to avoid.—*vi.* To lend aid.—*n.* Aid, remedy, an assistant.

hem, hem, *n.* The border of a garment, doubled and sewed to strengthen it, edge, border.—*interj.* and *n.* A sort of half cough, suggested by some feeling.—*vt.* (hemming, hemmed). To form a hem or border on; to enclose and confine; to make the sound expressed by the word hem.

hematite, he'ma-tit, *n.* A name of two ores of iron, red hematite and brown hematite.

hemisphere, he'mi-sfēr, *n.* One half of a sphere, half the celestial or terrestrial sphere.

hemlock, hem'lok, *n.* An umbelliferous plant whose leaves and root are poisonous.

hemorrhage, he'mor-āj, *n.* A bursting forth of blood, any discharge of blood from the blood-vessels.

hemorrhoids, he'mor-oidz, *n.pl.* Piles.

hemp, hemp, *n.* An annual herbaceous plant of the nettle family the fiber of which, also called hemp, is made into sail-cloth, ropes, etc.

hen, hen, *n.* The female of the domestic fowl; any female bird.

herald, he'rald, *n.* An officer whose business was to proclaim war or peace, bear messages, etc.; a forerunner, an officer who regulates matters relating to public ceremonies; one who records and blazons arms, etc.—*vt.* To introduce, as by a herald, to proclaim.

herbarium, hér-bā'ri-um, *n.; pl.* -iums and -ia. A collection of herbs or plants dried and preserved.

herbivorous, hérb-iv'or-us, *a.* Eating herbs; subsisting on herbaceous plants.

Herculean, hér-kū'lē-an, *a.* Belong-ing to or resembling Hercules, of extraordinary strength; very great or difficult.

herd, hérd, *n.* A number of animals feeding or driven together; flock; crowd, rabble, a keeper of cattle or sheep.—*vi.* and *t.* To unite into a herd, as beasts; to congregate.

hereafter, hér-af'tèr, *adv.* After this time, in a future state.—*n.* The time after this; a future state.

heresy, he're-si, *n.* A fundamental error in religion; error in doctrine; heterodoxy.

heretic, he're-tik, *n.* One guilty of heresy.

heritage, he'rit-āj, *n.* Inheritance lot or portion by birth.

hermit, her 'mit, *n.* One who lives in solitude, a recluse.

hernia, hér'ni-a, *n.* A protrusion of some organ of the abdomen through an interstice; a rupture.

heroin, her'o-in, *n.* A narcotic drug derived from morphia.

heroine, he'rō-in, *n.* A female hero.

heroism, he'rō-izm, *n.* The qualities of a hero; intrepidity; magnanimity.

heron, her'un, *n.* A wading bird with a long bill, long slender legs and neck.

herpes, hér'pez, *n.* A skin disease characterized by eruption or inflamed vesicles.

herpetology, hér-pe-tol'o-ji, *n.* The natural history of reptiles.

herring, he'ring, *n.* One of those small food fishes which go in shoals in northern seas.

herring-bone, he'ring-bōn, *a.* Applied to masonry, sewing, etc., which bears resemblance to the backbone of a herring.

hesitate, he'zi-tāt, *vi.* (hesitating, hesitated). To pause respecting decision or action; to stop in speaking; to stammer.

hesitation, he-zi-tā'shon, *n.* Act of hesitating; doubt; a stopping in speech.

hew, hū, *vt.* (*pret.* hewed, *pp.* hewed or hewn). To cut with an axe, etc.; to cut; to hack; to make smooth, as stone; to shape.

high-pressure, hī'pre-shūr, *a.* Having or involving a pressure exceeding that of the atmosphere, or having a pressure greater than 50 lbs. to the square inch.

highway, hī'wā, *n.* A public road; direct course, train of action.

hike, hīk, *vi.* To tramp; to go on a long or fairly long walking expedition.

hilarity, hi-la'ri-ti, *n.* Cheerfulness; merriment, good humor, jollity.

hill, hil, *n.* A natural elevation of less size than a mountain; an eminence.

hilt, hilt, *n.* A handle, particularly of a sword.

himself, him-self', *pron.* The emphatic and reflexive form of he and him.

hind, hīnd, *n.* The female of the reddeer or stag; a farm servant; a rustic.—*a.* Backward, back, pertaining to the backward part.

hinder, hīnd'èr, *a.* Posterior; in the rear, latter, after.

hinder, hin'dèr, *vt.* To prevent from moving or acting; to obstruct; to thwart to check.—*vi.* To interpose obstacles or impediments.

hint, hint, *vt.* To suggest indirectly; to insinuate.—*vi.* To make an indirect allusion.—*n.* A distant allusion; a suggestion.

hip, hip, *n.* The fleshy projecting part of the thigh; the haunch; the joint of the thigh; the fruit of the dog-rose or wild brier.—*interj.* Exclamation expressive of a call to anyone. *Hip, hip, hurrah!* the signal to cheer.

hire, hīr, *vt.* (hiring, hired). To procure for temporary use, at a certain price; to engage in service for a stipulated reward; to let; to lease (with out).—*n.* Price paid for temporary use of anything; recompense for personal service;

wages; pay.

hirsute, hèr-sūt', *a.* Hairy; shaggy.

history, his'to-ri, *n.* An account of facts, particularly respecting nations or states; that branch of knowledge which deals with past events, narration; a story; an account of existing things, as animals or plants.

histrionics, his-tri-on'iks, *n.* The art of theatrical representation.

hit, hit, *vt.* (hitting, hit). To strike or touch with some force to give a blow to; not to miss; to reach; to light upon; to suit.— *vi.* To strike; to come in contact, to reach the intended point; to succeed.—*n.* A stroke; a blow; a lucky chance; happy thought or expression.

hitch, hich, *vi.* To move by jerks; to be entangled, hooked, or yoked.—*vt.* To fasten; to hook, to raise by jerks.—*n.* A catch; act of catching, as on a hook, etc., knot or noose in a rope; a jerk; a temporary obstruction.

hither, hiTH'èr, *adv.* To this place.— *a.* Nearer; toward the person speaking.

hive, hīv, *n.* A box or receptacle for honey-bees; the bees inhabiting a hive; a place swarming with busy occupants.— *vt.* (hiving, hived). To collect into a hive; to lay up in store.—*vi.* To take shelter together; to reside in a collective body.

hoar, hōr, *a.* White or whitish; hoary.—*vi.* To become moldy or musty.

hoard, hōrd, *n.* A store, stock, or large quantity of anything, a hidden stock.— *vt.* To collect; to store secretly.—*vi.* To form a hoard; to lay up in store.

hoar frost, hōr'frost, *n.* The white particles of frozen dew, rime.

hoarse, hōrs, *a.* Having a grating voice, as when affected with a cold, discordant, rough, grating.

hobby, hob'i, *n.* A small but strong British falcon; an active, ambling nag; a hobby-horse; any favorite object or pursuit.

hod, hod, *n.* A kind of trough for carrying mortar and brick on the shoulder.

hodge-podge, hoj'poj, *n.* A mixed mass; a medley of ingredients; a hotch-potch.

hoe, hō, *n.* An instrument to cut up weeds and loosen the earth.—*vt.* (hoeing, hoed). To dig or clean with a hoe.—*vi.* To use a hoe.

hog, hog, *n.* A swine; a castrated boar; a sheep of a year old; a brutal or mean fellow.—*vi.* To bend, as a ship's bottom.

hogshead, hogz'hed, *n.* A large cask; an old measure of capacity, containing about 52-1/2 imperial gallons.

hoist, hoist, *vt.* To heave up, to lift upward by means of tackle.—*n.* Act of raising; apparatus for raising goods, etc., an elevator

hold, hōld, *vt.* (pret. held, pp. held,). To have in the grasp; to keep fast; to confine; to maintain; to consider; to contain; to possess; to withhold, to continue, to celebrate.—*vi.* To take or keep a thing in one's grasp; to stand as a fact or truth, not to give way or part, to refrain, to adhere; to derive title (with *of*).—*n.* A grasp; something which may be seized for support power of keeping, seizing, or directing; influence; place of confinement, stronghold, interior cavity of a ship.

hole, hōl, *n.* A hollow place in any solid body, a perforation, crevice, etc.; a den, a subterfuge.—*vt.* (holing, holed). To make a hole or holes in to drive into a hole.

holiday, ho'li-dā, *n.* A holy or sacred day; a festival; day of exemption from labor.—*a.* Pertaining to a festival.

holiness, hō'li-nes, *n.* State or quality of being holy; moral goodness, sanctity.— **His Holiness,** a title of the pope.

holometabolic, hol'o-met-a-bol"ik, *a.* Applied to insects which undergo a complete metamorphosis.

holster, hōl'ster, *n.* A leathern case for a pistol.

holy, hō'li, *a.* Free from sin; immaculate, consecrated, sacred.

homage, hom'āj, *n.* An act of fealty on the part of a vassal to his lord; obeisance, reverential worship.

home, hōm, *n.* One's own abode; the abode of one's family; residence; one' own country; an establishment affording the comforts of a home.—*a.* Domestic; close; severe, poignant.—*adv.* To one's own habitation or country; to the point; effectively.

homestead, hōm'sted, *n.* A house with the grounds and buildings contiguous; a home; native seat.

homeward, hōm'wèrd, *adv.* Toward one's habitation or country.—*a.* Being in the direction of home.

homiletics, ho-mi-let'iks, *n.* The art of preaching.

homily, ho'mi-li, *n.* A sermon, a familiar religious discourse; a serious discourse or admonition.

homologous, hō-mol'o-gus, *a.* Having the same relative position, proportion, or structure; corresponding.

homonym, ho'mŏ-nim, *n.* A word which agrees with another in sound, and perhaps in spelling but differs in signification.

hone, hōn, *n.* A stone of a fine grit used for sharpening instruments—*vt.* (honing, honed). To sharpen on a hone.

honest, on'est, *a.* Free from fraud; upright; just; sincere; candid; virtuous.

honey, hun'i, *n.* A sweet viscous juice collected by bees from flowers, sweetness, a word of tenderness.—*vt.* To sweeten.

honorary, on'ėr-a-ri, *a.* Relating to honor, conferring honor, possessing a title or place without performing services or without receiving a reward.

honor, on'ėr, *n.* Respect; esteem; testimony of esteem; dignity; good name; a nice sense of what is right, scorn of meanness, a title of respect or distinction, one of the highest trump cards; *pl.* civilities paid, public marks of respect, academic and university distinction.—*vt.* To regard or treat with honor, to bestow honor upon, to exalt; to accept and pay when due, as a bill.

honorable, on'ėr-a-bl, *a.* Worthy of honor; actuated by principles of honor; conferring honor, consistent with honor; performed with marks of honor, not base, honest fair; a title of distinction.

hood, hüd, *n.* A soft covering for the head; a cowl; a garment worn as part of academic dress, which indicates by its colors, material and shape the degree and University of its wearer; anything resembling a hood.—*vt.* To dress in a hood; to cover; to blind.

hoodwink, hüd'wingk, *vt.* To blind by covering the eyes of; to impose on.

hoof, hōf, *n.*, *pl.* **hoofs,** rarely hooves. The horny substance that covers the feet of certain animals, as the horse.

hook, hŏk, *n.* A bent piece of iron or other metal for catching; that which catches, a sickle.—*vt.* To catch with a hook, to ensnare.—*vi.* To bend; to be curving.

hoot, hŏt, *vi.* To shout in contempt; to cry as an owl.—*vt.* To utter contemptuous cries at.—*n.* A cry or shout in contempt.

hop, hop, *n.* A leap on one leg; a spring, a bitter plant of the hemp family used to flavor malt liquors.—*vi.* To leap or spring on one leg, to skip, to limp, to pick hops.—*vt.* To impregnate with hops.

hope, hōp, *n.* A desire of some good, accompanied with a belief that it is attainable; trust, one in whom trust or confidence is placed, the object of hope.—*vi.* (hoping, hoped). To entertain hope; to trust.—*vt.* To desire with some expectation of attainment.

horde, hōrd, *n.* A tribe or race of nomads; a gang; migratory crew; rabble.—*vi.* (hording, horded). To live together like migratory tribes.

horizon, ho-rī'zon, *n.* The circle which bounds the part of the earth's surface visible from given point; the apparent junction of the earth and sky.

hormones, hor'mōnz, *n.pl.* Products of the ductless glands, affecting other organs by way of the blood stream.

horn, horn, *n.* A hard projection on the heads of certain animals, the material of such horns; wind-instrument of music; extremity of the moon; drinking-cup; powder-horn, something resembling a horn; the feeler of a snail, etc.

horror, hor'rėr, *n.* A powerful feeling of fear and abhorrence, that which may excite terror, something frightful or shocking.

horse, hors, *n.* A well-known quadruped, used for draft and carriage in war; the male animal; cavalry; a name of various things resembling or analogous to a horse.—*vt.* (horsing, horsed). To supply with a horse; to carry on the back; to bestride.

horseradish, hors'rad-ish, *n.* A perennial plant, having a root of a pungent taste.

horseshoe, hors'shö, *n.* A shoe for horses, commonly of iron shaped like the letter U; anything shaped like a horse-shoe.— *a.* Having the form of a horse-shoe.

hortatory, hort'a-to-ri, *a.* Giving exhortation or advice, encouraging.

horticulture, hor'ti-kul-tūr, *n.* The art of cultivating gardens.

Hosanna, hō-zan'na, *n.* An exclamation of praise to God, or an invocation of blessings.

hose, hōz, *n. sing.* or *pl.* A covering for the thighs, legs, or feet; closefitting breeches, stockings, in these senses plural; a flexible pipe used for conveying water.

host, hōst, *n.* One who entertains a stranger or guest; an innkeeper; an army; any great number or multitude, the consecrated bread in the R. Catholic sacrament of the mass.

hostage, host'āj, *n.* A person delivered to an enemy, as a pledge to secure the performance of conditions.

hostel, hostelry, hos'tel, hos'tel-ri. *n.* An inn, a lodging-house.

hostile, hos'til *a.* Belonging to an enemy; unfriendly; antagonistic; adverse.

hostility, hos-til'i-ti, *n.* State or quality of being hostile; state of war between nations or states, the actions of an open enemy (in *pl.*); animosity, enmity, opposition.

hot, hot, *a.* Having sensible heat burning; glowing; easily exasperated; vehement; eager; lustful; biting; pungent in taste.

hour, our, *n.* The twenty-fourth part of a day, consisting of sixty minutes, the particular time of the day; an appointed time; *pl.* certain prayers in the R. Catholic Church.

house, hous *n.*, pl. **houses,** hou'zez. A building or erection for the habitation or use of man; any building or edifice, a dwelling a household; a family; a legislative body of men; audience or attendance, a commercial establishment.—*vt.* (housing, housed). To put or receive into a house, to shelter.—*vi.* To take shelter; to take up abode.

housing, houz'ing, *n.* A horsecloth, *pl.* the trappings of a horse.—*p.n.* Placing in houses; sheltering.

hovel, ho'vel, *n.* A mean house; an open shed for cattle, etc.—*vt.* To put in a hovel.

hover, ho'ver, *vi.* To hang fluttering in the air; to be in doubt; to linger near.

how, hou, *adv.* In what manner; to what extent; for what reason; by what means, in what state.

however, hou-ev'er, *adv.* In whatever manner or degree, in whatever state.—*conj.* Nevertheless yet; still; though.

howl, houl, *vi.* To cry as a dog or wolf; to utter a loud mournful sound; to roar, as the wind.—*vt.* To utter or speak with outcry.—*n.* A loud protracted wail; cry of a wolf, etc.

hub, hub, *n.* The central cylindrical part of a wheel in which the spokes are set.

hubbub, hub'bub, *n.* A great noise of many confused voices; tumult; uproar.

huckster, huk'ster, *n.* A retailer of small articles; a hawker.—*vi.* To deal in small articles; to higgle.— *vt.* To hawk.

huddle, hud'l, *vi.* (huddling, huddled). To crowd or press together promiscuously.—*vt.* To throw or crowd together in confusion, to put on in haste and disorder.—*n.* A confused mass; confusion.

huff, huf, *n.* A fit of peevishness or petulance; anger.—*vt.* To treat with inso-

lence, to bully; to make angry.—*vi.* To swell up; to bluster to take offense.

hug, hug, *vt.* (hugging, hugged). To press close in an embrace; to hold fast; to cherish; to keep close to.— *n.* A close embrace, a particular grip in wrestling.

Huguenot, hū 'ge-not, *n.* A French Protestant of the period of the religious wars in France in the 16th century.

hulk, hulk, *n.* the body of an old vessel; anything bulky or unwieldy.

hull, hul, *n.* The outer covering of anything particularly of a nut or of grain; husk; frame or body of a ship.—*vt.* To strip off the hull or hulls; to pierce the hull of a ship with a cannon-ball.

hum, hum, *vi.* (humming, hummed). To utter the sound of bees, to make an inarticulate buzzing sound.—*vt.* To sing in a low voice; to sing or utter inarticulately.—*n.* The noise of bees or insects, a low, confused noise, a low, inarticulate sound.—*interj.* A sound with a pause, implying doubt and deliberation.

human, hū'man, *a.* Belonging to man or mankind; having the qualities of a man.

humble, hum'bl, *a.* Of a low, mean, or unpretending character, lowly modest; meek.—*vt.* (humbling, humbled). To make humble, to abase, to lower.

humidity, hū-mid'i-ti, *n.* State of being humid moisture.

humiliate, hū-mil'i-āt, *vt.* To humble; to depress; to mortify.

humility, hū-mil'i-ti, *n.* Humbleness of mind; modesty; sense of insignificance.

humming-bird, hum'ing-berd, *n.* A family of minute but richly-colored birds that make a humming sound with their wings.

hummock, hum'ok. *n* A rounded knoll.

humorist, hu'mer-ist or u', *n.* One that makes use of a humorous style in speaking or writing; a wag.

humor, hu'mer or u'mer, *n.* Moisture or moist mater, fluid matter in an animal body, not blood, disposition; mood; a caprice; jocularity; a quality akin to wit, but depending for its effect less on point or brilliancy of expression.—*vt.* To comply with the inclination of, to soothe by compliance; to indulge.

hundred, hun'dred, *a.* Ten times ten.—*n.* The sum of ten times ten the number 100; a division or part of a county in England.

hundredweight, hun'dred-wat, *n.* A weight of a hundred and twelve pounds avoirdupois, twenty of which make a ton.

hunger, hung'ger, n. An uneasy sensation occasioned by the want of food, a craving of food, a strong or eager desire.— vi. To feel the uneasiness occasioned by want of food; to desire with great eagerness.

hungry, hung'gri, a. Feeling uneasiness from want of food; having an eager desire; lean; barren.

hunt, hunt, vt. To chase or search for, for the purpose of catching or killing; to follow closely; to use or manage, as hounds; to pursue animals over.—vi. To follow the chase, to search.—n. The chase of wild animals for catching them pursuit; an association of huntsmen, a pack of hounds.

hunter, hunt'èr, n. One who hunts a horse used in the chase; a kind of watch with a hinged case which protects the glass.

hurdle, hèr'dl, n. A movable frame made of twigs or sticks, or of bars or rods.— vt. (hurdling, hurdled). To make up, cover, or close with hurdles.

hurl, hèrl, vt. To send whirling through the air, to throw with violence; to utter with vehemence.—n. Act of throwing with violence.

hurricane, hu'ri-kan, n. A violent storm of wind traveling over 75 miles per hour.

hurry, hu'ri, vt. (hurrying, hurried). To drive or press forward with more rapidity, to urge to act with more celerity, to quicken.—vi. To move or act with haste; to hasten.—n. Act of hurrying; urgency; bustle.

hurt, hèrt, n. A wound; bruise; injury; harm.—vt. (pret. and pp. hurt) To cause physical pain to, to bruise; to harm; to impair; to injure; to wound the feelings of.

hurtle, hèr'tl, vi. (hurtling, hurtled). To meet in shock, to clash, to fly with threatening noise; to resound.

husband, huz'band, n. A married man; the correlative of wife, a good manager; a steward.—vt. To manage with frugality; to use with economy.

hush, hush, a. Silent; still; quiet.— n. Stillness; quiet.—vt. To make quiet; to repress, as noise.—vi. To be still, to be silent.

hut, hut, n. A small house, hovel, or cabin; a temporary building to lodge soldiers.—vt. (hutting, hutted); To place in huts, as troops.— vi. To take lodgings in huts.

hutch, huch, n. A chest or box, a corn bin; a box for rabbits, a low wagon used in coal-pits; a measure of 2 bushels.

hyacinth, hi'a-sinth, n. A flowering, bulbous plant, of many varieties; a red variety of zircon tinged with yellow or brown: also applied to varieties of garnet, sapphire, and topaz.

hydrogen, hi'drō-jen, n. The gaseous elementary substance which combines with oxygen to form water.

hydrophobia, hi-drō-fō'bi-a, n. A morbid dread of water; a disease produced by the bite of a mad animal, especially a dog.

hyena, hi -ē 'na, n. A carnivorous quadruped of Asia and Africa feeding chiefly on carrion.

hygiene, hī'ji-ēn, n. A system of principles designed for the promotion of health, sanitary science.

hymnal, him'nal, n. A collection of hymns, generally for use in public worship.

hyperbola, hi-pèr'bō-la, n. A conic section, a curve formed by a section of a cone, when the cutting plane makes a greater angle with the base than the side of the cone makes.

hyperbole, hi-pèr'bō-lē, n. Exaggeration, a figure of speech exceeding the truth.

hyperborean, hi-pèr-bō'rē-an, a. Being in the extreme north, arctic frigid.—n. An inhabitant of the most northern regions.

hypercritic, hi-per-krit'ik, n. One critical beyond measure; a captious censor.

hyphen, hī'fen, n. A character, thus (-), implying that two words or syllables are to be connected.

hypnotism, hip'no-tizm, n. A sleeplike condition caused by artificial means.

hypochondria, hi-po-kon'dri-a, n. An ailment characterized by exaggerated anxiety, mainly as to the health; low spirits.

hypocrisy, hi-pok'ri-si, n. A feigning to be what one is not, insincerity; a counterfeiting of religion.

hypocrite, hi'po-krit, n. One who feigns to be what he is not; a dissembler.

hysteria, hysterics, his-tē'ri-a, hister'iks. n. A nervous affection chiefly characterized by laughing and crying, convulsive struggling, sense of suffocation, etc.

I

I, î, *pron.* The pronoun of the first person in the nominative case; the word by which a speaker or writer denotes himself

ice, îs, *n.* Water or other fluid congealed; ice-cream.—*vt.* (icing, iced). To cover with ice; to convert into ice; to cover with concreted sugar, to freeze.

iconoclast, î-kon'o-klast, *n.* A breaker of images; one who attacks cherished beliefs.

iconography, î-ko-nog'ra-fi, *n.* The knowledge of ancient statues, paintings, gems, etc.

icy, îs'i, *a.* Abounding with ice; made of ice, resembling ice, chilling; frigid; destitute of affection or passion.

idea, î-dē'a, *n.* That which is seen by the mind's eye; an image in the mind; object of thought; notion; conception; abstract principle; ideal view.

ideal, î-dē'al, *a.* Existing in idea or fancy; visionary; imaginary; perfect.—*n.* An imaginary model of perfection.

idealism, î'dē'al-izm, *n.* The system that makes everything to consist in ideas, and denies the existence of material bodies, or which denies any ground for believing in the reality of anything but percipient minds and ideas.

idealize, î-dē'al-iz, *vt.* To make ideal, to embody in an ideal form.

identical, î-den'tik-al, *a.* The same.

identify, î-den'ti-fi, *vt.* To make to be the same, to consider as the same in effect; to ascertain or prove to be the same.

identity, î-den'ti-ti, *n.* Sameness, as distinguished from similitude and diversity; sameness in every possible circumstance.

idiopathy, id-i-op'a-thi, *n.* A morbid state not produced by any preceding disease.

idiosyncrasy, id'i-o-sin"kra-si, *n.* Peculiarity of temperament or constitution; mental or moral characteristic distinguishing an individual.

idle, î'dl, *a.* Not engaged in any occupation; inactive; lazy; futile; affording leisure; trifling; trivial.— *vi.* (idling, idled). To be idle; to lose or spend time in inaction.—*vt.* To spend in idleness.

idol, î'dol, *n.* An image or symbol of a deity consecrated as an object of worship, a person honored to adoration; anything on which we set our affections inordinately.

ignorance, ig-nō-rans, *n.* State of being illiterate, uninformed, or uneducated; want of knowledge.

ignore, ig-nōr', *vt.* (ignoring, ignored). to pass over or overlook as if ignorant of, to disregard.

iguana, ig-wä'na, *n.* An American reptile of the lizard family.

ill, il, *a.* Bad or evil; producing evil, unfortunate, cross, crabbed, sick or indisposed; impaired; ugly; unfavorable, rude.—*n.* Evil, misfortune; calamity; disease, pain.— *adv.* Not well; badly; with pain or difficulty.

illegitimate, il-lē-jit'i-māt, *a.* Not legitimate, born out of wedlock, illogical; not authorized.—*vt.* To render illegitimate.

illuminate, il-lūm'in-āt, *vt.* (illuminating, illumined). To light up; to adorn with festal lamps or bonfires, to enlighten intellectually, to adorn with colored pictures, etc., as manuscripts.

illustrate, il-lus'trāt or il'lus-trāt, *vt.* (illustrating, illustrated). To make clear or obvious, to explain, to explain and adorn by means of pictures: drawings. etc.

illustration, il-lus-trā'shon, Act of illustrating; that which illustrates; an example; design to illustrate the text of a book.

illustrious, il-lus'tri-us, *a.* Renowned; celebrated; noble; conferring honor or renown, glorious.

image, im'ā j, *n.* A representative of any person or thing, a statue; an idol; embodiment; a picture drawn by fancy; the appearance of any object formed by the reflection or refraction of the rays of light.—*vt.* (imaging, imaged). To represent by an image; to mirror; to form a likeness of in the mind.

imagination, im-aj'in-ā"shon, *n.* The act of imagining; the faculty by which we form a mental image or new combinations of ideas, mental image; a mere fancy; notion.

imagine, im-aj'in, *vt.* (imagining, imagined). To picture to oneself, to fancy, to contrive, to think; to deem.—*vi.* To conceive; to have a notion or idea.

imbroglio, im-brō'lyō, *n.* An intricate and perplexing state of affairs, a misunderstanding of a complicated nature.

imitate, im'i-tāt, *vt.* (imitating, imitated). To follow as a model or example; to copy; to mimic; to counterfeit.

imitation, im-i-tā'shon, *n.* Act of imitating; that which is made or produced as a copy, resemblance, a counterfeit

immediate, im-mē'di-āt, *a*. Without anything intervening; acting without a medium; direct; not acting by secondary causes; present; without intervention of time.

immemorial, im-me-mō'ri-al, *a*. Beyond memory; extending beyond the reach of record or tradition.

immerge, im-merj', *vt*. (immerging, immerged). To dip or plunge; to immerse.—*vi*. To disappear by entering into any medium.

immerse, im-mérs', *vt*. (immersing, immersed). to plunge into water or other fluid; to overwhelm; to engage deeply.

immigrate, im'mi-grāt, *vi*. To come into a country for permanent residence .

immolate, im'mō-lā t, *vt*. (immolating, immolated). To sacrifice, to kill, as a victim offered in sacrifice; to offer in sacrifice.

immunity, im-mū'ni-ti, *n*. Freedom from service or obligation, particular privilege or prerogative; state of not being liable.

imp, imp, *n*. A young or little devil; a mischievous child.—*vt*. (imping, imped). To graft, to mend a deficient wing by the insertion of a feather, to strengthen.

impact, im'pakt, *n*. A forcible touch; a blow; the shock of a moving body that strikes against another.

impale, im-pāl', *vt*. (impaling, impaled). To put to death by fixing on a stake; to join, as two coats of arms on one shield, with an upright line between.

impalpable, im-pal'pa-bl, *a*. Not to be felt; so fine as not to be perceived by the touch; not easily or readily apprehended by the mind.

impassive, im-pas'iv, *a*. Not susceptible of pain or suffering; impassible, unmoved.

impatient, im-pā'shent, *a*. Not patient; uneasy under given conditions and eager for change, not suffering quietly; not enduring de lay.

impeach, im-pēch', *vt*. To charge with a crime; to bring charges of maladministration against a minister of state, etc., to call in question; to disparage

impediment, im-ped'i-ment, *n*. That by which one is impeded; obstruction.

impel, im-pel', *vt*. (impelling, impelled). To drive or urge forward to press on; to instigate; to incite, to actuate.

imperceptible, im-pér-sep'ti-bl, *a*. Not perceptible; not easily apprehended by

the senses; fine or minute.

imperfect, im-pėr'fekt, *a*. Not perfect; not complete; not perfect in a moral view; faulty; *imperfect tense*, a tense expressing an uncompleted action or state, especially in time past.

imperforate, im-pėr'fo-rāt, *a*. Not perforated or pierced; having no opening or pores.

imperial, im-pē'ri-al, *a*. Pertaining to an empire or emperor, supreme; suitable for an emperor; of superior excellence.—*n*. A tuft of hair beneath a man's lower lip; a size of paper measuring 30 by 22 inches.

impersonal, im-pér'son-al, *a*. Not having personal existence; not endued with personality; not referring to any particular person; *impersonal verb*, a verb (such as *it* rains) used only with an impersonal nominative.—*n*. That which wants personality; an impersonal verb.

impersonate, im-pėr'son-āt, *vt*. To invest with personality, to assume the character of; to represent in character, as on the stage.

impetuous, im-pe'tū-us, *a*. Rushing with great force; forcible; precipitate; vehement of mind; hasty; passionate.

impiety, im-pī-e-ti, *n*. Want of piety; irreverence toward the Supreme Being; ungodliness; an act of wickedness.

impinge, im-pinj', *vi*. (impinging, impinged). To dash against; to clash.

implicate, im'pli-kāt, *vt*. (implicating, implicated). To involve or bring into connection with; to prove to be connected or concerned, as in an offense.

implication, im-pli-kā'shon, *n*. Act of implicating; state of being implicated, entanglement, a tacit inference; something to be understood though not expressed.

implicit, im-pli'sit, *a*. Implied; fairly to be understood, though not expressed in words; trusting to another; unquestioning.

implore, im-plōr', *vt*. and *i*. (imploring, implored). To call upon or for, in supplication; to beseech, entreat.

imply, im-plī', *vt*. (implying, implied). To involve or contain in substance or by fair inference; to signify indirectly; to presuppose.

importance, im-pōrt'ans, *n*. Quality of being important; weight; moment, rank or standing; weight in self-estimation.

importune, im-pōr-tūn', *vt*. (importuning importuned). To press with solicitation;

to urge with frequent application.—*vi.* To solicit earnestly and repeatedly.

impose, im-pōz', *vt.* (imposing, imposed). To place, set, or lay on; to lay on, as a tax, penalty, duty, etc.; to lay on, as hands; to obtrude fallaciously, to palm or pass off.—*vi.* Used in phrase to *impose on* or *upon,* to deceive; to victimize.

impotent, im-pō-tent, *a.* Entirely wanting vigor of body or mind feeble, destitute of the power of begetting children.

impound, im-pound', *vt.* To confine in a pound or close pen, to confine to take possession of for use when necessary.

impoverish, im-po'vėr-ish, *vt.* To make poor, to reduce to indigence; to exhaust the strength or fertility of, as of soil.

impress, im-pres', *vt.* To press into; to imprint, to stamp on the mind to inculcate; to compel to enter into public service, as seamen; to take for public use.—*n.* im'press. That which is impressed; mark made by pressure, impression character, act of compelling to enter into public service.

impression, im-pre'shon, *n.* Act of impressing, that which is impressed; mark; effect produced on the mind, an indistinct notion idea, copy taken by pressure from type, etc.; edition; copies forming one issue of a book.

impressionist, im-pre'shon-ist, *n.* One who lays stress on impressions, an artist who depicts scenes by their most striking characteristics as they first impress the spectator.

impromptu, im-promp'tū, *n.* A saying, poem, etc., made off-hand; an extemporaneous composition.—*a.* Off-hand; extempore.—*adv.* Offhand.

improper, im-pro'pér, *a.* Not proper; unfit; not decent; erroneous; wrong.

impropriety, im-prō-prī'e-ti, *n.* Quality of being improper, that which is improper; an unsuitable act, expression, etc.

improve, im-prōv', *vt.* (improving improved). To better; to ameliorate; to mend; to rectify; to use to good purpose; to apply to practical purposes.—*vi.* To grow better.

improvement, im-prōv'ment, *n.* Act of improving; state of being improved, a change for the better that which improves, a beneficial or valuable addition or alteration.

improvise, im-pro-vīz', To form on the spur of the moment to compose and recite, etc., without previous prepara-

tion.

impulse, im'puls, *n.* Force communicated instantaneously, effect of a sudden communication of motion, influence acting on the mind motive; sudden determination.

in, in, *prep.* Within; inside of; surrounded by, indicating presence or situation within limits, whether of place, time, circumstances, etc.—*adv.* In or within some place state, circumstances, etc.; not out.

inadvertence, inadvertency, in-ad-vėrt-ens, in-ad-vėrt'en-si, *n.* Quality of being inadvertent; any oversight or fault which proceeds from negligence or want of attention.

inadvertent, in-ad-vėrt'ent, *a.* Not paying strict attention; heedless; unwary; negligent.

inappropriate, in-ap-prō'pri-āt, *a.* Not appropriate; unsuited; not proper.

inarticulate, in-är-tik'ū-lāt, *a.* Not articulate, not jointed or articulated; not uttered distinctly.

inaugurate, in-ä'gū-rāt, *vt.* To induct into an office with suitable ceremonies, to perform initiatory ceremonies in connection with.

incalculable, in-kal'kū-la-bl, *a.* Not calculable; very great.

incandescent, in-kan-des'ent, *a.* White or glowing with heat.—**incandescent light,** a form of gas light, a form of electric light given forth from a filament of carbon inclosed in an airless glass globe.

incantation, in-kan-tā'shon, *n.* The act of using certain words and ceremonies to raise spirits, etc.; the form of words so used; a magical charm or ceremony.

incapable, in-kā'pa-bl, *a.* Not capable; possessing inadequate power or capacity; not susceptible; incompetent, unqualified or disqualified.—*n.* One physically or mentally weak.

incarnate, in-kär'nāt, *vt.* To clothe with flesh; to embody in flesh.—*a.* Invested with flesh; embodied in flesh.

incense, in'sens, *n.* Aromatic substance burned in religious rites odors of spices and gums, burned in religious rites; flattery or agreeable homage.—*vt.* (incensing, incensed). To perfume with incense.

inceptive, in-sep'tiv, *a.* Pertaining to inception; beginning, applied to a verb which expresses the beginning of an action.—*n.* An inceptive verb.

incessant, in-ses'ant, *a.* Unceasing unintermitted; continual; constant.

incest, in 'sest, n. Sexual commerce between near blood relations.

inch, insh, n. The twelfth part of a foot in length, a small quantity or degree.—vt. To drive or force by inches.

incite, in-sīt', vt. (inciting, incited). To move to action by impulse or influence, to instigate, to encourage.

inclination, in-klin-ā'shon, n. The act of inclining; deviation from a normal direction; a leaning of the mind or will; tendency; bent; bias; predilection liking.

incline, in-klīn', vi. (inclining, inclined). To deviate from a direction regarded as normal, to slope; to be disposed; to have some wish or desire.—vt. To cause to lean or bend towards or away from; to give a leaning to; to dispose.—n. An ascent or descent; a slope.

inclose, in-klōz', vt. (inclosing, inclosed). To shut up or confine on all sides; to environ; to cover with a wrapper or envelope.

inclosure, in-klō'zhūr, n. Act of inclosing, what is inclosed, a space inclosed or fenced; something inclosed with a letter, etc.

inclusive, in-klö'siv a. Inclosing; comprehended in the number or sum; comprehending the stated limit.

incognito, in-kog'ni-tō, pred.a. or adv. In disguise.—n. (fem. being **incognita**). One passing under an assumed name; assumption of a feigned character.

incoherent, in-kō-hēr'ent, a. Not coherent; wanting rational connection, as ideas, language, etc.; rambling and unintelligible.

incombustible in-kom-bust'i-bl, a. Not combustible; that cannot be burned.

income, in'kum, n. Receipts or emoluments regularly coming in from property or employment; annual receipts; revenue.

incomparable, in-kom'pa-ra-bl, a. Not comparable, that admits of no comparison with others; matchless.

incompatibility, in-kom-pat'i-bil"iti, n. State or quality of being incompatible; inconsistency; disposition or temper entirely out of harmony.

incompatible, in-kom-pat'i-bl, a. Not compatible; inconsistent; irreconcilably different; that cannot be made to accord.

incompetence, incompetency, inkom'pē-tens, in-kom'pē-ten-si, n. State or quality of being incompetent, want of suitable faculties, adequate means, or proper qualifications.

incompetent, in-kom'pē-tent, a. Not competent; incapable; wanting legal qualifications, not admissible.

incondite, in-kon'dīt, a. Rude; unpolished, said of literary compositions.

inconsistence, inconsistency, in-konsist'ens, in-kon-sist'en-si, n. The condition or quality of being inconsistent; opposition or disagreement of particulars; self contradiction; incongruity; discrepancy.

inconstant, in-kon'stant, a. Not constant, subject to change of opinion or purpose, not firm in resolution; fickle.

incontinent, in-kon'ti-nent, a. Not continent; not restraining the passions or appetites, unchaste, unable to restrain discharges.

inconvenience, in-kon-vē'ni-ens, n. The quality of being inconvenient annoyance; molestation; trouble disadvantage.—vt. To put to inconvenience; to trouble.

inconvertible, in-kon-vėrt'i-bl, a. Not convertible, that cannot be changed into or exchanged for something else.

incorporate, in-kor'pō-rāt, vt. To form into one body; to unite; to blend; to associate with another whole, as with a government, to form into a legal body or corporation.—vi. To unite; to grow into or coalesce.—a. Incorporated; united m one body.

incorruptible, in-ko-rupt'i-bl, a. Not corruptible; that cannot corrupt or decay; inflexibly just and upright.

increase, in-krēs', vi. (increasing, increased). To become greater; to augment, to advance in any quality, good or bad; to multiply by the production of young.—vt. To make greater or larger, to add to.—n. in'krēs. A growing larger in size, quantity, etc.; augmentation; addition; increment; profit; interest; offspring.

incredulous, in-kred'ū-lus, a. Not credulous; refusing or withholding belief

increment, in'krē-ment, n. Act or process of increasing; increase; increase in the value of real property from adventitious causes.

incubator, in'kū-bā t-ėr, n. One who or that which incubates, an apparatus for hatching eggs by artificial heat.

incubus, in'kū-bus, n., pl. -buses or -bi. A name of nightmare; something that weighs heavily on a person; burden or incumbrance, dead weight.

inculpate, in-kul'pāt, vt. To show to be in

fault; to impute guilt to; to incriminate.

incumbent, in-kum'bent, *a.* Lying on; resting on a person, as duty or obligation.—*n.* One in possession of an ecclesiastical benefice or other office.

indecency, in-dē'sen-si, *n.* The quality of being indecent; what is indecent in language, actions, etc.; indecorum; immodesty.

indelicate, in-de'li-kāt, *a.* Wanting delicacy; offensive to modesty or nice sense of propriety; somewhat immodest.

indemnify, in-dem'ni-fī, *vt.* To make safe from loss or harm; to reimburse or compensate.

indemnity, in-dem'ni-ti, *n.* Security given against loss, damage, or punishment; compensation for loss or injury sustained.

indent, in-dent', *vt.* To notch, to cut into points or inequalities, to bind by indenture.—*n.* A cut or notch; an indentation.

indenture, in-den'tūr, *n.* That which is indented; a deed under seal between two or more parties each having a duplicate.—*vt.* To indent, to bind by indenture.

independence, in-dē-pend'ens, *n.* State of being independent; complete exemption from control, self-reliance; political freedom.

index, in'deks, *n.; pl.* **indexes** or **indices,** in'dek-sez, in'di-sez. Something that points out; the hand ☞ used by printers, etc.; a table of contents, list of books disapproved of by R. Catholic authorities; the forefinger; the figure denoting to what power any mathematical quantity is involved.—*vt.* To provide with an index; to place in an index.

Indian, In'di-an, *a.* Pertaining to India, or to the Indies, East or West pertaining to the aborigines of America.

indicative, in-dik'a-tiv, *a.* That serves to point out, serving as an indication; designating a mood of the verb that declares directly or asks questions.—*n.* The indicative mood.

indigestion, in-di-jest'yon, *n.* Incapability of or difficulty in digesting; dyspepsia.

indignation, in-dig-nā'shon, *n.* A feeling of displeasure at what is unworthy or base; anger, mingled with contempt, disgust, or abhorrence; violent displeasure.

indigo, in 'di-go, *n.* A blue vegetable dye, from India and other places the leguminous plant that produces the dye.

indirect, in-di-rekt', *a.* Not direct; circuitous; not tending directly to a purpose or end, not straightforward; not resulting directly.

indissoluble, in-dis'sō-lū-bl, *a.* Not capable of being dissolved, perpetually binding or obligatory; not to be broken.

indistinct, in-dis-tingkt', *n.* Not distinct; faint; confused; imperfect or dim.

individual, in-di-vid'ū-al, *a.* Subsisting as one indivisible entity; pertaining to one only, peculiar to a single person or thing.—*n.* A being or thing forming one of its kind, a person.

indoor, in'dōr, *a.* Being within doors, being within the house.

indoors, in'dorz, *adv.* Within doors, inside a house.

indubitable, in-dū'bit-a-bl, *a.* Not to be doubted, too plain to admit of doubt, evident.

induce, in-dūs', *vt.* (inducing, induced). To lead by persuasion or argument; to prevail on; to actuate, to produce or cause.

induct, in-dukt', *vt.* To lead or bring into; to put in possession of an ecclesiastical living or office, with customary ceremonies.

indulge, in-dulj', *vt.* (indulging, indulged). To give free course to, to gratify by compliance, to humor to excess.—*vi.* To indulge oneself; to practice indulgence.

indulgence, in-dulj'ens, *n.* The act or practice of indulging; a favor; intemperance, gratification of desire; tolerance; remission of the penance attached to certain sins.

indurate, in'dū-rāt, *vi.* To grow hard.—*vt.* To make hard; to deprove of sensibility.

industrious, in-dus'tri-us, *a.* Given to or characterized by industry; diligent, active.

industry, in'dus-tri, *n.* Habitual diligence steady attention to business; the industrial arts generally. or any one of them; manufacture; trade.

ineptitude, in-ept'i-tū d *n.* Condition or quality of being inept; unfitness, silliness.

inequality, in-ė-kwol'i-ti, *n.* Condition of being unequal; want of equality, an elevation or depression in a surface; diversity.

inert, in-ėrt', *a.* Destitute of the power of moving itself, or of active resistance to motion impressed; lifeless; sluggish; inactive.

inertia, in-ėr'shi-a, *n.* Passiveness inactivity; the property of matter by which it tends to retain its state of rest or of uniform rectilinear motion.

inexorable, in-eks'ōr-a-bl, *a*. Not to be persuaded by entreaty or prayer; unbending; unrelenting; implacable.

inexpedient, in-eks-pē'di-ent, *a*. Not expedient; not advisable or judicious.

inexplicable, in-eks'pli-ka-bl, *a*. That cannot be explained or interpreted; unaccountable; mysterious.

infamous, in'fa-mus, *a*. Notoriously vile; detestable, branded with infamy.

infamy, in'fa-mi, *n*. Total loss of reputation; public disgrace; qualities detested and despised; extreme vileness.

infancy, in'fan-si, *n*. State of being an infant, early childhood, period from birth to the age of twenty-one; first age of anything.

infant, in'fant, *n*. A very young child; one under twenty-one years of age.—*a*. Pertaining to infants.

infatuate, in-fa'tū-āt, *vt*. To make foolish; to inspire with an extravagant passion.

infatuation, in-fa'tū- ā"shon, *n*. Act of infatuating, state of being infatuated; foolish passion.

inferior, in-fē'ri-ėr, *a*. Lower in place, station, age, value, etc., subordinate.—*n*. A person lower in rank, importance, etc.

infernal, in-fėr 'nal, *a*. Pertaining to the lower regions or hell; very wicked and detestable, diabolical.—**infernal machine,** an explosive apparatus contrived for assassination or other mischief.

infidel, in'fi-del, *n*. A disbeliever; a skeptic, one who does not believe in God or in Christianity.—*a*. Unbelieving, skeptical.

infinitive, in-fin'it-iv, *a*. Designating a mood of the verb which expresses action without limitation of person or number, as, to love.— *n*. The infinitive mood.

infinity, in-fin'i-ti, *n*. State or quality of being infinite, unlimited extent of time, space, quantity, etc.; immensity.

infirmary, in-fėrm'a-ri *n*. A place where the sick and injured are nursed, a hospital.

infirmity, in-fėrm'i-ti, *n*. State of being infirm; unsound state of the body; weakness of mind or resolution; failing; malady.

inflame, in-flām', *vt*. To set on fire; to kindle; to excite or increase, to incense; to make morbidly red and swollen.—*vi*. To grow hot, angry, and painful, to take fire.

inflammation, in-flam-ā'shon, *n*. Act of inflaming, state of being inflamed; a redness and swelling attended with heat, pain, and feverish symptoms.

inflection, in-flek'shon, *n*. Act of inflecting; state of being inflected; grammatical variation of nouns verbs, etc.; modulation of the voice, deflection or diffraction.

inflexibility, in-fleks'i-bil"i-ti *n*. Firmness of purpose; unbending pertinacity or obstinacy.

inflexible, in-fleks'i-bl, *a*. That cannot be bent; firm in purpose; pertinacious, inexorable.

inflow, in'flō, *n*. The act of flowing in or into; that which flows in; influx.

influence, in'flū-ens, *n*. Agency or power serving to affect, modify, etc.; sway; effect; acknowledged ascendency with people in power.—*vt*. To exercise influence on, to bias, to sway.

informal, in-form'al, *a*. Not in the usual form or mode, not with the official or customary forms; without ceremony.

information. in-form-ā'shon, *n*. The act of informing; intelligence communicated or gathered; a charge or accusation before a magistrate.

infringe, in-frinj', *vt*. (infringing, infringed) To break, as laws, agreements, etc., to violate, to contravene.— *vi*. To encroach (with *on* or *upon*).

infuse, in-fūz', *vt*. (infusing, in-fused). To pour in, as a liquid, to instill, as principles, to steep in liquor without boiling, in order to extract solutions, etc.

infusion, in-fū'zhon, *n*. Act or process of infusing; that which is infused; liquor obtained by infusing or steeping.

ingenious, in-jē'ni-us, *a*. Possessed of cleverness or ability, apt in contriving; contrived with ingenuity; witty or well conceived.

ingenuity, in-jen-ū'i-ti, *n*. Quality of being ingenious; ready invention; skill in contrivance.

ingredient, in-grē'di-ent, *n*. That which is a component part of any mixture; an element, component, or constituent.

inhabit, in-ha'bit, *vt*. To live or dwell in, to occupy as a place of settled resident.—*vi*. To dwell, to live, to abide.

inherit, in-he'rit, vt. To come into possession of as an heir, to receive by nature from a progenitor, to hold as belonging to one's lot.—*vi*. To take or have possession of property.

inheritance, in-he'rit-ans, *n*. Act of inheriting, that which is or may be inherited; what falls to one's lot; possession.

inhospitable, in-hos'pit-a-bl, *a.* Not hospitable; incapable of being satisfied or appeased.

inscribe, in-skrīb', *vt.* (inscribing inscribed). To write down, to imprint on, as on the memory; to address or dedicate, to mark with letters or words; to draw a figure within another.

inscrutable, in-skrö'ta-bl, *a.* Unsearchable, that cannot be penetrated or understood by human reason.

insect, in'sekt, *n.* One of those small animals that have three divisions of the body—head, thorax, and abdomen—and usually three pairs of legs and two pairs of wings, as flies, etc.; a puny, contemptible person.—*a.* Pertaining to insects; like an insect; mean.

insensible, in-sens'i-bl *a.* Not perceived or perceptible by the senses; void of feeling; unfeeling; callous, indifferent.

inseparable, in-sep'a-ra-bl, *a.* Not separable; not to be parted; always together.

insert, in-sért', *vt.* To put, bring, or set in; to thrust in; to set in or among.

insertion, in-sér'shon, *n.* Act of inserting; thing inserted; place or mode of attachment of a part or organ to its support.

inside, in'sīd, *n.* The interior side or part of a thing.—*a.* Interior; internal.—*prep.* In the interior of; within.

insinuate, in-sin'u-āt, *vt.* To introduce by windings or gently; to work gradually into favor; to introduce by gentle or artful means, to hint.—*vi.* To creep or wind; to make an insinuation, to wheedle.

insolvent, in-sol'vent, *a.* Not solvent; not having money, etc., sufficient to pay debts.—*n.* One unable to pay his debts.

inspiration, in-spi-rā'shon *n.* The act of inspiring; the drawing in of breath, the divine influence by which the sacred writers were instructed; influence emanating from any object; the state of being inspired, something conveyed to the mind when under extraordinary influence.

inspire, in-spīr', *vt.* (inspiring, inspired). To breathe in; to breathe into, to communicate divine instructions to; to infuse ideas or poetic spirit into; to animate in general.—*vi.* To draw in breath; to inhale air into the lungs.

instant, in'stant, *a.* Pressing or urgent; immediate; making no delay; present or current.—*n.* A moment.

instill, in-stil', *vt.* (instilling, instilled). To pour in, as by drops; to infuse by degrees; to insinuate imperceptibly.

instinct, in'stingkt, *n.* Spontaneous or natural impulse the knowledge and skill which animals have without experience; intuitive feeling.—*a.* in-stingkt'. Animated or stimulated from within; inspired.

institute, in'sti-tūt, *vt.* To set up or establish; to found; to begin; to appoint to an office; to invest with a benefice.—*n.* That which is instituted, established law, principle, a literary or scientific body; an institution, *pl.* a book of elements or principles.

insulate, in'sū-lāt, *vt.* To make into an island, to detach, to separate as an electrified body, by interposition of non-conductors.

insulator, in 'sū-lāt-ér, *n.* One who or that which insulates; a body that interrupts the communication of electricity; non-conductor.

insulin, ins'ū-lin, *n.* A substance extracted from the pancreas of animals, and found beneficial in diabetes.

insult, in'sult, *n.* Any gross affront or indignity; act or speech of insolence or contempt.—*vt.* in-sult'. To treat with insult or insolence.—*vi.* To behave with insolent triumph.

insure, in-shör', *vt.* (insuring, insured). To make sure; to contract for the receipt of a certain sum in the event of loss, death, etc.

insurgent, in-sér'jent, *a.* Rising in opposition to lawful authority, rebellious.—*n.* One who rises in opposition to authority.

integral, in'ti-gral, *a.* Whole; forming a necessary part of a whole not fractional.—*n.* A whole; an entire thing.

intelligent, in-tel'i-jent, *a.* Endowed with the faculty of understanding or reason; endowed with a good intellect well informed.

intelligible, in-tel'i-ji-bl, *a.* Capable of being understood; comprehensible; clear.

intemperate, in-tem'pér-ēt, *a.* Not temperate; addicted to an excessive use of alcoholic liquors, excessive or immoderate.—*n.* One not temperate.

intercede, in-tér-sēd', *vi.* (interceding, interceded). To mediate; to plead in favor of one; to make intercession.

intercept, in-tér-sept', *vt.* To take or seize on by the way; to stop on its passage; to obstruct the progress of; to cut or shut off.

intercession, in-tẻr-se'shon, *n*. Act of interceding; mediation; prayer or solicitation to one party in favor of another.

interest, in'tẻr-est, *vt*. To concern; to engage the attention of.—*n*. Concern or regard, advantage, profit profit per cent from money lent or invested influence with a person.

interfere, in-ter-fẻr', *vi*. (interfering, interfered). To clash; to interpose, to take a part in the concerns of others.

interior, in-tẻ'ri-ẻr, *a*. Internal, being within; inland.—*n*. The inner part of a thing, the inside; the inland part of a country, etc.

interlude, in'tẻr-lūd, *n*. A short entertainment between the acts of a play, or between the play and the afterpiece; a piece of music between certain more important passages.

interminable, in-tẻr'min-a-bl, *a*. Admitting no limit; boundless; endless.

international, in-tẻr-na'shon-al, *a*. Relating to or mutually affecting nations, regulating the mutual intercourse between nations.

interpretation, in-tẻr'pret-ā"shon *n*. Act of interpreting; explanation, representation of a character on the stage.

interregnum, in-tẻr-reg'num, *n*. The time between reigns; intermission or break in succession.

interrogate, in-te'rō-gāt, *vt*. To question; to examine by asking questions.

interrogation, in-te'rō-gā"shon, *n*. Act of interrogating; question put; a sign that marks a question, thus (?).

interrupt, in-tẻr-rupt', *vt*. To break in upon the progress of; to cause to stop in speaking.

interstice, in-tẻrs'tis, *n*. A narrow space between things closely set; a chink.

interval, in'tẻr-val, *n*. A space between things; amount of separation between ranks, degrees, etc.; difference in gravity or acuteness between sounds.

interview, in'tẻr-vū, *n*. A meeting between persons; a conference.— *vt*. To have an interview with to get information for publication.

interweave, in-tẻr-wẻv', *vt*. To weave together; to unite intimately; to interlace.

intestate, in-test'āt, *a*. Dying without having made a will; not disposed of by will.—*n*. A person who dies without making a will.

intestine, in-tes'tῐn, *a*. Internal; domestic; not foreign. *n*. The canal extending from the stomach to the anus; *pl*. entrails or viscera in general.

intimate, in'ti-māt, *a*. Inward or internal; close in friendship; familiar, close.—*n*. An intimate or familiar friend.—*vt*. (intimating, intimated). To hint or indicate; to announce.

intolerable, in-tol'ẻr-a-bl, *a*. That cannot be borne, unendurable; insufferable.

intolerant, in-tol'ẻr-ant, *a*. That cannot bear, not enduring difference of opinion or worship; refusing to tolerate others.

intone, in-tōn', *vi*. To use a musical monotone in pronouncing. *vt*. To pronounce with a musical tone; to chant.

intoxicate, in-toks'i-kāt, *vt*. To make drunk; to elate to enthusiasm or madness.—*vi*. To cause intoxication.

intrigue, in-trēg', *n*. An underhand plot or scheme, plot of a play, etc.; an illicit intimacy between a man and woman.— *vi*. (intriguing, intrigued). To engage in an intrigue; to carry on forbidden love.

intrinsic, **intrinsical**, in-trin'sik, intrin'sik-al, *a*. Being within; inherent; essential.

introduce, in-trō-dūs', *vt*. To lead or bring in; to insert; to bring to be acquainted; to present; to make known, to import; to bring before the public.

introduction, in-trō-duk'shon, *n*. Act of introducing, act of making persons known to each other; act of bringing something into notice; a preliminary discourse.

introspection, in-trō-spek'shon, *n*. The act of looking inwardly; examination of one's own thoughts or feelings.

intrude, in-trŏd', *vi*. (intruding, intruded). to thrust oneself in, to force an entry or way in without permission, right, or invitation; to encroach.—*vt*. To thrust in.

intuition, in-tū-i'shon, *n*. A looking on; direct apprehension of a truth without reasoning.

intuitive, in-tū'it-iv, *a*. Perceived by the mind immediately without reasoning; based on intuition; self-evident.

invalid, in'va-lēd, *n*. One weak or infirm; a person disabled for active service.—*a*. In ill health; infirm disabled.—*vt*. To render an invalid; to enroll on the list of invalids.

invention, in-ven'shon, *n*. Act of inventing, contrivance of that which did not before exist; device; power of inventing; ingenuity; faculty by which an author produces plots, etc.

inventory, in'ven-to-ri, *n.* An account of catalogue of the goods and chattels of a deceased person; a catalogue of particular things.— *vt.* to make an inventory of.

inverse, in'vèrs or in-ve˙ rs', *a.* Opposite in order or relation; inverted

invest, in-vest', *vt.* To clothe, to array, to clothe with office or authority; to endow; to besiege; to lay out as money in some species of property.—*vi.* To make an investment.

investigate, in-ves'ti-gāt, *vt.* To search into, to make careful examination of.

invincible, in-vin'si-bl, *a.* Not to be conquered or overcome, insurmountable.—*n.* One who is invincible.

invitation, in-vi-tā'shon, *n.* Act of inviting; bidding to an entertainment, etc.

invite, in-vīt', *vt.* (inviting, invited). To ask to do something; to ask to an entertainment, etc., to allure or attract.—*vi.* To give invitation; to allure.

involute, in'vō-lūt, *n.* A curve traced by any point of a tense string when it is unwound from a given curve.—*a.* Involved; rolled inward from the edges.

involve, in-volv', *vt.* (involving, involved). To roll up; to envelop to imply; to include; to implicate; to complicate, in algebra, etc., to raise a quantity to any assigned power.

inward, in'wèrd, *a.* Internal; being within; intimate; in the mind, soul, or feelings.—*adv.* Toward the inside; into the mind.—*n.pl.* The inner parts of an animal; the viscera.

iron, ī'ern, *n.* The most common and useful metal, an instrument made of iron; a utensil for smoothing cloth, *pl.* fetters; chains, handcuffs.—*a.* Made of iron; consisting of or like iron, harsh, severe, binding fast, vigorous; inflexible.—*vt.* To smooth with an iron; to fetter; to furnish or arm with iron.

irony, ī'ron-i, *n.* A mode of speech which expresses a sense contrary to that conveyed by the words; a subtle kind of sarcasm.

irradiation, ir-rā'di-ā"shon. *n.* Act of irradiating; illumination; apparent enlargement of an object strongly illuminated.

irregular, ir-re'gū-lèr, *a.* Not regular; not according to rule or custom; anomalous, vicious, crooked variable; deviating from the common rules in its inflections.—*n.* A soldier not in regular service.

irrepressible, ir-rē-pres'i-bl, *a.* Not repressible; incapable of being repressed.

irreproachable, ir-rē-prōch'a-bl, *a.* Incapable of being reproached upright; faultless.

irresistible, ir-rē -zist'i-bl, *a.* Not resistible; that cannot be resisted; resistless.

irrigate, ir'ri-gāt, *vt.* To bedew or sprinkle; to water by means of channels or streams.

irritant, ir'rit-ant, *a.* Irritating, producing inflammation.—*n.* That which irritates; a medical application that causes pain or heat.

irritation, ir-rit-ā'shon, *n.* Act of irritating; exasperation, annoyance; vital action in muscles or organs caused by some stimulus.

isolationist, ī s-ō-lā'shon-ist, *n.* One who favors keeping aloof from other countries politically.

isometric, isometrical, ī-sō-met'rik, ī-sō-met'rik-al, *a.* Pertaining to or characterized by equality of measure.

isosceles, ī-sos'e-lēz, *a.* Having two legs or sides only that are equal (an *isosceles* triangle).

issue, ish'ū, *n.* The act of passing or flowing out; delivery; quantity issued at one time, event; consequence; progeny; offspring; an artificial ulcer to promote a secretion of pus; matter depending in a lawsuit.—*vi.* (issuing, issued). To pass or flow out; to proceed, to spring to grow or accrue; to come to an issue in law, to terminate.—*vt.* To send out; to put into circulation, to deliver for use

isthmus, ist'mus or is'mus, *n.* A neck of land connecting two much larger portions.

italic, i-ta'lik, *a.* Pertaining to Italy the name of a printing type sloping towards the right.—*n.* An italic letter or type.

itch, ich, *n.* A sensation in the skin causing a desire to scratch, a constant teasing desire; —*vi.* To feel an itch; to have a teasing sensation impelling to something.

itinerant, i- or ī-tin'èr-ant, *a.* Passing or travelling from place to place; not settled.—*n.* One who travels from place to place.

itinerary, i- or ī-tin'èr-a-ri, *n.* A work containing notices of places of a particular line of road; a travel route; plan of a tour.—*a.* Travelling; pertaining to a journey.

ivory, ī'vo-ri, *n.* The substance composing the tusks of the elephants, etc. something made of ivory.—*a.* Consisting or made of ivory.

I

J

jabber, jab'ẻr, *vi.* To gabble; to talk rapidly or indistinctly; to chatter.*vt* To utter rapidly with confused sounds.—*n.* Rapid and indistinct talk.

jacket, jak'et, *n.* A short outer garment; a casing of cloth, felt, wood etc.

jag, jäg, *vt.* (jagging, jagged). To cut into notches or teeth; to notch.—*n.* A notch; a ragged protuberance.

jaguar, ja-gwär', *n.* The American tiger, a spotted carnivorous animal, the most formidable feline quadruped of the New World.

jail, jāl, *n.* A prison; place of confinement.

jailer, jailor, jāl'er, *n.* The keeper of a jail.

jam, jam, *n.* A conserve of fruits boiled with sugar and water.—*vt.* (jamming, jammed). To crowd; to squeeze tight, to wedge in.

jargon, jär'gon, *n.* Confused, unintelligible talk; gibberish; phraseology peculiar to a sect, profession, etc.; a variety of zircon.

jasmine, jas'min, *n.* A fragrant shrub, bearing white or yellow flowers.

jaunt, jänt, *vi.* To ramble here and there; to make an excursion.—*n.* A trip; a tour; an excursion; a ramble.

jaunty, jän'ti, *a.* Gay and easy in manner or actions; airy; sprightly; showy.

javelin, jav'lin, *n.* A light spear thrown from the hand.

jaw, jä, *n.* The bones of the mouth in which the teeth are fixed.

jazz, jaz, *n.* Syncopated or rag-time music, originally of Negro origin.

Jehovah, jē-hō'va, *n.* An old Hebrew name of the Supreme Being.

jelly, je'li, *n.* Matter in a glutinous state; the thickened juice of fruit boiled with sugar, transparent matter obtained from animal substances by boiling.—*vi.* To become a jelly.

jelly-fish, jel'i-fish, *n.* A gelatinous marine animal.

jeopardy, je'pẻrd-i, *n.* Hazard; risk exposure to death, loss, or injury.

Jesus, jē'zus, *n.* The Savior of men; Christ.

jettison, jet'i-son, *n.* Jetsam.—*vt.* To throw overboard

Jew, jū, *n.* A Hebrew or Israelite.

jewel, jū'el, *n.* A personal ornament of precious stones, a precious stone.—*vt.*

(jewelling, jewelled). To adorn with jewels.

jilt, jilt, *n.* A woman who gives her lover hopes and capriciously disappoints him.—*vt.* To deceive in love.—*vi.* To play the jilt.

jingle, jing'gl, *vi.* and *t.* (jingling, jingled). To sound with a tinkling metallic sound, to clink.—*n.* A rattling or clinking sound.

jockey, jok'i, *n.* A man who rides horses in a race; a dealer in horses; one who takes undue advantage in trade.—*vt.* To play the jockey to; to ride in a race; to jostle by riding against; to cheat.

joiner, join'ẻr, *n.* A mechanic who does the wood-work of houses; a carpenter.

joist, joist, *n.* One of the pieces of timber to which the boards of a floor or the laths of a ceiling are nailed.—*vt.* To fit with joists.

joke, jōk, *n.* A jest; something said to excite a laugh, raillery, what is not in earnest.—*vi.* (joking, joked). To jest; to sport.—*vt.* To cast jokes at; to rally.

jot, jot, *n.* An iota; a tittle.—*vt.* (jotting, jotted). To set down in writing.

journal, jẻr'nal, *n.* A diary; an account of daily transactions, or the book containing such; a daily or periodical paper, a narrative of the transactions of a society, etc.; that part of an axle which moves in the bearings.

journalist, jẻr'nal-ist, *n.* The writer of a journal; a newspaper editor or contributor.

journey, jẻr'ni, *n.* A traveling from one place to another; tour; excursion; distance traveled.—*vi.* To travel from place to place.

Judaism, jū'dā-izm, *n.* The religious doctrines and rites of the Jews, conformity to the Jewish rites and ceremonies.

Judaize, jū'da-iz, *vi.* and *t.* To conform to the religious doctrines and rites of the Jews.

Judas, jū'das, *n.* A treacherous person.

judgment, juj'ment, *n.* Act of judging; good sense; discernment; opinion or estimate; mental faculty by which man ascertains the relations between ideas; sentence pronounced, a calamity regarded as a punishment of sin; final trial of the human race.

jug, jug, *n.* A vessel for liquors, generally with a handle; a mug; a pitcher.—*vt.* (jugging, jugged). To put in a jug; to cook by Putting into a jug, and this into boiling water (*jugged* hare).

jumble, jum'bl, *vt.* (jumbling, jumbled). To mix in a confused mass.—*vi.* To meet, mix, or unite in a confused manner.—*n.* Confused mass disorder, confusion.

jump, jump, *vi.* To leap; to skip; to spring; to agree, tally, coincide.—*vt.* To pass over by a leap; to pass over hastily.—*n.* Act of jumping; leap; spring; bound.

junction, jungk'shon, *n.* Act or operation of joining; state of being joined; point of union; place where railways meet.

juncture, jungk'tūr, *n.* A joining or uniting; line or point of joining; point of time; point rendered critical by circumstances.

June, jūn, *n* The sixth month of the year.

jungle, jung'gl, *n.* Land covered with trees, brushwood, etc., or coarse, reedy vegetation.

junior, jū'ni-ėr, *a.* Younger, later or lower in office or rank.—*n.* A per son younger than another or lower in standing.

juniper, jū'ni-pėr, *n.* A coniferous shrub, the berries of which are used to flavor gin.

junket, jung'ket, *n.* Curds mixed with cream, sweetened and flavored, a sweetmeat, a feast.—*vi.* and *t.* To feast.

juridical, jū-rid'ik-al, *a.* Relating to the administration of justice or to a judge.

jurisdiction, jū-ris-dik'shon, *n.* Judicial power, right of exercising authority; district within which power may be exercised.

jurisprudence, jū-ris-prö'dens, *n.* The science of law; the knowledge of the laws, customs, and rights of men necessary for the due administration of justice.

jurist, jū'rist, *n.* A man who professes the science of law; one versed in the law, or more particularly, in the civil law.

just, just, *a.* Right; acting rightly; upright, impartial, fair, due, merited; exact.—*adv.* Exactly, precisely; near or nearly; almost; merely; barely.

justice, jus'tis, *n.* Quality of being just, rectitude, propriety, impartiality; fairness; just treatment; merited reward or punishment, a judge holding a special office.

J

K

kaleidoscope, ka-lī'dos-kōp, *n*. An optical instrument which exhibits an endless variety of colored figures.

kangaroo, kang'ga-rö, *n*. An Australian marsupial quadruped that moves forward by leaps.

keel, kēl, *n*. The principal timber in a ship, extending from stem to stern at the bottom; the corresponding part in iron vessels; the whole ship, something resembling a keel, a coal-barge.—*vi*. To capsize.

keen, kēn, *a*. Acute of mind; shrewd; sharp; eager; piercing; severe, bitter.

keep, kēp, *vt*. (keeping, kept). To hold, to preserve; to guard; to detain; to attend to; to continue any state, course, or action; to obey; to perform; to observe or solemnize; to confine to one's own knowledge; not to betray; to have in pay.—*vi*. To endure; not to perish or be impaired.—*n*. Care; guard; sustenance; a donjon or strong tower.

kettle, ket'l, *n*. A vessel of iron or other metal, used for heating and boiling water, etc.

key, kē, *n*. An instrument for shutting or opening a lock; a little lever by which certain musical instruments are played on by the fingers; fundamental tone in a piece of music, that which serves to explain a cipher, etc.—*vt*. To furnish or fasten with a key.

kick, kik, *vt*. To strike with the foot; to strike in recoiling, as a gun.—*vi*. To strike with the foot or feet; to manifest opposition to restraint; to recoil.—*n*. A blow with the foot or feet recoil of a firearm.

kid, kid, *n*. A young goat; leather made from its skin, a small wooden tub.—*vt*. (kidding, kidded). To bring forth a kid.

kidnap, kid'nap, *vt*. (kidnapping, kidnapped). To steal or forcibly abduct a human being.

kidney, kid'ni, *n*. Either of the two glands which secret the urine; sort or character.

kill, kil, *vt*. To deprive of life; to slay; to slaughter for food; to deaden (pain), to overpower.

kiln, kil, *n*. A fabric of brick or stone, which may be heated to harden or dry anything.

kin, kin, *n*. Race; family, consanguinity or affinity, kindred.—*a*. Kindred; congenial.

kind, kīnd, *n*. Race; genus; variety; nature, character.—**In kind**, to pay with produce or commodities.—*a*. Humane, having tenderness or goodness of nature; benevolent, friendly.

kindergarten, kin'd'ér-gär-tn, *n*. An infants' school in which amusements are systematically combined with instruction.

kindle, kin'dl, *vt*. (kindling, kindled). To set on fire; to light; to rouse, to excite to action.—*vi*. To take fire; to be roused or exasperated.

kindly, kīnd'li, *a*. Of a kind disposition, congenial, benevolent mild.—*adv*. In a kind manner; favorably.

kink, kingk, *n*. A twist in a rope or thread, a crotchet.—*vi*. To twist or run into knots.

kinsfolk kinz'fölk *n*. People of the same kin; kindred; relations.

kinsman, kinz'man, *n*. A man of the same kin, a relative.

kipper, kip'ér, *n*. A salmon at the spawning season, a fish split open, salted, and dried or smoked.—*vt*. To cure (fish) by splitting open, salting, and drying.

kismet, kis'met, *n*. Fate or destiny.

kiss, kis, *vi*. To touch with the lips to caress by joining lips; to touch gently.—*vi*. To join lips; to come in slight contact.—*n*. A salute given with the lips.

kitchen, ki'chen, *n*. The room of a house appropriated to cooking.

kitchen-garden, ki'chen-gär-dn, *n*. A garden for raising vegetables for the table.

kite, kīt, *n*. A bird of the falcon family; a light frame of wood and paper constructed for flying in the air.

kith, kith, *n*. Relatives or friends collectively.

kitten, kit'n, *n*. A young cat.—*vi*. To bring forth young, as a cat.

kleptomania, klep-tō-mā'ni-a, *n*. An irresistible mania for pilfering

knack, nak, *n*. Facility of performance; dexterity.

knap, nap, *vt*. (knapping, knapped). To break short (as flints); to snap; to bite off.—*n*. A short sharp noise; a snap.

knapsack, nap'sak, *n*. A bag for necessaries borne on the back by soldiers, etc.

knave, nāv, *n*. A petty rascal; a dishonest man, a card with a soldier or servant on it.

knead, nēd, *vt*. To work into a mass or suitable consistency for bread, etc.

knee, nē, *n.* The joint connecting the two principal parts of the leg a similar joint; piece of bent timber or iron used in a ship, etc

knife, nīf, *n.;* pl. **knives,** nīvz. A cutting instrument consisting of a blade attached to a handle, cutting part of a machine.

knob, nob, *a.* A hard protuberance; a boss; a round ball at the end of anything.

knock, nok, *vt.* To strike with something thick or heavy; to strike against; to clash.—*vi.* To strike.—*n.* A stroke, a blow, a rap.

knocker, nok'ėr, *n.* One who knocks; something on a door for knocking.

knoll, nōl, *n.* A little round hill; ringing of a bell, knell.—*vt.* and *i.* To sound, as a bell.

knot, not, *n.* A complication of threads or cords; a tie, ornamental bunch of ribbon, etc.; hard protuberant joint of a plant, a knob bunch; group; a difficult question a nautical mile (= 1.151 ordinary mile).— *vt.* (knotting, knotted). To tie in a knot; to unite closely.—*vi.* To become knotted, to knit knots.

know, nō, *vt.* (pret. knew, pp. known). To perceive with certainty, to understand, to be aware of; to distinguish, to be acquainted with; to have experience of—*vi.* To have knowledge; not to be doubtful.

knowledge, nol'ej, *n.* The result or condition of knowing; clear perception; learning; information; skill; acquaintance.

K

L

label, lā'bel, *n*. A slip of paper, etc. affixed to something and stating name, contents, etc., a slip affixed to deeds to hold the seal.—*vt*. (labeling, labeled). To affix a label to.

labor, lā'bėr, *n*. Exertion, physical or mental, toil, work done or to be done; laborers in the aggregate the pangs and efforts of childbirth.—*vi*. To engage in labor, to work; to proceed with difficulty, to be burdened.—*vt*. To cultivate; to prosecute with effort.

laborer, lā'bėr-ėr, *n*. One who labors; a man who does work that requires little skill, as distinguished from an artisan.

labyrinth, lab'i-rinth, *n*. A place full of intricacies, a maze, an inexplicable difficulty; a part of the internal ear

lace, lās, *n*. A cord used for fastening boots, etc., ornamental cord or braid; a delicate fabric of interlacing threads.—*vt*. (lacing, laced). To fasten with a lace; to adorn with lace; to interlace; to mingle in small quantity.

lack, lak, *vt*. To want; to be without; to need, to require.—*vi*. To be in want—*n*. Want; deficiency; need; failure.

ladder, lad'er, *n*. An article of wood rope, etc., consisting of two long side-pieces connected by crosspieces forming steps; means of rising to mienence; vertical flaw in stocking, etc.

lag, lag, *a*. Coming behind, sluggish; tardy.—*n*. Quantity of retardation of some movement.—*vi*. (lagging, lagged). To loiter, tarry.

laity, lā'i-ti, *n*. The people, as distinguished from the clergy; non-professional people.

lake, lāk, *n*. A body of water wholly surrounded by land; a pigment of earthy substance with red (or other) coloring matter.

lamb, lam, *n*. The young of the sheep one as gentle or innocent as a iamb.—*vi*. To bring forth young, as sheep.

lame, lām, *a*. Crippled in a limb or limbs; disabled; limping; defective, not satisfactory, not smooth.—*vt*. (laming, lamed). To make lame; to render imperfect and unsound.

lamp, lamp, *n*. A vessel for containing oil to be burned by means of a wick, any contrivance for supply artificial light.

lampoon, lam-pön', *n*. A scurrilous or personal satire in writing, a satiric attack.—*vt*. To write a lampoon against.

lamprey, lam'prā, *n*. The name of eel-like, scaleless fishes with suctorial mouths, inhabiting fresh and salt waters.

lance, lans, *n*. A weapon consisting of a long shaft with a sharp-pointed head, a long spear.—*vt*. (lancing, lanced). To pierce with a lance, to open with a lancet.

land, land, *n*. The solid matter which constitutes the fixed part of the surface of the globe; soil; estate, country, people of a country or region.—*vt*. and *i*. To set or go on the land, to disembark.

landscape, land'skāp, *n*. A portion of land which the eye can comprehend in a single view; a country scene; picture representing a piece of country.

landslip, landslide, land'slip, land'slīd, *n*. A portion of a hill which slips down, the sliding down of a piece of land.

land-surveying, land'sėr-vā-ing, *n*. Act of surveying land, art of determining the boundaries and extent of land.

languid, lang'gwid, *a*. Wanting energy; listless; dull or heavy; sluggish.

languish, lang'gwish, *vi*. To be or become faint, feeble or spiritless to fade; to sink under sorrow or any continued passion, to look with tenderness.

languor, lang'gér, lang'gwer, *n*. Languidness; lassitude; a listless or dreamy state.

lanolin, lan'ō-lin, *n*. A greasy substance obtained from unwashed wool, used as an ointment.

lantern, lan'tėrn, *n*. A case in which a light is carried; part of a lighthouse in which is the light; erection on the top of a dome, etc., to give light, a tower with the interior open to view.—*vt*. To provide with a lantern.

lanyard, lan'yärd, *n*. A short piece of rope or line, used in ships.

lap, lap, *n*. The loose lower part of a garment; the clothes on the knees of a person when sitting; the knees in this position part of a thing that covers another; single round of a course in races; a lick, as with the tongue, sound as of water rippling on the beach.—*vt*. (lapping, lapped). To lap; to infold, to lick up, to wash gently against.—*vi*. To lie or be turned over; to lick up food; to ripple gently.

larceny, lär'se ni, *n*. Theft of goods or personal property.

lard, lärd, *n*. The fat of swine, after being melted and separated from the flesh.—*vt*. To apply lard to; to fatten, to stuff with bacon, to interlard.

large, lärj, *a*. Great in size, number etc., not small, copious, big; bulky; wide.— **At large**, without restraint, with all details.

lariat, lä'ri-at. *n*. The lasso a long cord or thong of leather with a noose used in catching wild horses, etc.

larva, lär'va, *n*., pl. **larvae**. An insect in the caterpillar or grub state.

larynx, la'ringks, *n*., pl. **larynxes, larynges**, la'ringks-ez, la-rin'jēz; The upper part of the windpipe, a cartilaginous cavity serving to modulate the sound of the voice.

lascivious, las-si'vi-us, *a*. Wanton; lewd; lustful.

lash, lash, *n*. The thong of a whip, a whip; a stroke with a whip; a stroke of satire; a cutting remark.—*vt*. To strike with a lash, to satirize; to dash against, as waves; to tie with a rope or cord.— *vi*. To ply the whip; to strike at.

lasso, las'sō, *n*. A rope with a running noose, used for catching wild horses, etc.—*vt*. To catch with a lasso.

last, läst, *a*. That comes after all the others; latest, final, next before the present; utmost.—*adv*. The last time in conclusion.—*vi*. To continue in time; to endure; not to decay or perish.—*vt*. To form on or by a last.—*n*. A mold of the foot on which boots are formed; a weight of 4000 lbs.

late, lāt, *a*. Coming after the usual time; slow; not early; existing not long ago, but not now, deceased recent; modern; last or recently in any place, office, etc.—*adv*. At a late time or period; recently.

Latin, la'tin, *a*. Pertaining to the Latins, a people of Latium, in Italy; Roman.—*n*. The language of the ancient Romans

latitude, la'ti-tūd, *n*. Breadth; width; extent from side to side scope, laxity; distance north or south of the equator, measured on a meridian; distance of a star north or south of the ecliptic.

laud, läd, *n*. Praise; a hymn of praise; *pl*. a service of the church comprising psalms of praise.—*vt*. To praise; to celebrate.

laudanum, lä'da-num, *n*. Opium prepared in spirit of wine; tincture of opium.

laugh, läf, *vi*. To make the involuntary noise which sudden merriment excites; to treat with some contempt; to appear gay, bright, or brilliant.—*vt*. To express by laughing; to affect or effect by laughter.—*n*. The act of laughing; short fit of laughing.

laughter, läf'tèr, *n*. Act or sound of laughing, expression of mirth peculiar to man

launch, länsh, *vt*. To throw, to cause to slide into the water, to put out into another sphere of duty, etc. —*vi*. To glide, as a ship into the water, to enter on a new field of activity, to expatiate in language.—*n*. Act of launching the largest boat carried by a man-of-war.

laundry, län'dri, *n*. Place where clothes are washed and dressed.

lavish, lav'ish, *a*. Profuse, liberal to a fault; extravagant; superabundant.—*vt*. To expend with profusion, to squander.

law, lä, *n*. A rule prescribed by authority; a statute; a precept; such rules or statues collectively, legal procedure; litigation; a principle deduced from practice or observation; a formal statement of facts observed in natural phenomena.

lax, laks, *a*. Loose; flabby; soft; slack; vague; equivocal; not strict remiss; having too frequent discharges from the bowels.

laxative, laks'at iv, *a*. Having the power of relieving from constipation.—*n*. A gentle purgative.

lay, lā, *vt*. (pret. and pp. laid). To place in a lying position; to set or place in general, to impose, to bring into a certain state; to settle; to allay; to place at hazard; to wager; to contrive.—*vi*. To bring forth eggs; wager.—*n*. A stratum; a layer; one rank in a series reckoned upward, a song a narrative poem.—*a*. Not clerical; not professional.

layer, lā'èr, *n*. One who or that which lays, a stratum; a coat, as of paint; a row of masonry, etc.; a shoot of a plant, not detached from the stalk, partly laid underground for growth.—*vt*. To propagate by bending a shoot into the soil.

lead, lēd, *vt*. (pret. and pp. led). To guide or conduct, to direct and govern; to precede, to entice; to influence, to spend, to begin.—*vi*. To go before and show the way; to be chief or commander; to draw; to have a tendency.—*n*. Guidance; precedence.

leader, lēd'èr, *n*. One who leads; a guide; captain; head of a party; editorial article in a newspaper.

leaf, lēf, *n*.; pl. **leaves**, lēvz. One of the thin, expanded, deciduous growths of a plant, a part of a book containing two pages; a very thin plate, the movable side of a table, one side of a double door.—*vi.* To shoot out leaves; to produce leaves.

league, lēg, *n.* A combination between states for their mutual aid; an alliance, a compact, a measure of three miles or knots.—*vi.* (leaguing, leagued). To form a league; to confederate.

leak, lēk, *n.* A fissure in a vessel that admits water, or permits it to escape; the passing of fluid through an aperture.—*vi.* To let water in or out of a vessel through a crevice.

lean, lēn, *vi.* (pret. and pp. leaned). To slope or slant, to incline, to tend; to bend so as to rest on something; to depend.—*vt.* To cause to lean; to support or rest.

learn, lèrn, *vt.* (pret. and pp. learned). To gain knowledge of or skill in, to acquire by study.—*vi.* To gain knowledge; to receive instruction.

least, lēst, *a.* Smallest.—*adv.* In the smallest or lowest degree.—**At least, at the least**, to say no more; at the lowest degree.

leave, lēv, *n.* Permission; liberty granted; a formal parting of friends.—*vt.* (leaving, left). To let remain; to have remaining at death; to bequeath, to quit, to abandon to refer.—*vi.* To depart; to desist.

leaven, lev'n, *n.* A substance that produces fermentation, as in dough; yeast; barm.—*vt.* To mix with leaven; to excite fermentation in, to imbue.

lecher, lech'èr, *n.* A man given to lewdness.—*vi.* To practice lewdness, to indulge lust.

lecture, lek'tūr, *n.* A discourse on any subject; a reprimand; a formal reproof.—*vi.* (lecturing, lectured). To deliver a lecture or lectures.—*vt.* To reprimand; to reprove.

leer, lēr, *n.* A side glance, an arch or affected glance.—*vi.* To give a leer; to look meaningly.—*vt.* To turn with a leer, to affect with a leer.

leeway, lē'wā, *n.* The drifting of a ship to the leeward.—**To make up leeway**, to overtake work in arrears.

left, left, *a.* Denoting the part opposed to the right of the body.—*n.* The side opposite to the right.

left-handed, left'hand-ed, *a.* Using the left hand and arm with more dexterity than the right; sinister; insincere, awkward.

leg, leg, *n.* The limb of an animal, a lower or posterior limb; the long or slender

support of anything.

legal, lē'gal, *a.* According to, pertaining to, or permitted by law lawful; judicial.

legion, lē'jon, *n.* A Roman body of infantry soldiers, in number from 3000 to above 6000; a military force, a great number.

legislation le-jis-lā'shon, *n.* Act of making a law or laws; laws or statutes enacted.

leisure, lē'zhur or lezh'ūr, *n.* Freedom from occupation; vacant time.—*a.* Not spent in labor; vacant.

lemon, le'mon, *n.* An acid fruit of the orange kind; the tree that produces this fruit.

lemonade, le-mon-ād', *n.* A beverage, usually aerated, consisting of lemonjuice mixed with water and sweetened.

lemur, lē'mèr, *n.* A quadrumanous mammal, allied to monkeys and rodents.

lend, lend, *vt.* (lending, lent). To furnish on condition of the thing being returned; to afford or grant *refl.* to accommodate.

length, length, *n.* State or quality of being long; extent from end to end, extension, long duration, extent or degree.—**At length**, at full extent; at last.

leprosy, lep'rō-si, *n.* A foul cutaneous disease characterized by dusky red or livid tubercles on the face or extremities.

less, les, *a.* Smaller; not so large or great.—*adv.* In a smaller or lower degree.—*n.* A smaller quantity.

lessen, les'n, *vt.* To make less, to lower to depreciate.—*vi.* To become less; to abate.

lesson, les'n, *n.* Portion which a pupil learns at one time; portion of scripture read in divine service; something to be learned, severe lecture; truth taught by experience.

let, let, *vt.* (letting, let). To permit; to allow, to lease.—*vi.* To be leased or let.

let, let, *vt.* To hinder; to impede.—*n.* A hindrance, impediment.

letter, let'èr, *n.* A mark used as the representative of a sound; a written message, an epistle, the literal meaning; in *printing,* a single type; *pl.* learning; erudition.—*vt.* To impress or form letters on.

level, le'vel, *n.* An instrument for detecting variation from a horizontal surface; an instrument by which to find a horizontal line; a horizontal line or plane; a surface without inequalities, usual elevation; equal elevation with something else; horizontal gallery in a mine.—*a.* Horizontal, even, flat having no degree of superiority.— *vt.* (leveling leveled).

To make level, to lay fiat on the ground, to reduce to equality; to point, in taking aim.—*vi.* To point a gun, etc.; to aim.

lexicon, leks'i-kon, *n.* A word-book; a dictionary a vocabulary containing an alphabetical arrangement of the words in a language with the definition of each.

liable, li'a-bl, *a.* Answerable for consequences; responsible; subject; exposed: with *to.*

liaison, lē-ā-zōng, *n.* A bond of union; an illicit intimacy between a man and woman.

libation, li-bā'shon, *n.* Act of pouring a liquor, usually wine, on the ground or on a victim in sacrifice in honor of some deity; the wine or other liquor so poured.

libel, li'bel, *n.* A defamatory writing; a malicious publication; the written statement of a plaintiff's ground of complaint against a defendant.—*vt.* (libeling, libeled). To frame a libel against, to lampoon to exhibit a charge against in court.

liberal, li'bēr-al, *a.* Generous; ample; profuse; favorable to reform or progress; not too literal or strict; free.—*n.* One who advocates great political freedom.

liberty, li'bēr-ti, *n.* State or condition of one who is free; privilege; immunity, license, district within which certain exclusive privileges may be exercised; freedom of action or speech beyond civility or decorum; state of being disengaged.

library, li'bra-ri, *n.* A collection of books, edifice or apartment for holding books.

librate, li'brāt, *vt.* To poise; to balance.—*vi.* To move, as a balance to be poised.

lick, lik, *vt.* To draw the tongue over the surface of, to lap, to take in by the tongue, to beat.—*n.* A drawing of the tongue over anything; a slight smear or coat; a blow.

lie, li, *vi.* (lying, lied). To utter falsehood with deceitful intention.—*n.* A falsehood; an intentional violation of truth.

lie, li, *vi.* (lying, pret. lay, pp. lain). To occupy a horizontal position; to rest on anything lengthwise; to be situated, to remain, to be incumbent; to exist; to depend; to be sustainable in law.—**To lie in,** to be in childbed.—**To lie to,** to stop and remain stationary.—*n.* Relative position of objects; general bearing or direction.

life, lif, *n.; pl.* lives, livz. State of animals and plants in which the natural functions are performed; vitality; present state of existence; time from birth to death; manner of living; animal being; spirit; vivacity, the living form, exact resemblance; rank in society; human affairs, a person, narrative of a life, eternal felicity.

lift, lift, *vt.* To raise to a higher position to hoist, to elevate, to raise in spirit; to collect when due.; vi. To raise; to rise.—*n.* Act of lifting; assistance, that which is to be raised; an elevator or hoist.

ligament, li'ga-ment, *n.* That which unites one thing to another; a band; a substance serving to bind one bone to another.

light, lit, *n.* That by which objects are rendered visible; day; that which gives or admits light; illumination of mind knowledge, open view; explanation; point of view; situation, spiritual illumination.—*a.* Bright, clear, not deep, as color; not heavy; not difficult; easy to be digested, active, not laden, slight moderate; unsteady; gay; trifling, wanton, sandy, having a sensation of giddiness; employed in light work.—*adv.* Lightly; cheaply.—*vt.* (pret. and pp. lighted or lit). To give light to, to enlighten to ignite.—*vi.* To brighten; to descend, as from a horse, etc., to alight, to come by chance.

like, lik, *a.* Equal; similar; resembling; likely; feeling disposed.—*adv.* or *prep.* In the same manner similarly; likely.—*vt.* (liking, liked). To be pleased with; to approve.—*vi.* To be pleased, to choose.—*n.* Some person or thing resembling another; a counterpart; a liking; a fancy.

lilt, lilt, *vt.* and *i.* To sing cheerfully; to give musical utterance.—*n.* A song; a tune.

limb, lim, *n.* The arm or leg, especially the latter; a branch of a tree; graduated edge of a quadrant etc.; border of the disc of the sun moon, etc.—*vt.* To supply with limbs, to tear off the limbs of.

limber, lim'bēr, *a.* Flexible, pliant.—*n.* A carriage with ammunition boxes attached to the guncarriage.—*vt.* and *i.* To attach the limber to the gun-carriage.

limbo, lim'bo, *n.* A supposed region beyond this world for souls of innocent persons ignorant of Christianity; any similar region; a prison of confinement.

lime, lim, *n.* Any viscous substance, calcareous earth used in cement; mortar made with lime; the linden-tree, a tree producing an inferior sort of lemon.—*vt.*

L

(liming, limed). To smear or manure with Lime, to ensnare, to cement.

line, lin. *n*. A small rope or cord; a thread-like marking; a stroke or score, a row of soldiers, ships words, etc.; a verse; an outline; a short written communication; course of procedure, etc., connected series, as of descendants; series of public conveyances, as steamers, the twelfth part of an inch; the equator; the regular infantry of an army; *pl*. works covering extended positions and presenting a front in only one direction to the enemy.—*vt*. (lining lined). To draw lines upon; to set with men or things in lines; to cover on the inside, to put in the inside of.

lineament, lin'ē-a-ment, *n*. One of the lines which mark the features feature; form.

linen, lin'en, *n*. Cloth made of flax under clothing.—*a*. Made of flax, resembling linen cloth.

linger, ling'gėr, *vi*. To delay; to loiter; to hesitate; to remain long.— *vt*. To spend wearily.

link, lingk, *n*. A single ring of a chain anything closed like a link; anything connecting; a measure of 7.92 inches; a torch.—*vi*. To be connected.—*vt*. To join or connect, as by links to unite.

linseed, lin'sēd, *n*. Flax-seed.

lintel, lin'tel, *n*. The horizontal part of the door or window frame.

lion, lī'on, *n*. A carnivorous animal of the cat family; a sign in the zodiac Leo; an object of interest and curiosity.

liquefy, lik'wē-fī, *vt*. To melt, to dissolve by heat.—*vi*. To become liquid.

liqueur, li-kūr' or li-kör', *n*. An alcoholic beverage sweetened and containing some infusion of fruits or aromatic substances.

liquid, lik'wid, *a*. Fluid; not solid; soft, smooth, devoid *of* harshness.—*n*. A fluid; a letter with a smooth flowing sound, as l and r.

liquidate, lik'wid-āt, *vt*. To clear from obscurity; to adjust; to settle, adjust, and apportion, as a bankrupt's affairs.

lisp, lisp, *vi*. To pronounce the sibilant letters imperfectly, as in pronouncing th for s, to speak imperfectly, as a child.—*vt*. To pronounce with a lisp, or imperfectly.—*n*. The habit or act of lisping.

list, list, *n*. The selvedge of cloth; a limit or border, a roll or catalogue: inclination to one side, *pl*. a field inclosed for a combat.—*vt*. To enroll, to enlist.—*vi*.

To enlist, as in the army; to desire; to be disposed; to hearken.

literature, li'tėr-a-tūr, *n*. Learning; literary knowledge; collective writings of a country or period belles-lettres; the literary profession.

lithology, li-thol'o-ji, *n*. The knowledge of rocks; study of the mineral structure of rocks.

litigant, li'ti-gant, *a*. Disposed to litigate; engaged in a lawsuit.—*n*. One engaged in a lawsuit.

litigate, li'ti-gāt, *vt*. To contest in law. *vi*. To carry on a suit by judicial process.

little, lit'l, *a*. Small in size or extent; short in duration; slight; mean.—*n*. A small quantity, space, etc.—**A little,** somewhat.—*adv*. In a small degree or quantity.

liturgy, li'ter-ji, *n*. A ritual or established formulas for public worship.

live, liv, *vi*. (living, lived). To exist; to be alive, to dwell, to conduct oneself in life; to feed or subsist; to acquire a livelihood, to be exempt from spiritual death—*vt*. To lead, pass or spend.

live, līv, *a*. Having life, alive, not dead, ignited; vivid, as color.

load, lōd, *vt*. To charge with a load; to burden; to encumber, to bestow in great abundance; to charge, as a gun.—*n*. A burden, cargo, a grievous weight; something that oppresses.

loaf, lōf, *n*.; *pl*. **loaves,** lōvz. A mass of bread formed by the baker; a conical lump of sugar.—*vi*. To lounge.—*vt*. To spend idly.

loath, loth, lōth, *a*. Disliking; unwilling; averse; not inclined; reluctant.

loathe, lōTH, *vt*. (loathing, loathed). To feel disgust at, to abhor, to abominate.—*vi*. To feel nausea or abhorrence.

loathing, lōTH'ing, *n*. Extreme disgust or aversion; abhorrence; detestation.

loathness, lōTH'sum, *a*. Exciting disgust; disgusting; detestable; abhorrent.

lob, lob, *n*. A dolt, a lout.—*vt*. (lobbing, lobbed). To throw or toss slowly.

lobby, lob'i, *n*. An apartment giving admission to others; an entrance-hall.

lobe, lōb, *n*. A round projecting part of something; such a part of the liver, lungs, brain, etc., the lower soft part of the ear.

lobster, lob'stėr, *n*. A ten-footed crustacean with large claws, allied to the crab.

local, lō'kal, *a*. Pertaining to a particular place, confined to a spot or definite district.—*n.* A local item of news; a local railway train.

lock, lok, *n.* An appliance for fastening doors, etc.; mechanism by which a firearm is discharged; a fastening together, inclosure in a canal, with gates at either end; a tuft or ringlet of hair.— *vt.* To fasten with a lock and key, to shut up or confine; to join firmly; to embrace closely.—*vi.* To become fast, to unite closely by mutual insertion.

lodge, loj, *n.* A small country house, a temporary abode, place where members of a society, as freemasons, meet; the society itself.—*vt.* (lodging, lodged). To furnish with temporary accommodation; to set or deposit for keeping; to beat down (growing crops).—*vi.* To have a temporary abode; to settle, to reside.

loft, loft, *n.* The space below and between the rafters; a gallery raised within a larger apartment or in a church.

log, log, *n.* A bulky piece of timber unhewed; a floating contrivance for measuring the rate of a ship's velocity; a log-book.

loiter, loi'tèr, *vi.* To be slow in moving; to spend time idly; to hang about.—*vi.* To waste carelessly with *away.*

loll, lol, *vi.* (lolling, lolled). To lean idly, to lie at ease, to hang out, as the tongue of a dog.—*vt.* To suffer to hang out.

lone, lōn, *a.* Solitary; unfrequented; single.

long, long, *a.* Drawn out in a line; drawn out in time, tedious protracted; late; containing much verbal matter.—*n.* Something that is long.—*adv.* To a great extent in space or in time, at a point of duration far distant.—*vi.* To desire eagerly; with *for.*

longitude, lon'ji-tūd, *n.* Length; distance on the surface of the globe east or west, measured by meridians.

look, lük, *vi.* To direct the eye so as to see; to gaze; to consider; to expect; to heed; to face; to appear.— *vt.* To see, to express by a look.—*n.* Act of looking; sight; gaze; glance; mien, aspect.

loose, lös, *a.* Not attached; untied not dense or compact; vague, careless, having lax bowels, unchaste.—*vt.* (loosing, loosed). To untie or unbind; to detach; to set free; to relax; to loosen.

loot, löt, *n.* Booty; plunder, especially such as is taken in a sacked city.—*vt.* To plunder.

lord, lord, *n.* A master; a ruler; proprietor of a manor, a nobleman, a British title applied to peers, sons of dukes and mar-

quises, and the eldest sons of earls; honorary title of certain high officials, (with *cap.*) the Supreme Being.—*vi.* To act as a lord; to rule with arbitrary or despotic sway.

lose, löz, *vt.* (losing, lost). To cease to possess, as through accident, to fail to keep; to forfeit; not to gain or win, to miss, to cease or fail to see or hear; to misuse.— *vi.* To suffer loss; not to win.

lost, lost, *p.a.* Gone from our hold, view, etc., not to be found, ruined wasted; forfeited; perplexed; alienated.

lot, lot, *n.* A person's part or share fate which falls to one; part in life allotted to a person a distinct portion, a considerable quantity or number; something used to decide what is yet undecided.— *vt.* (lotting, lotted). To assign by lot; to sort; to portion.

lounge, lounj, *vi.* (lounging lounged). To loiter; to loll.—*n.* An idle gait or stroll; act of reclining at ease; a place for lounging.

love, luv, *vt.* (loving loved). To regard with affection, to like, to delight in.—*vi.* To be in love; to be tenderly attached.— *n.* Warm affection; fond attachment; the passion between the sexes, the object beloved a word of endearment, Cupid, the god of love; the score of nothing at tennis, etc.

low, lō, *a.* Depressed below any given surface or place; not high; deep; below the usual rate; not loud, wanting strength, mean, dishonorable; not sublime; plain.— *adv.* Not aloft, under the usual price; near the ground, not loudly.

luck, luk, *n.* That which happens to a person; chance; hap; fortune; success.

lucky, luk'i, *a.* Meeting with good luck or success; fortunate; auspicious.

ludicrous, lü'di-krus, *a.* That serves for sport; laughable; droll ridiculous.

luggage, lug'äj, *n.* Anything cumbersome and heavy; a traveller's baggage.

lull, lul, *vt.* To sing to, as to a child; to soothe.—*vi.* To subside, to become calm.—*n.* A season of quiet or cessation.

lumber, lum'bèr, *n.* Anything useless and cumbersome, in America timber sawed or split for use.—*vt.* To fill with lumber; to heap together in disorder.—*vi.* To move heavily, as a vehicle, in America to cut and prepare timber.

lump, lump, *n.* A small mass of matter; a mass of things.—*vt.* To throw into a mass; to take in the gross.

lunge, lunj, *n.* A sudden thrust or pass, as with a sword.—*vi.* (lunging, lunged). To make a thrust.

lurch, lèrch, *vi.* To lurk; to roll or sway to one side.—*n.* A sudden roll or stagger; a difficult or helpless position.

lure, lūr, *n.* Something held out to call a trained hawk; a bait; any enticement.—*vt.* (luring, lured). To attract by a lure or bait; to entice.

lust, lust, *n.* Longing desire; carnal appetite; depraved affections.—*vi.* To desire eagerly; to have carnal desire.

luster, lus'ter, *n.* Brightness; brilliancy, renown, a branched chandelier ornamented with cut glass a glossy fabric for dress.

luxury, luks'ū-ri, *n.* Extravagant indulgence; that which gratifies a fastidious appetite; anything delightful to the senses.

lymphatic, lim-fat'ik, *a.* Pertaining to lymph; phlegmatic; sluggish.— *n.* A vessel in animal bodies which contains or conveys lymph.

lynx, lingks, *n.* A carnivorous anima;resembling the cat, noted for its keen sight.

lyric, lyrical, li'rik, li'rik-al, *a.* Pertaining to a lyre; designating that species of poetry which has reference to the individual emotions of the poet, such as songs.—**lyric,** li'rik, *n.* A lyric poem; an author of lyric poems.

M

Machiavelian, ma'ki-a-vē l"i-an, *a.* Pertaining to *Machiavelli,* or denoting his principles; cunning in political management.

machine, ma-shēn', *n.* Any contrivance which serves to regulate the effect of a given force or to produce or change motion, an organized system; a person who acts as the tool of another.—*vt.* To apply machinery to; to produce by machinery.

mad, mad, *a.* Disordered in intellect; insane; crazy; frantic; furious; infatuated.—*vt.* (madding, madded). To make mad.

Magi, mā'jī, *n.pl.* The caste of priests among the ancient Medes and Persians; holy men or sages of the East.

magic, ma'jik, *n.* The art of producing effects by superhuman means, sorcery, enchantment; power similar to that of enchantment. —*a.* Pertaining to magic working or worked by or as if by magic.

magnesia, mag-nē'si-a, *n.* Oxide of magnesium, a white slightly alkaline powder.

magnet, mag'net, *n.* The loadstone, which has the property of attracting iron; a bar of iron or steel to which the properties of the loadstone have been imparted.

magnificence, mag-nif'i-sens, *n.* Grandeur of appearance; splendor, pomp.

magnify, mag'ni-fī, *vt.* To make great or greater, to increase the apparent dimensions of; to extol; to exaggerate.—*vi.* To possess the quality of causing objects to appear larger.

maiden, mā d'n, *n.* A maid or virgin, an old Scottish instrument of capital punishment resembling the guillotine.—*a.* Pertaining to maidens; unpolluted; unused; first.

mail, māl, *n.* A bag for conveying letters, etc.; letters conveyed; person or conveyance carrying the mail; armor of chain-work, etc.—*vt.* (mailing, mailed). To send by mail; to post; to arm with mail.

main, mān, *a.* Chief, or most important mighty; vast; directly applied; used with all one's might.—*n.* Strength; great effort; chief or main portion; the ocean; a principal gas or water pipe in a street; a hand at dice, a match at cockfighting.

major, mā'jėr, *a.* The greater in number, quantity, or extent; the more important.—*n.* A military officer next above a captain; a person aged twenty-one years complete.

majority, ma-jo'ri-ti, *n.* The greater number; excess of one number over another; full age; rank or commission of a major.

make, māk, *vt.* (making, made). To produce or effect; to cause to be; to compose; to constitute; to perform; to cause to have any quality to force; to gain; to complete; to arrive at, to have within sight.—*vi.* To act or do; to tend; to contribute; to flow toward land.—*n.* Form; structure texture.

malcontent, mal'kon-tent, *n.* A discontented person.—*a.* Discontent-ed with the rule under which one lives.

male, māl, *a.* Pertaining to the sex that begets young; masculine.—*n.* One of the sex that begets young; a plant which has stamens only.

malt, mält, *n.* Barley or other grain steeped in water till it germinates, then dried in a kiln and used in brewing.—*vt.* To make into malt.—*vi.* To become malt.

man, man, *n.*, *pl.* **men**, men. A human being; a male adult of the human race; mankind; the male sex; a male servant; a piece in a game as chess, etc.—*vt.* (manning, manned). To furnish with men, to guard with men; *refl.* To infuse courage into.

manacle, man'a-kl, *n.* An instrument of iron for fastening the hands; a handcuff; used chiefly in the plural.—*vt.* (manacling, manacled). To put manacles on; to fetter.

manage, man'āj, *vt.* (managing, managed). To wield, to direct in riding; to conduct or administer; to have under command, to treat with judgment.—*vi.* To conduct affairs.

mandatory, man'da-to-ri, *a.* Containing a command; preceptive directory.

maneuver, ma-nū'vėr or ma-nö'vėr, *n.* A regulated movement, particularly of troops or ships; management with address; stratagem.—*vi.* (maneuvering, maneuvered). To perform military or naval maneuvers; to employ stratagem; to manage with address.—*vt.* To cause to perform maneuvers.

mangle, mang'gl, *vt.* (mangling mangled). To mutilate; to lacerate, to smooth, as linen.—*n.* A rolling press or small cal-

M

ender for smoothing cotton or linen.

manicure, man'i-kūr, n. One whose occupation is to trim the nails, etc., of the hand.

manifest, man'i-fest, a. Clearly visible; evident; obvious.—vt. To make manifest; to display or exhibit.—n. A document stating a ship's cargo, destination, etc.

manifold, man'i-fōld, a. Numerous and various, of divers kinds.—vt. To multiply impressions of, as by a copying apparatus.

manipulate, ma-nip'ū-lāt, vt. To treat with the hands: to handle; to operate upon so as to disguise.

manner, man'ėr n. The mode in which anything is done; method; bearing or conduct; pl. carriage or behavior; civility in society; sort or kind

mannerism, man'ėr-izm, n. Adherence to the same manner; tasteless uniformity of style; peculiarity of personal manner.

mantle, man'tl, n. A kind of cloak worn over other garments; something that covers and conceals; incandescent hood for gas jet.—vt. (mantling, mantled). To cloak; to cover as with a mantle.—vi. To become covered with a coating; to cream; to display superficial changes of hue.

manual, man'ū-al, a. Performed by the hand; used or made by the hand.—n. A small book; a compendium, the service-book of the R. Catholic Church; keyboard of an organ.

manufacture, man-ū-fak'tūr, n. The process of making anything by hand or machinery; something made from raw materials.—vt. (manufacturing, manufactured). To fabricate from raw materials; to fabricate without real grounds.—vi. To be occupied in manufactures.

manure, man-ūr', vt. (manuring, manured). To fertilize with nutritive substances.—n. Any substance added to soil to accelerate or increase the production of the crops.

manuscript, man'ū-skript, n. A paper written with the hand often contracted to MS pl. MSS.—a. Written with the hand.

many, me'ni, a. Forming or comprising a number; numerous.— **The many**, the great majority of people; the crowd..— **So many**, the same number of; a certain number indefinitely.

marble, mär'bl, n. A calcareous stone of compact texture; a little hard ball used by boys in play; an inscribed or sculptured marble stone.—a. Made of or like marble.—vt. (marbling, marbled). To stain like marble.

march, märch, vi. To move by steps and in order, as soldiers; to walk in a stately manner; to progress; to be situated next. vt. To cause to march.—n. The measured walk of a body of men; a stately walk; distance passed over; a musical composition to regulate the march of troops etc., a frontier or boundary (usually in pl.); the third month of the year.

marine, ma-rēn', a. Pertaining to the sea; found in the sea; used at sea naval, maritime.—n. A soldier who serves on board of a man-of-war; collective shipping of a country; whole economy of naval affairs.

maritime, ma'ri-tīm, a. Relating to the sea; naval; bordering on the sea; having a navy and commerce by sea.

mark, märk, n. A visible sign or impression on something; a distinguishing sign; indication or evidence, preeminence or importance, a characteristic; heed or regard, object aimed at; proper standard, extreme estimate; a German coin.—vt. To make a mark or marks on, to denote (often with out), to regard, observe, heed.—vi. To note; to observe critically; to remark.

market, mär'ket, n. An occasion on which goods are publicly exposed for sale; place in which goods are exposed for sale; rate of purchase and sale; demand for commodities; privilege of keeping a public market.—vi. To deal in a market.—vt. To offer for sale in a market.

maroon, ma-rön, n. A fugitive slave in the W. Indies; a brownish crimson or claret color.—vt. To land and leave on a desolate island.

marrow, ma'rō, n. A soft substance in the cavities of bones; the best part; a kind of gourd, also called vegetable marrow.

marry, ma'ri, vt. (marrying, married). To unite in wedlock, to dispose of in wedlock; to take for husband or wife.—vi. To take a husband or a wife.—interj. Indeed; forsooth.

marshal, mär'shal, n. One who regulates rank and order at a feast, procession, etc.; a military officer of the highest rank, Generally called field-marshal.— vt. (marshalling, marshalled). To dispose in order, to array.

masculine, mas'kū-lin, a. Male manly;

robust; bold or unwomanly; designating nouns which are the names of male animals, etc.

mash, mash, *n.* A mixture of ingredients beaten or blended together; a mixture of ground malt and warm water yielding wort.—*vt.* To mix; to beat into a confused mass.

mask, mask, *n.* A cover for the face; a masquerade; a sort of play common in the 16th and 17th centuries; pretense.—*vt.* To cover with a mask; to disguise; to hide.

masquerade, mas-kėr-ā d', *n.* An assembly of persons wearing masks; a disguise.—*vi.* To assemble in masks; to go in disguise.

mass, mas, *n.* A body of matter, a lump; magnitude; an assemblage collection; the generality; the communion service in the R. Catholic Church.—**The masses,** the populace.—*vt.* and *i.* To form into a mass; to assemble in crowds.

massacre, mas'sa-kėr, *n.* Ruthless, unnecessary, or indiscriminate slaughter—*vt.* (massacring, massacred) To kill with indiscriminate violence, to slaughter.

massage, ma-säzh' or mas'ā j, *n.* A process of kneading, rubbing, pressing, etc., parts of a person s body to effect a cure.—*vt.* (massaging, massaged). To treat by this process.

massive, mas'iv, *a.* Bulky and heavy; ponderous; pertaining to a mass; not local or special.

mast, mäst, *n.* A long upright timber in a vessel, supporting the yards, sails, and rigging, the fruit of the oak, beech, etc. (no *pl.*).—*vt.* To supply with a mast or masts.

master, mäs'tėr, *n.* One who rules or directs; an employer; owner; captain of a merchant ship teacher in a school; a man eminently skilled in some art; a word of address for men (written Mr. and pron. mis'ter) and boys (written in full); a vessel having masts.—*vt.* To bring under control to make oneself master of.—*a.* Belonging to a master, chief.

mat, māt, *n.* An article of interwoven rushes, twine, etc., used for cleaning or protecting, anything growing thickly or closely interwoven.—*vt.* (matting, matted). To cover with mats, to entangle.—*vi.* To grow thickly together.

matador, ma-ta-dōr', *n.* The man appointed to kill the bull in bullfights; a card in ombre and quadrille

match, mach, *n.* A person or thing equal to another, union by marriage, one to be married; a contest; a small body that catches fire readily or ignites by friction.—*vt.* To equal; to show an equal to; to set against as equal in contest; to suit, to marry.—*vi.* To be united in marriage; to suit; to tally.

mate, māt, *n.* A companion; a match, a husband or wife; second officer in a ship.—*vt.* (mating, mated). To equal; to match, to marry; to checkmate.

material, ma-tē'ri-al, *a.* Consisting of matter not spiritual, important; essential; substantial.—*n.* Anything composed of matter, substance of which anything is made.

materialize, ma-tē'ri-al-īz, *vt.* To reduce to a state of matter; to regard as matter.

mathematics, ma-thē-ma'tiks, *n.* The science of magnitude and number, comprising arithmetic, geometry, algebra, etc.

matron, mā'tron *n.* An elderly married woman or an elderly lady; head nurse or superintendent of a hospital, etc.

matter, mat'ėr, *n.* Not mind; body; that of which anything is made; substance as distinct from form; subject, business, circumstance; import; moment; pus.—*vi.* To be of importance; to signify; to form pus.

May, mā, *n.* The fifth month of the year, hawthorn blossom—*vi.* To celebrate the festivities of Mayday.—*v. aux.* (pret. might, mit). Used to imply possibility, opportunity, permission, desire, etc.

mead, mēd, *n.* A fermented liquor made from honey and water; a meadow: *poet.*

meadow, me'dō, *n.* A low level tract of land under grass.—*a.* Belonging to a meadow.

meal, mēl, *n.* Portion of food taken at one time; a repast; ground grain, flour.

mealy-mouthed, mē l'i-mouTHd, *a.* Unwilling to tell the truth in plain language; soft-spoken; inclined to hypocrisy.

mean, mēn, *a.* Low in rank or birth; humble, base contemptible; occupying a middle position; middle; intermediate.—*n.* What is intermediate average rate or degree; medium; *pl.* measure or measures adopted; agency (generally used as *sing.*), income or resources.—*vt.* (pret. and pp. *meant*). To have in the mind, to intend; to signify; to import.—*vi.* To have thought or ideas, or to have meaning.

M

measure, me'zhūr, *n.* The extent or magnitude of a thing; a standard of size, a measuring rod or line; that which is allotted; moderation; just degree; course of action; legislative proposal; musical time; meter; a grave solemn dance; *pl.* beds or strata.—*vt.* (measuring, measured). To ascertain the extent or capacity of; to estimate; to value; to pass through or over, to proportion; to allot.—*vi.* To have a certain extent.

measurement, me'zhūr-ment, *n.* Act of measuring; amount ascertained.

meat, mēt, *n.* Food in general; the flesh of animals used as food; the edible portion of something (the *meat* of an egg).

mechanic, me-kan'ik, *a.* Mechanical.—*n.* An artisan, an artisan employed in making and repairing machinery.

mechanical, me-kan'ik-al, *a.* Pertaining to mechanism or machinery, resembling a machine; done by the mere force of habit; pertaining to material forces, physical.

medicate, med'i-kā t, *vt.* (medicating, medicated). To treat with medicine; to impregnate with anything medicinal.

medicine, med'sin, *n.* Any substance used as a remedy for disease; a drug; the science and art of curing diseases.

mediocrity, mē-di-ok'ri-ti, *n.* State of being mediocre, a moderate degree or rate; a person of mediocre talents or abilities.

meditate, med'i-tāt, *vi.* (meditating, meditated). To dwell on anything in thought, to cogitate.—*vt.* To think on; to scheme; to intend.

Mediterranean, med'i-te-rā'nē-an, *a.* Surrounded by land: now applied exclusively to the *Mediterranean* Sea.

medium, mē 'di-um, *n.*; pl. -ia, -iums. Something holding a middle position; a mean; means of motion or action, agency of transmission; instrumentality.—*a.* Middle; middling.

meet, mēt, *vt.* (meeting, met). To come face to face with; to come in contact with, to encounter, to light on, to receive; to satisfy.—*vi.* To come together; to encounter; to assemble.—*n.* A meeting, as of huntsmen.—*a.* Fit; suitable; proper.

mellow, mel'ō, *a.* Soft with ripeness; soft to the ear, eye, or taste; toned down by time; half-tipsy.— *vt.* To make mellow, to soften.—*vi.* To become mellow.

melodrama, me-lō-dra'ma, *n.* Properly a musical drama, a serious play, with startling incidents, exaggerated sentiment, and splendid decoration.

melody, me'lō-di, *n.* An agreeable succession of sounds; sweetness of sound the particular air or tune of a musical piece.

melt, melt, *vt.* To reduce from a solid to a liquid state by heat; to soften; to overcome with tender emotion.—*vi.* To become liquid; to dissolve; to be softened to love, pity, etc.; to pass by imperceptible degrees.

member, mem'bēr, *n.* An organ or limb of an animal body, part of an aggregate; one of the persons composing a society, etc.; a representative in a legislative body.

memoir, mem'oir, mem'wär, *n.* A written account of events or transactions; a biographical notice; recollections of one's life (usually in the *pl.*).

memorial, mē-mō'ri-al, *a.* Pertaining to memory or remembrance; serving to commemorate.—*n.* That which preserves the memory of something; a monument; memorandum, a written representation of facts, made as the ground of a petition.

memory, mem'ō-ri, *n.* The faculty of the mind by which it retains knowledge or ideas, remembrance, recollection; the time within which a person may remember what is past; something remembered.

mend, mend, *vt.* To repair; to restore to a sound state, to amend.— *vi.* To advance to a better state; to improve.

meningitis, men-in-jī'tis, *n.* Inflammation of the membranes of the brain or spinal cord.

mercenary, mėr'se-na-ri, *a.* Hired venal, that may be hired; greedy of gain; sordid.—*n.* One who is hired; a soldier hired into foreign service.

merchant, mėr'chant *n.* One who carries on trade on a large scale; a man who exports and imports goods.—*a.* Relating to trade; commercial.

mercy, mėr'si, *n.* Willingness to spare or forgive; clemency; pity; a blessing, benevolence, unrestrained exercise of authority.

mere, mēr, *a.* This or that and nothing else, simple absolute, entire, utter.—*n.* A pool or small lake; a boundary.

meretricious, me-rē-tri'shus, *a.* Pertaining to prostitutes; alluring by false show, gaudy.

merge, mėrj, *vt.* (merging, merged). To cause to be swallowed up or incorporated.—*vi*. To be sunk, swallowed, or lost.

meridian, mē-rid'i-an, *n*. Pertaining to midday or noon, pertaining to the acme or culmination.—*n*. Mid-day; point of greatest splendor, any imaginary circle passing through both poles, used in marking longitude; a similar imaginary line in the heavens passing through the zenith of any place.

mermaid, mèr'mād, *n*. A fabled marine creature, having the upper part like a woman and the lower like a fish.

mesentery, me'sen-te-ri, *a*. A membrane retaining the intestines in a proper position.

mesh, mesh, *n*. The space between the threads of a net; something that entangles, implement for making nets.—*vt*. To catch in a net.

mess, mes, *n*. A dish of food, food for a person at one meal; a number of persons who eat together, especially in the army or navy, a disorderly mixture; muddle.—*vi*. To take meals in common with others.

metabolism, me-tab'ol-izm, *n*. Change or metamorphosis; chemical change of nutriment taken into the body.

metal, me'tal, *n*. An elementary substance, such as gold, iron, etc., having a peculiar luster and generally fusible by heat; the broken stone for covering roads.

metallurgy, me'tal-èr-ji, *n*. Art of working metals; art or operation of separating metals from their ores by smelting.

metaphysics, me-ta-fi'ziks, *n*. The science of the principles and causes of all things existing; the philosophy of mind as distinguished from that of matter.

meteor, mē'tē-èr, *n*. An atmospheric phenomenon; a transient luminous body; something that transiently dazzles.

meteoric, mē-tē-or'ik, *a*. Pertaining to or consisting of meteors; proceeding from a meteor; transiently or irregularly brilliant.

mew, mū, *n*. A sea-mew, a gull moulting of a hawk; a coop for fowls, a place of confinement, the cry of a cat.—*vt*. To moult, to shut up, as in a cage.—*vi*. To moult; to cry as a cat.

miasma, mī-az'ma, *n*., pl. **miasmata**, mi-az'ma-ta. The effluvia of any putrefying bodies; noxious emanation, malaria.

middle, mid'l, *a.; no compar.; superl*. middlemost. Equally distant from the extremes, intermediate intervening.— **Middle Ages**, the period from the fall of the Roman Empire to about 1450.—*n*. Point or part equally distant from the extremities; something intermediate.

mildew, mil'dū, *n*. A minute parasitic fungus that causes decay in vegetable matter, condition so caused.—*vt*. and *i*. To taint with mildew.

militarism, mil'i-ta-rizm, *n*. The system that leads a nation to pay excessive attention to military affairs.

military, mil'i-ta-ri, *a*. Pertaining to soldiers or war, martial; soldierly belligerent.—*n*. The whole body of soldiers, the army.

milk, milk, *n*. A whitish fluid secreted in female animals, serving as nourishment for their young what resembles milk; white juice of plants.—*vt*. To draw milk from.

mill, mil, *n*. A machine for making meal or flour; a machine for grinding, etc.; building that contains the machinery for grinding, etc.— *vt*. To pass through a mill; to stamp in a coining press, to throw as silk; to full, as cloth.

milling, mil'ing, *n*. The process of grinding or passing through a mill, the transverse grooves on the edge of a coin.

mimic, mim'ik, *a*. Imitative; consisting of imitation.—*n*. One who imitates or mimics.—*vt*. (mimicking, mimicked). To imitate, especially for sport; to ridicule by imitation.

mind, mīnd, *n*. The intellectual power in man, understanding cast of thought and feeling; inclination; opinion; memory.— *vt*. To attend to, to observe, to regard.

mindful, mīnd'ful, *a*. Bearing in mind; attentive; regarding with care; heedful.

mine, mīn, *adj. pron. My;* belonging to me.—*n*. A pit from which coal, ores, etc. are taken an underground passage in which explosives may be lodged for destructive purposes, a contrivance floating on or near the surface of the sea, to destroy ships by explosion; a rich source or store of wealth.—*vi*. (mining, mined). To dig a mine; to dig for ores, etc.; to burrow.—*vt*. To undermine; to sap.

mineral, mi'ne-ral, *n*. An inorganic body existing on or in the earth.—*a*. Pertaining to or consisting of minerals; impregnated with mineral matter.

mingle, ming'gl, *vt*. (mingling, mingled). To mix up together; to blend; to debase by mixture.—*vi*. To be mixed; to join.

miniature, min'i-a-tūr, *n*. A painting of very small dimensions, usually in water-

M

colors, on ivory, vellum, etc.; anything represented on a greatly reduced scale a small scale.—*a.* On a small scale; diminutive.

minister, min'is-tèr, *n.* A servant; attendant, agent, a member of a government; a political representative or ambassador, the pastor of a church.—*vt.* To give, to supply.—*vi.* To perform service; to afford supplies, to contribute.

minnow, min'ō, *n.* A very small British fish inhabiting fresh-water streams.

minor, mī'nor, *a.* Lesser, smaller, of little importance; petty; in music. Less by a lesser semitone.—*n.* A person not yet 21 years of age.

minority, mi-no'ri-ti, *n.* State of being a minor, period from birth until 21 years of age, the smaller number or a number less than half; the party that has the fewest votes.

minute, mi-nūt *a.* The sixtieth part of an hour or degree; short sketch of an agreement, etc., in writing; a note to preserve the memory of anything.—*vt.* (minuting, minuted). To write down a concise state or note of.

mirror, mi'rèr, *n.* A looking-glass; any polished substance that reflects images; an exemplar—*vt.* To reflect, as in a mirror

misadventure, mis-ad-ven'tūr, *n.* An unlucky accident; misfortune; ill-luck.

misalliance, mis-al-lī'ans, *n.* Improper association; an unequal marriage.

misanthrope, misanthropist, mis'an-thr'ōp, mis-an'thr'ōp-ist, *n.* A hater of mankind.

misapprehend, mis-ap'pē-hend", *vt.* To misunderstand; to take in a wrong sense.

misbecome, mis-bē-kum', *vt.* Not to become, to suit ill.

miscalculate, mis-kal'kū-lāt, *vt.* To calculate erroneously.

miscarry, mis-ka'ri, *vi.* To fail to reach its destination, to fail of the intended effect, to bring forth young before the proper time.

miscellaneous, mis-sel-lā'nē-us, *a.* Consisting of several kinds, promiscuous; producing written compositions of various sorts.

miserly, mī'zèr-li, *a.* Like a miser in habits; penurious; sordid; niggardly.

misery, miz'èr-i, *n.* Great unhappiness; extreme distress; wretchedness.

misfeasance, mis-fē'zans, *n.* In *law,* a wrong done; wrong-doing in office

misfit, mis-fit', *n.* A bad fit.—*vt.* To make

(a garment, etc.) of a wrong size; to supply with something not suitable.

misfortune, mis-for'tūn, *n.* Ill fortune; calamity; mishap.

misinform, mis-in-form', *vt.* To give erroneous information to.

misinterpret, mis-in-tér 'pret, *vt.* To interpret erroneously.

misjudge, mis-juj', *vt.* To judge erroneously.—*vi.* To err in judgment.

misplace, mis-plās, *vt.* To put in a wrong place; to set on an improper object.

misprint, mis-print', *vt.* To print wrongly.—*n.* A mistake in printing.

missile, mis'il *a.* Capable of being thrown.—*n.* A weapon or projectile thrown with hostile intention as an arrow, a bullet.

mission, mi'shon, *n.* A sending or delegating, duty on which one is sent; destined end or function; persons sent on some political business or to propagate religion, a station of missionaries.

missive, mis'iv, *a.* Such as is sent proceeding from some authoritative source.—*n.* A message; a letter or writing sent.

misspell, mis-spel', *vt.* To spell wrongly.

misspent, mis-spent', *p.a.* Ill-spent; wasted.

misstatement, mis-stāt'ment, *n.* A wrong statement.

mist, mist, *n.* Visible watery vapor aqueous vapor falling in numerous but almost imperceptible drops; something which dims or darkens.

mistake, mis-tāk', *vt.* To misunderstand or misapprehend; to regard as one when really another.—*vi.* To err in opinion or judgment.—*n.* An error in opinion or judgment; blunder, fault.

mistress, mis'tres, *n.* The female appellation corresponding to *master,* a woman who has authority, ownership, etc.; a female teacher, a concubine, a title of address applied to married women (written *Mrs.* and pronounced mis'iz).

mite, mīt, *n.* A minute animal of the class Arachnida (cheese-mite, etc.); a very small coin formerly current; a very little creature.

mixture, miks'tūr, *n.* Act of mixing state of being mixed; a compound, a liquid medicine of different ingredients.

moan, mōn, *vi.* To utter a low dull sound through grief or pain.—*vt.* To bewail or deplore.—*n.* A low dull sound due to grief or pain; a sound resembling this.

moat, mōt, *n.* A deep trench round a castle

or other fortified place.—*vt.* To surround with a ditch for defense.

mob, mob, *n.* A crowd, disorderly assembly; rabble.—*vt.* (mobbing mobbed). To attack in a disorderly crowd, to crowd round and annoy.

moccasin, mok'a-sin, *n.* A shoe of deerskin or soft leather, worn by N. American Indians; a venomous serpent of the United States.

mock, mok, *vt.* To mimic in contempt or derision; to flout, to ridicule; to set at naught; to defy.—*vi.* To use ridicule, to gibe or jeer.—*n.* A derisive word or gesture; ridicule; derision.—*a.* Counterfeit; assumed.

mockery, mok'è-ri, *n.* Derision; sportive insult; counterfeit appearance, vain effort.

model, mo'del, *n.* A pattern, an image, copy, facsimile; standard, plan, or type; a person from whom an artist studies his proportions, postures, etc.—*vt.* (modelling, modelled). To plan after some model; to form in order to serve as a model; to mold.—*vi.* To make a model.

moderate, mo'de-rāt, *vt.* To restrain from excess; to temper, lessen, allay.—*vi.* To become less violent or intense; to preside as a moderator.—*a.* Not going to extremes; temperate, medium, mediocre.— *n.* One not extreme in opinions.

modulus, mod'ū-lus, *n.* In *mathematics, etc.*, a constant quantity used in connection with some variable quantity.

mohair, mō'hār, *n.* The hair of the Angora goat; cloth made of this hair; an imitation wool and cotton cloth.

mold, mōld, *n.* Fine soft earth; mustiness or mildew, dust from incipient decay, form in which a thing is cast; model; shape; character.—*vt.* To cause to contract mold, to cover with mold or soil, to model; to shape; to fashion.—*vi.* To become moldy.

molding, mōld'ing, *n.* Anything cast in a mold; ornamental contour or form in wood or stone along an edge or a surface.

mole, mōl, *n.* A small discolored protuberance on the human body; a mound or break-water to protect a harbor from the waves, a small burrowing insectivorous animal.

molecule, mo'le-kūl, *n.* A very minute particle of matter.

mole-hill, mōl'hil, *n.* A little hillock of earth thrown up by moles; a very small

hill.

mollify, mol'i-fī, *vt.* (mollifying, mollified). To soften; to assuage; to appease; to reduce in harshness; to tone down.

mollusc, mollusk, mol'usk, *n.* An animal whose body is soft, as mussels, snails, cuttle-fish, etc.; one of the *Mollusca.*

monarch, mon'ärk, *n.* A supreme governor of a state, a sovereign one who or that which is chief of its kind.—*a.* Supreme, ruling.

monarchy, mon'är-ki, *n.* Govern ment in which the supreme power is lodged in a single person, actually or nominally; a kingdom.

monastery, mon'as-te-ri, *n.* A house for monks, sometimes for nuns abbey; priory; convent.

monatomic, mon-a-tom'ik, *a.* Said of an element one atom of which will combine with only one atom of another element.

money, mun'i, *n.* Coin; pieces of gold, silver, or other metal, stamped by public authority and used as the medium of exchange a circulating medium; wealth; affluence.

Mongol, Mongolian, mon'gol, mongō'li-an, *n.* A native of Mongolia.— *a.* Belonging to Mongolia.

monitor, mo'ni-tè r, *n.* One who admonishes; one who warns of faults or informs of duty, a senior pupil in a school appointed to instruct and look after juniors; a lizard.

monk, mungk, *n.* A male inhabitant of a monastery, bound to celibacy.

monogamy, mon-og'a mi, *n.* The practice or principle of marrying only once; the marrying of only one at a time.

monopoly, mo-nop'o-li, *n.* An exclusive trading privilege; assumption of anything to the exclusion of others.

monotony, mon-ot'o-ni, *n.* Uniformity of sound; a dull uniformity, an irksome sameness or want of variety.

monsoon, mon-sön', *n.* The trade-wind of the Indian seas, blowing from N.E. from November to March, and s.w. from April to October.

monster, mon'stèr, *n.* An animal of unnatural form or of great size; one unnaturally wicked or evil.—*a.* Of inordinate size.

month, munth, *n.* The period measured by the moon's revolution (the lunar month, about 29-1/2 days), one of the twelve parts of the year (the calendar month, 30 or 31 days).

M

monthly, munth'li, *a.* Done or happening once a month, or every month.—*n.* A publication appearing once a month.—*adv.* Once a month; in every month.

monument, mon'ū-ment, *n.* Any-thing by which the memory of a person or of an event is preserved; a memorial; a singular or notable instance.

mood, mŏd, *n.* Temper of mind; disposition, a fit of sullenness, a form of verbs expressive of certainty contingency, etc.; a form of syllogism.

moon, mŏn, *n.* The changing luminary of the night; the heavenly body next to the earth, revolving round it in about 29-1/2 days; a satellite of any planet, a month.

moonlight, mŏn'līt, *n.* The light afforded by the moon.—*a.* Illuminated by the moon, occurring during moonlight.—**moon-lit,** mŏn 'lit *a.* Illuminated by the moon.

moonshine, mŏn'shīn, *n.* The light of the moon; show without substance; pretense; illegally distilled corn whiskey.

moonstone, mŏn'stōn, *n.* A translucent variety of felspar used in trinkets, etc.

moor, mör, *n.* A tract of waste land or of hilly ground on which game is preserved, a native of the northern coast of Africa.—*vt.* To secure a ship in a particular station, as by cables and anchors.—*vi.* To be confined by cables.

mooring, mör'ing, *n.* Act of one who moors; *pl.* the anchor, etc., by which a ship is moored; the place where a ship is moored.

mop, mop, *n.* A cloth or collection of yarns fastened to a handle, and used for cleaning; a grimace.—*vt.* (mopping mopped). To rub with a mop; to wipe.—*vi.* To grimace.

mope, mŏp, *vi.* (moping, moped). To show a downcast air; to be spiritless or gloomy.—*n.* One who mopes.

moral, mo'ral, *a.* Relating to morality or morals; ethical; virtuous; supported by reason and probability. —*n.* The practical lesson inculcated by any story; *pl.* general conduct as right or wrong, mode of life; ethics.

moralist, mo'ral-ist, *n.* One who teaches morals; a writer or lecturer on ethics; one who inculcates or practices moral duties.

morality, mō-ral'i-ti, *n.* The doctrine of moral duties; ethics; moral character or quality; quality of an action in regard to right and wrong, an old form of drama in which the personages were allegorical representations of virtues, vices, etc.

morass, mō-ras', *n.* A tract of low soft, wet ground; a marsh; a swamp, a fen.

Mormon, mor'mon, *n.* A member of a sect founded in the United States in 1830, who practice polygamy; a Latter-day Saint. Also **Mormonite, Mormonist.**

morning, morn'ing, *n.* The first part of the day; the time between dawn and the middle of the forenoon; the first or early part. Often used as an *adj.*

Morocco, mō-rok'ō, *n.* A fine kind of leather prepared from goat skin.

mortality, mor-tal-i-ti, *n.* State of being mortal; actual death of great numbers of men or beasts; deathrate.

mortise, mor'tis, *n.* A hole cut in one piece of material to receive the tenon of another piece.—*vt.* To cut a mortise in; to join by a tenon and mortise.

mortuary, mor'tū-a-ri, *n.* A place for the temporary reception of the dead.—*a.* Pertaining to the burial of the dead.

mosaic, mō-zā'ik, *n.* Inlaid work of marble, precious stones, etc., disposed on a ground of cement so as to form designs.—*a.* Pertaining to or composed of mosaic.

moss, mos, *n.* A small plant with simple branching stems and numerous small leaves, a bog, a place where peat is found,—*vt.* To cover with moss by natural growth.

most, mŏst, *a.* superl. of more. Greatest in any way.—*adv.* In the greatest degree, quantity, or extent; mostly; chiefly.—*n.* The greatest number; the majority; greatest amount; utmost extent, degree, etc.

mother, muTH'ėr, *n.* A female parent; a woman who has borne a child, source or origin, an abbess or other female at the head of a religious institution; a slimy substance that gathers in vinegar etc.—*a.* Native; natural; inborn, vernacular.

mother-country, muTH'ėr-kun-tri *n.* A country which has sent out colonies, a country as the producer of anything.

motion, mō'shon, *n.* Act or process of moving; power of moving; movement, internal impulse, proposal made; evacuation of the intestines.—*vi.* To make a significant gesture with the hand.

motive, mō'tiv, *n.* That which incites to action; cause, inducement; purpose, theme in a piece of music; prevailing idea of an artist.—*a.* Causing motion.—*vt.* To supply a motive to or for, to prompt.

motley, mot'li, *a*. Variegated in color, parti colored, heterogeneous; diversified—*n*. A dress of various colors.

motor, mō'tor, *n*. A moving power; force or agency that sets machinery in motion; a motor-car—*a*. Imparting motion.

mottle, mot'l, *n*. A blotched or spotted character of surface.—*vt*. (mottling, mottled). To mark with spots or blotches as if mottled.

motto, mot'tō, *n.; pl.* -oes, or -os. A short sentence or phrase, or a single word, adopted as expressive of one's guiding idea.

moult, mōlt, *vi*. and *t*. To shed or cast the hair, feathers, skin, horns, etc., as birds and other animals.— *n*. Act or process of changing the feathers, etc.; time of moulting.

mound, mound. *n*. An artificial elevation of earth; a bulwark, a rampart; the globe which forms part of the regalia.

mount, mount, *n*. A hill; a mountain, that with which something is fitted, a setting, frame, etc.; opportunity or means of riding on horseback, a horse.—*vi*. To rise; to get on horseback or upon any animal; to amount.—*vt*. To raise aloft, to climb to place oneself upon, as on horseback; to furnish with horses; to set in or cover with something; to set off to advantage.

mountain, moun'tin, *n*. An elevated mass larger than a hill, anything very large.— *a*. Pertaining to a mountain; found on mountains.

mountaineer, moun-tin-ēr', *n*. An inhabitant of a mountainous district a climber of mountains.—*vi*. To practice the climbing of mountains.

mountebank, moun'ti-bangk, *n*. One who mounts a bench or stage in a public place, and vends medicines or nostrums, a quack: any boastful and false pretender.

mounting, mount 'ing, *n*. Act of one who mounts: that with which an article is mounted or set off; trimming, setting, etc.

mourn, mōrn, *vi*. To sorrow: to lament; to wear the customary habit of sorrow.— *vt*. To grieve for: to deplore.

mourning, mōrn'ing, *n*. Lamentation, dress worn by mourners.—*a*. Employed to express grief.

mouse, mous, *n*., pl. **mice**, mîs, A small rodent quadruped that infests houses, fields, etc.—*vi*. mouz (mousing, moused). To hunt for or catch mice.

mouth, mouth, *n.; pl*. **mouths**, mouTHz. The opening in the head of an animal into which food is received, and from which voice is uttered; opening of anything hollow, as of a pitcher. or of a cave, pit, etc., the part of a river, etc., by which it joins with the ocean.—*vt*. mouTH. To take into the mouth; to utter with a voice affectedly big.—*vi*. To speak with a loud, affected voice; to vociferate.

mouth-organ, mouth-or'gan, *n*. A small popular wind-instrument, flat in shape, with openings for the various notes, which are produced by inhalation and exhalation.

move, mōv, *vt*. (moving, moved). To cause to change place, posture, or position, to set in motion, to affect; to rouse, to prevail on; to propose, as a resolution.—*vi*. To change place or posture; to stir; to begin to act; to shake; to change residence to make a proposal to a meeting.—*n*. The act of moving; a movement; proceeding; action taken.

movement, mōv'ment, *n*. Act of moving; motion; change of position, manner of moving; gesture; an agitation to bring about some result desired, wheel-work of a clock.

mow, mō, *vt*. (pret. mowed, pp. mowed or mown). To cut down, as grass, etc.; to cut the grass from; to cut down in great numbers.—*vi*. To cut grass; to use the scythe.

much, much, *a.;* comp. more, superl. most. Great in quantity or amount, abundant.—*adv*. In a great degree; by far; greatly.—*n*. A great quantity; something strange or serious.

mucilage, mū'si-lāj, *n*. A solution in water of gummy matter, a gummy substance found in certain plants.

muck muk, *n*. Dung in a moist state, something mean, vile, or filthy.—*vt*. To manure with muck; to remove muck from.

mucous, mucose, mū'kus, *a*. Pertaining to mucus, or resembling it; slimy.— **mucous membrane**, a membrane that lines all the cavities of the body which open externally, and secretes mucus.

mud, mud, *n*. Moist and soft earth; sediment from turbid waters mire.—*vt*. (mudding, mudded). To soil with mud; to make turbid.

muddle, mud'l, *vt*. (muddling, muddled). To make muddy; to intoxicate partially, to confuse, to make a mess of.—*vi*. To

M

become muddy to act in a confused manner.—*n.* A mess, confusion, bewilderment.

muffle, muf'l, *vt.* (muffling, muffled). To cover close, particularly the neck and face; to conceal; to deaden the sound of by wrapping cloth, etc., round.—*n.* The tumid and naked portion of the upper lip and nose of ruminants and rodents.

muffler, muf'lẽr, *n.* A cover for the face or neck; a stuffed glove for lunatics.

multiple, mul'ti-pl, *a.* Manifold; having many parts or divisions.—*n.* A number which contains another an exact number of times.

multiplication, mul'ti-pli-kā"shon, *n.* Act or process of multiplying state of being multiplied; reproduction of animals.

multiply, mul'ti-plī, *vt.* (multiplying, multiplied). To increase in number; to add to itself any given number of times.—*vi.* To increase in number, or to become more numerous by reproductive; to extend.

multitude, mul'ti-tūd, *n.* State of being many; a great number, collectively or indefinitely, a crowd.— **The multitude,** the populace.

mumble, mum'bl, *vi.* (mumbling, mumbled). To mutter; to speak with mouth partly closed, to eat with the lips close.—*vt.* To utter with a low, inarticulate voice.

mummy, mum'i, *n.* A dead human body embalmed after the manner of the ancient Egyptians, with wax, balsams, etc.

mumps, mumps, *n.* Silent displeasure, sullenness, a disease consist ing in an inflammation of the salivary glands.

municipality, mū-ni'si-pal"i-ti, *n.* A town possessed of local self-government; community under municipal jurisdiction.

munificence, mū-ni'fi-sens, *n.* A be-stowing liberally; liberality; generosity.

munition, mū-ni'shon, *n.* Military stores; ammunition; material for any enterprise.

murder, mẽr'dẽr, *n.* Act of killing a human being with premeditated malice.—*vt.* To kill (a human being) with premeditated malice; to mar by bad execution.

murmur, mẽr'mẽr, *n.* A low continued or repeated sound, a hum, a grumble or mutter.—*vi.* To utter a murmur or hum, to grumble.—*vt.* To utter indistinctly, to mutter.

Muscadel, Muscatel, Muscadine,

mus'ka-del, mus'ka-tel, mus'ka-dīn, *a.* and *n.* A sweet and strong Italian or French wine; the grapes which produce this wine; a delicious pear.

muscle, mus'l, *n.* A definite portion of an animal body consisting of fibers susceptible of contraction and relaxation, and thus effecting motion, a mussel.

muscular, mus'ku-lẽr, *a.* Pertaining to or consisting of muscle; performed by a muscle; strong; brawny; vigorous.

muse, mūz, *n.* One of the nine sister goddesses of the Greeks and Romans presiding over the arts; poetic inspiration; a fit of abstraction.—*vi.* (musing mused). To ponder; to meditate in silence; to be absent in mind.—*vt.* To meditate on.

mushroom, mush'röm, *n.* An edible fungus; an upstart.—*a.* Pertaining to mushrooms; resembling mushrooms in rapidity of growth.

music, mū'zik, *n.* Melody of harmony, the science of harmonious sounds; the written or printed score of a composition.

muster, mus'tẽr, *vt.* To collect, as troops; to assemble or bring together—*vi.* To assemble, to meet in one place.—*n.* An assembling of troops; register of troops mustered an array

mutation, mū-tā'shon, *n.* Act or process of changing, change, alteration, either in form or qualities, modification.

mute, mūt, *a.* Silent, incapable of speaking; dumb; not pronounced, or having its sound checked by a contact of the vocal organs, as certain consonants *(t, p, k, etc.).*—*n.* A dumb person; a hired attendant at a funeral, a mute consonant.—*vi.* (muting, muted). To eject the contents of the bowels as birds.

myself, mī -self', *compd. pron.*, pl. **Ourselves,** our-selvz'. As a nominative it is used, generally after I, to express emphasis—I, and not another; in the objective often used reflexively and without any emphasis.

mysterious, mis-tē'ri-us, *a.* Containing mystery, beyond human comprehension; untelligible; enigmatical.

mystery, mis'tẽr-i, *n.* Something above human intelligence; a secret, an old form of drama in which the characters and events were drawn from sacred history; a trade craft, or calling.

myth, mith, *n.* A tradition or fable embodying the notions of a people as to their gods, origin early history etc., an invented story.

N

nab, nab, *vt.* (nabbing, nabbed). To catch or seize suddenly or unexpectedly.

nail, nāl, *n.* The horny substance at the end of the human finger and toes; a claw; a small pointed piece of metal, to be driven into timber etc., a stud or boss, a measure of 2-1/4 inches.—*vt.* To fasten or stud with nails; to hold fast or make secure.

naked, nā'ked, *a.* Not having clothes on; bare; nude; open to view; mere, bare, simple; destitute, unassisted.

name, nām, *n.* That by which a person or thing is designated; appellation; title, reputation, eminence sound only; not reality; authority, behalf; a family.—*vt.* (naming, named). To give a name to; to designate; to style; to nominate; to speak of or mention as.

namely, nām'li, *adv. By* name; particularly; that is to say.

nap, nap *n.* The woolly substance on the surface of cloth, etc.; the downy substance on plants, a short sleep.—*vi.* (napping napped). To have a short sleep; to drowse.

nape, nāp, *n.* The prominent joint of the neck behind; the back part of the neck.

nard, närd, *n.* An aromatic plant, usually called spikenard; an unguent prepared from the plant.

narrative, nar'a-tiv, *a.* Pertaining to narration.—*n.* That which is narrated or related; a relation orally or in writing.

narrow, na'rō, *a.* Of little breadth not wide or broad, very limited straitened; not liberal; bigoted, near; close; scrutinizing.—*n.* A narrow channel, a strait: usually in *pl.*—*vt.* To make narrow.—*vi.* To become narrow, to contract in breadth.

nasal, nā'zal, *a.* Pertaining to the nose, formed or affected by the nose, as speech.—*n.* An elementary sound uttered partly through the nose.

national, na'shon-al, *a.* Pertaining to a nation; public; attached to one's own country.

nationality, na-shon-al'i-ti, *n.* Quality of being national; national character; strong attachment to one's own nation; a nation.

native, nā'tiv, *a.* Pertaining to the place or circumstances of one's birth; indige-nous; inborn; occurring in nature pure or unmixed.— *n.* One born in a place or country; an indigenous animal or plant; an oyster raised in an artificial bed.

natural, na'tūr-al, *a.* Pertaining to nature; produced or effected by nature consistent with nature not artificial; according to the life, not revealed; bastard; unregenerated.—*n.* An idiot; a fool.

naturalization, na'tūr-al-izā"shon, *n.* Act of investing an alien with the privileges of a native citizen.

nature, nā'tūr, *n.* The universe, the total of all agencies and forces in the creation; the inherent or essential qualities of anything, individual constitution; sort; natural human instincts; reality as distinct from that which is artificial.

navigate, na'vi-gat, *vi.* To conduct or guide a ship, to sail.—*vt.* To manage in sailing, as a vessel; to sail or guide a ship over.

navy, nā'vi, *n.* All the ships of a certain class belonging to a country; the whole of the ships of war belonging to a nation.

near, nēr, *a.* Not distant in place, time, or degree, intimate, affecting one's interest or feelings, parsimonious; narrow; on the left of a horse, not circuitous.—*prep.* Close to; nigh.—*adv.* Almost; within a little; close to the wind.—*vt.* and *i.* To approach, to come near.

neat, nēt, *n.* Cattle of the bovine genus.— *a.* Pure; clean; trim; tidy; clever; smart, without water added

nebula, neb'ū-la, *n. pl.* -ae. Celestial objects like white clouds, generally clusters of stars.

necessary, ne'ses-sa-ri, *a.* Such as must be, inevitable, essential acting from necessity.—*n.* Anything indispensably requisite.

necrology, nek-rol 'o-ji, *n.* A register of deaths; a collection of obituary notices.

necromancy, nek'rō-man-si, *n.* The revealing of future events through pretended communication with the dead, sorcery.

Necropolis, nek-rō'po-lis, *n.* A city of the dead, a cemetery.

need, nēd, *n.* A state that requires supply or relief; urgent want; necessity; poverty; destitution.—*vt.* To have necessity or need for, to lack, require.—*vi.* To be necessary: used impersonally.

needle, nē'dl, *n.* An instrument for interweaving thread; a small steel instrument for sewing, a magnetized piece of steel in a compass attracted to the pole; anything in the form of a needle.

needless, nĕd'les, *a.* No needed or wanted; unnecessary; not requisite; useless.

needle-work, nē'dl-wêrk, *n.* Work done with a needle; business of a seamstress.

negative, neg'at-iv, *a.* That denies; implying denial or negation; implying absence, the opposite of positive.—*n.* A word which denies, as *not*, *no*, a proposition by which something is denied; a veto, a photographic picture on glass or celluloid, in which the lights and shades are the opposite of those in nature.—*vt.* To prove the contrary of; to reject by vote.

negotiate, nē-gō'shi-āt, *vi.* To treat with another respecting purchase and sale; to hold diplomatic intercourse; to conduct communications in general.—*vt.* To procure or bring about by negotiation to pass into circulation (as a bill of exchange).

neighborhood, nā'bêr-hud, *n.* Condition of being neighbors; neighbors collectively, vicinity, locality.

neither, nē'THêr or nī'THêr, *pron.* and *pron. adj.* Not either; not the one or the other—*conj.* Not either; nor.

nematoid, nem'a-toid, *n.* A roundworm; one of an order of entozoa or intestinal worms.—*a.* Pertaining to or resembling the nematoids.

Nemesis, nem'e-sis, *n.* A female Greek divinity personifying retributive justice; just retribution or punishment.

nerve, nêrv, *n.* One of the fibrous threads in animal bodies whose function is to convey sensation and originate motion; fortitude; courage; energy; something resembling a nerve.—*vt.* (nerving, nerved). To give strength or vigor to; to steel.

nervous, nêrv'us, *a.* Pertaining to the nerves, affecting the nerves having the nerves easily affected, easily agitated; having nerve or bodily strength, vigorous; sinewy.

nest, nest, *n.* The place or bed formed by a bird for laying and hatching her eggs; a number of persons frequenting the same haunt; a snug abode.—*vi. To* build a nest, to nestle.

nestle, nes'l, *vi.* (nestling, nestled). To make or occupy a nest; to lie close and snug.—*vt.* To shelter, as in a nest, to cherish.

net, net, *n.* A texture of twine, etc., with meshes, commonly used to catch fish, birds, etc.; a snare.—*vt.* (netting, netted). To make into a net; to take in a net; to capture by wile.

net, **nett**, net, *a.* Being clear of all deductions, estimated apart from all expenses.—*vt.* (netting, netted). To gain as clear profit.

neuter, nū'têr, *a.* Neutral; neither masculine nor feminine; neither active nor passive, as a verb.—*n.* An animal or neither sex; a plant with neither stamens nor pistils; a noun of the neuter gender.

neutral, nū-tral, *a.* Not siding with any party in a dispute; indifferent; neither acid nor alkaline.—*n.* A person or nation that takes no part in a contest between others.

neutralize, nū-tral-īz, *vt.* To render neutral or inoperative; to counteract.

neutron, nū-tron, *n.* An uncharged particle of the same mass as a proton.

nevertheless, nev'êr-THê-les", *adv.* Not the less, notwithstanding; yet; however.

new, nū, *a.* Recent in origin, novel not before known; different; unaccustomed, fresh after any event not second-hand.—*adv.* Newly; recently.

newel, nū'el, *n.* The upright structure in a winding staircase supporting the steps.

Newfoundland, nū-found'land or nu'found-land, *n.* A large dog, remarkable for sagacity and swimming powers.

newspaper, nūz'pa-per, *n.* A sheet of paper printed periodically for circulating news.

next, nekst, *a.* superl. of nigh. Nearest in place, time rank, or degree.—*adv.* At the time or turn nearest.

nick, nik, *n.* The exact point of time, the critical time; a notch; a score.—*vt.* To hit upon exactly; to make a nick in, to mark with nicks.

nickel, nik'el, *n.* A valuable metal of a white color and great hardness, magnetic, and when pure malleable and ductile.

nickel-silver, nik'el-sil-vêr, *n.* An alloy composed of copper, zinc, and nickel.

nickname, nik'nām, *n.* A name given in contempt or jest.—*vt.* To give a nickname to.

nicotine, nik'ō-tin, *n.* A volatile alkaloid from tobacco, highly poisonous.

night, nīt, *n.* The daily period of darkness; the time from sunset to sunrise, a state or time of darkness, depression, etc.; ignorance; obscurity, death.

nihilism, nī'hil-izm, *n.* Nothingness; the doctrine that nothing can be known; principles of a Russian secret society of communists.

nimble, nim'bl, *a.* Quick in motion; moving with ease and celerity; agile, prompt.

nimbus, nim'bus, *n.* A rain-cloud; a halo surrounding the head in representations of divine or sacred personages.

niter, nī'tėr, *n.* Nitrate of potassium or saltpeter, used for making gunpowder, in dyeing, medicine, etc.

nitrogen, nī'tro-gen. *n.* The elementary unflammable gas constituting about four-fifths of the atmospheric air.

nitro-glycerine, nī-trō-glis'ėr-in, *n.* A powerful explosive produced by the action of nitric and sulphuric acids on glycerine.

nitrous, nī'trus, *a.* Pertaining to niter; applied to compounds containing less oxygen than those called nitric.

nival, nī'val, *a.* Snowy; growing among snow, or flowering during winter.

no, nō, *adv.* A word of denial or refusal; not in any degree; not.—*n.* A denial; a negative vote.—*a.* Not any; none.

noble, nō'bl, *a.* Of lofty lineage; belonging to the peerage, illustrious, lofty in character; magnanimous, magnificent; stately.—*n.* A person of rank; a peer; an old English gold coin.

nocturn, nok'tėrn, *n.* A religious service formerly used in the R. Catholic Church at midnight, now a part of matins.

nod, nod, *vi.* (nodding, nodded). To make a slight bow, to let the head sink from sleep; to incline the head, as in assent or salutation, etc.—*vt.* To incline; to signify by a nod.—*n.* A quick inclination of the head.

node, nōd, *n.* A knot, a protuberance; a sort of knot on a stem where leaves arise, one of the two points in which two great circles of the celestial sphere intersect.

nominal, no'mi-nal, *a.* Pertaining to a name; titular; not real; merely so called.

nonagon, non'a-gon, *n.* A plane figure having nine sides and nine angles.

non-conductor, non-kon-dukt'ėr, *n.* A substance which does not conduct, or transmits with difficulty heat, electricity, etc.

nonconformist, non-kon-form'ist, *n.* One who does not conform to the established church.

nonconformity, non-kon-form'i-ti, *n.* Neglect or failure of conformity, refusal to unite with an established church.

nondescript, non'dē-skript, *a.* That has not been described, abnormal; odd;

indescribable.—*n.* A person or thing not easily described or classed.

nonentity, non-en'ti-ti, *n.* Non-existence; a thing not existing; a person utterly without consequence or Importance.

nonesuch, nun'such, *n.* A person or thing that has not its equal or parallel.

noonday, nön'dā, *n.* Mid-day noon.—*a.* Pertaining to mid-day, meridional.

noose, nös or nöz, *n.* A running knot, which binds the closer the more it is drawn.—*vt.* (noosing. noosed). To tie or catch in a noose, to entrap.

nor, nor, *conj.* A word used to render negative a subsequent member of a clause or sentence, correlative to neither or other negative; also equivalent to *and not.*

Nordic, nor'dik *a.* Of or belonging to those peoples of Northern Europe who are long-headed, tall blue-eyed and fair-haired.

normal, nor'mal, *a.* According to a rule, conforming with a certain type or standard; regular; perpendicular.—**normal school**, a training-college for teachers. *n.* A perpendicular.

nose, nöz, *n.* The organ of smell employed also in respiration and speech; the power of smelling; scent, sagacity, a nozzle.—*vt.* and *i.* (nosing, nosed). To smell; to wange through the nose; to pry officiously.

nostalgia, nos-tal'ji-a, *n.* Vehement desire to revisit one's native country, home-sickness.

nostrum, nos'trum, *n.* A quack medicine, the ingredients of which are kept secret.

note, nōt, *n.* A mark, sign, or token; an explanatory or critical comment; a memorandum; a bill, account; a paper promising payment, a communication in writing notice, reputation; distinction; a character representing a musical sound, or the sound itself.—*vt.* (noting, noted). To observe carefully; to mark; to set down in writing.

noteworthy, nōt-wėr-THi, *a.* Deserving notice; worthy of observation or notice.

notice, nōt'is, *n.* Act of noting; regard; information; order; intimation; civility; a brief critical review.—*vt.* (noticing, noticed). To take note of; to perceive; to make observations on; to treat with attention.

notify, nōt'i-fī, *vt.* To make known; to declare; to give notice to; to inform.

notoriety, nō-tō-rī'e-ti, *n.* State of being notorious; discreditable publicity; one who is notorious.

novel, no'vel, *a.* Of recent origin or introduction, new and striking unusual.—*n.* A fictitious prose narrative picturing real life.

novelist, no'vel-ist, *n.* A writer of novels.

noxious, nok'shus, *a.* Hurtful, pernicious, unwholesome; corrupting to morals.

nozzle, noz'l, *n.* The projecting spout of something; terminal part of a pipe.

nucleus, nū'klē-us, *n.;* pl. **-lei.** A kernel or something similar, a mass about which matter is collected, body of a comet.

number, num'ber, *n.* An aggregate of units, or a single unit; a numeral; many; one of a numbered series of things, part of a periodical, metrical arrangement of syllables; difference of form in a word to express unity or plurality.—*vt.* To reckon; to enumerate; to put a number on; to reach the number of.

numeral, nū'mėr-al, *a.* Pertaining to number; consisting of or representing number.—*n.* A figure used to express a number.

numerate, nū'me˙ r-āt, *vt.* (numerating, numerated). To count; to enumerate.

numerator, nū'mėr-āt-er, *n.* One who numbers; the number (above the line) in vulgar fractions which shows how many parts of a unit are taken.

numerous, nū'mėr-us, *a.* Consisting of a great number of individuals, many.

nurse, nėrs, *n.* One who suckles or nourishes a child, one who tends the young, sick, or infirm; an attendant in a hospital, one who or that which nurtures or protects.— *vt.* (nursing, nursed). To act as nurse to, to suckle, to rear, to tend in sickness or infirmity; to foment; to foster.

nursery, nėr'sė-ri, *n.* The place in which children are nursed and taken care of; a place where trees, plants, etc., are propagated.

nurture, nėr'tūr, *n.* Upbringing education, nourishment.—*vt.* (nurturing, nurtured). To nourish, to educate; to bring or train up.

nut, nut, *n.* A fruit containing a seed or kernel within a hard covering; a small block of metal or wood with a grooved hole, to be screwed on the end of a bolt.—*vi.* (nutting, nutted). To gather nuts.

nutation, nū-tā'shon, *n.* A nodding a slight gyratory movement of the earth's axis.

nutmeg, nut'meg, *n.* The aromatic kernel of the fruit of a tree of the Malay Archipelago.

nymph, nimf, *n.* A goddess of the mountains, forests, meadow, or waters, a young and attractive woman; a maiden; the chrysalis of an insect.

O

O, ō, An exclamation used in earnest or solemn address; often distinguished from *Oh,* which is more strictly expressive of emotion.

obedience, ō-bē'di-ens, *n.* Act of obeying; quality of being obedient, submission to authority.

obelisk o'be-lisk, *n.* A tall four-sided pillar, tapering as it rises and terminating in a small pyramid, a mark (†) used in printing.

obey, ō-bā', *vt.* To comply with, as commands or requirements; to be ruled by; to yield to.—*vi.* To submit to authority.

obituary, ō-bit'ū-a-ri, *n.* An account of a person or persons deceased, list of the dead.—*a.* Relating to the decease of a person.

object, ob'jekt *n.* That about which any faculty of the mind is employed; end; purpose; a concrete reality; the word, clause, etc., governed by a transitive verb or by a preposition.—*vt.* ob-jekt'. To oppose, to offer as an objection.—*vi.* To oppose in words or arguments.

objective, ob-jek'tiv, *a.* Pertaining to an object; relating to whatever is exterior to the mind (also *pron.* ob'jek-tiv), belonging to the case which follows a transitive verb or preposition.—*n.* The objective case, object, place, etc., aimed at.

oblige, ō-blīj', *vt.* (obliging, obliged). To constrain, to bind by any restraint; to lay under obligation of gratitude; to render service or kindness to.

oblivion, ob-li'vi-on, *n.* State of being forgotten; forgetfulness; act of forgetting.

obscure, ob-skūr', *a.* Darkened dim; not easily understood; abstruse; unknown to fame; indistinct.—*vt.* (obscuring obscured). To darken; to make less visible, legible, or intelligible; to tarnish.

observe, ob-zé rv', *vt.* (observing observed). To take notice of, to behold with attention; to remark; to keep religiously; to celebrate; to comply with; to practice.—*vi.* To remark; to be attentive.

obsession, ob-sesh'on, *n.* Act of besieging; persistent attack; state of being beset.

obstruction, ob-struk'shon, *n.* Act of obstructing, that which impedes progress; obstacle; impediment; check.

obstruent, ob'strü-ent, *a.* Obstructing.—*n.* Anything that obstructs the natural passages in the body.

obtain, ob-tān', *vt.* To get possession of; to acquire; to earn.—*vi.* To be received in common use, to prevail; to hold good.

obverse, ob'vèrs, *n.* and *a.* That side of a coin or medal which has the face or head or principal device on it.

obviate, ob'vi-ā t, *vt.* (obviating, obviated). To meet, as difficulties or objections; to get over, to remove.

occupancy, ok'kū-pan-si, *n.* Act of occupying; a holding in possession; term during which one is occupant.

occupation, ok-kū-pā'shon, *n.* Act of occupying; act of taking possession; tenure; business; employment; vocation.

occupy, ok'kū-pī, *vt.* (occupying, occupied). To take possession of; to hold and use; to cover or fill; to employ; to engage: often *refl.*—*vi.* To be an occupant.

occur, ok-kèr', *vi.* (occurring, occurred). To come to the mind; to happen; to be met with; to be found here and there.

occurrence, ok-ku'rens, *n.* The act of occurring or taking place; any incident or accidental event, an observed instance.

ocean, ō'shan, *n.* The vast body of water which covers more than three-fifths of the globe; the sea; one of the great areas into which the sea is divided, any immense expanse.—*a.* Pertaining to the great sea.

odd, od, *a.* Not even, not exactly divisible by 2; not included with others; incidental; casual; belonging to a broken set, queer

odds, odz, *n. sing.* or *pl.* Inequality excess; difference in favor of one, advantage; amount by which one bet exceeds another.

off, of, *adv.* Away, distant, not on from; not toward.—**Well off, ill off,** in good or bad circumstances. *a.* Distant, farther away, as applied to horses; right hand—*prep.* Not on; away from; to seaward from.— *interj.* Begone!

offense, of-fens', *n.* Injury, an affront, insult, or wrong; displeasure; transgression of law; misdemeanor.

offend, of-fend', *vt.* To displease; to shock; to cause to sin or neglect duty.—*vi.* To sin, to commit a fault to cause dislike or anger.

offensive, of-fens'iv, *a.* Causing offense; causing displeasure or annoyance; disgusting; impertinent; used in attack, aggressive.—*n.* Act or posture of attack

offer, of'er, *vt.* To present for acceptance or rejection; to tender; to bid, as a price or wages.—*vi.* To present itself; to declare a willingness, to make an attempt.—*n.* Act of offering; act of bidding a price; the sum bid.

offertory, of'er-to-ri, *n.* Sentences read or repeated in church while the alms or gifts are collecting the alms collected.

off-hand, of'hand, *a.* Done without thinking or hesitation, unpremeditated.—*adv.* On the spur of the moment; promptly.

office, of'is, *n.* Special duty or business; high employment or position under government; function; service, a formulary of devotion, a place where official or professional business is done; persons entrusted with certain duties, persons who transact business in an office; pl. kitchens, outhouses, etc., of a mansion or farm.

officer, of'is-er, *n.* A person invested with an office one who holds a commission in the army or navy.—*vt.* To furnish with officers.

official, of-fi'shal, *a.* Pertaining to an office or public duty, made by virtue of authority.—*n.* One invested with an office of a public nature.

officiate, of-fi'shi-āt, *vi.* To perform official duties, to act in an official capacity.

oil, oil, *n.* An unctuous inflammable liquid drawn from various animal and vegetable substances, a similar substance of mineral origin; an oil-color.—*vi.* To smear or rub over with oil.

oleander, ö-lē-an'der, *n.* An evergreen flowering shrub.

olfactory ol-fak'to-ri, *a.* Pertaining to smelling; having the sense of smelling.—*n.* An organ of smelling.

oligarchy, o'li-gär-ki, *n.* Govern-ment in which the supreme power is in a few hands, those who form such a class or body.

olive, o'liv, *n.* An evergreen tree its fruit, from which a valuable oil is expressed; the color of the olive; the emblem of peace.—*a.* Relating to, or of the color of the olive.

Olympiad, ö-lim'pi-ad, *n.* A period of four years reckoned from one celebration of the Olympic games to another,

the first Olympiad beginning 776 B.C.

omen, ö'men, *n.* An event thought to portend good or evil; an augury; presage.—*vi.* To augur, to betoken.—*vt.* To predict.

ominous, o'min-us, *a.* Containing an omen, and especially an ill omen; inauspicious.

omission, ö-mi'shon, *n.* Act of omitting; neglect or failure to do something required; failure to insert or mention, something omitted.

omit, ö-mit', *vt.* (omitting, omitted) To pass over or neglect; not to insert or mention.

omnivorous, om-niv'or-us, *a.* All-devouring; eating food of every kind.

on, on, *prep.* Above and touching by contact with the surface or upper part; in addition to; at or near; immediately after and as a result in reference or relation to, toward or so as to affect; at the peril of among the staff of; pointing to a state, occupation, etc.—*adv.* On ward; in continuance, adhering not off

once, wuns, *adv.* One time, formerly; immediately after; as soon as.—**At once,** all together; suddenly, forthwith.

one, wun, *a.* Being but a single thing or a unit, closely united forming a whole; single.—*n.* The first of the simple units; the symbol representing this (= 1).—**At one,** in union or concord.—*pron.* Any single person; any man; any person, a thing, particular thing.

only, ön'li, *a.* Single; sole; alone.— *adv.* For one purpose alone; simply; merely; solely.—*conj.* But; excepting that.

onomatopoeia, on'o-ma-tō-pē"a, *n.* The formation of words by imitation of sounds.

ooze, öz, *n.* A soft flow, as of water; soft mud or slime; liquor of a tanvat.—*vi.* (oozing, oozed). To flow or issue forth gently; to percolate.— *vt.* To emit in the shape of moisture.

opal, ö-pal, *n.* A precious stone, which exhibits changeable reflections of green, blue, yellow, and red.

open, ö'pn, *a.* Not shut, covered, or blocked; not restricted, accessible; public; spread out; free, liberal, bounteous, candid, clear, exposed, fully prepared, attentive amenable; not settled; enunciated with a full utterance.—*n.* An open or clear space.—*vt.* To make open; to unclose; to cut into; to spread out; to begin; to make public; to declare open; to reveal.—*vi.* To unclose itself; to be parted; to begin. **opening**, ō'pn-ing, a. First in order; beginning.—n. Act of one who or that which opens; an open place; aperture; beginning; vacancy; opportunity of commencing a business, etc.

opera, o'pe-ra, n. A dramatic composition set to music and sung and acted on the stage; a theater where operas are performed.

opossum, ō-pos'um, n. The name of several marsupial mammals of America.

opponent, op-pō'nent, a. Opposing; antagonistic; opposite.—n. One who opposes; an adversary; an antagonist.

opposition, op-pō-zi'shon, n. Act of opposing; attempt to check or defeat; contradiction, inconsistency; the collective body of opponents of a ministry.

oppressive, op-pres'iv, a. Burden-some, unjustly severe, tyrannical.

optics, op'tiks, n. The science which treats of the nature and properties of light and vision, optical instruments, etc.

optimism, op'tim-izm, n. The opinion or doctrine that everything is for the best, tendency to take the most hopeful view.

or, or, conj. A particle that marks an alternative, and frequently corresponds with either and whether.—adv. Ere before.—n. Heraldic name for gold.

oracle, o'ra-kl, n. Among the Greeks and Romans, the answer of a god to an inquiry respecting some future event, place where the answers were given, the sanctuary of the ancient Jews; any person reputed uncommonly wise, a wise or authoritative utterance.

orange, o'ranj n. An evergreen fruit-tree and also its fruit, the color of this fruit, a reddish yellow.—a. Belonging to an orange; colored as an orange.

orange-peel, o'ranj-pēl, n. The rind of an orange separated from the fruit, the peel of the bitter orange dried and candied.

orchestra, or'kes-tra, n. That part of the Greek theater allotted to the chorus; that part of a theater, etc. appropriated to the musicians; a body of musicians.

order, or'dėr, n. Regular disposition; proper state; established method, public tranquillity, command; instruction to supply goods or to pay money; rank, class, division, or dignity, a religious fraternity; division of natural objects; pl. clerical character, specially called holy orders.—**In order**, for the purpose.—vt. To place in order; to direct; to command; to give an order or com-

mission for—vi. To give command.

ordinal, or'din-al, a. Expressing order or succession.—n. A number denoting order (as first); a book containing an ordination service.

ordinance, or'din-ans, n. That which is ordained; law, statute, edict, decree.

ordinary, or'din-a-ri, a. Con-formable to order; regular; customary; common; of little merit.—n. An ecclesiastical judge; a judge who takes cognizance of causes in his own right; an eating-house where the prices are settled.—**In ordinary**, in actual and constant service; statedly attending, as a physician: but a ship in ordinary is one laid up.

ordinate, or'din-āt, a. Regular, methodical.—n. In geometry, a line of reference determining the position of a point.

organ, or'gan, n. An instrument or means; a part of an animal or vegetable by which some function is carried on; a medium of conveying certain opinions; a newspaper; the largest wind instrument of music.

organization, or'gan-i-zā"shon, n. Act or process of organizing suitable disposition of parts for performance of vital functions.

organize, or'gan-īz, vt. To give an organic structure to; to establish and systematize, to arrange so as to be ready for service.

Orient, ō'ri-ent, a. Rising, as the sun; eastern; oriental; bright.—n. The East, luster as that of a pearl.—vt. To define the position of; to cause to lie from east to west.

orientation, ōr'i-en-tā"shon, n. A turning towards the east; position east and west.

origin, o'ri-jin, n. Source, beginning; derivation; cause; root; foundation.

original, ō-ri'jin-al, a. Pertaining to origin; primitive, first in order; having the power to originate, not copied.—n. Origin; source; first copy; model; that from which anything is translated or copied, a person of marked individuality.

originate, ō-ri'jin-āt, vt. (originating, originated). To give origin to; to produce.—vi. To have origin; to be begun.

Orthodox, or'thō-doks, a. Sound in opinion or doctrine; sound in religious doctrines; in accordance with sound doctrine.

orthography, or-thog'ra-fi, n. The art of writing words with the proper letters; spelling.

O

Orthopter, Orthopteran, or-thop'tėr, or-thop'tėr-an, *n.* One of an order of insects including cockroaches, grasshoppers, and locusts.

osmose, os'mōs, *n.* The tendency of fluids to pass through porous partitions and mix.

osprey, os'prā, *n.* A kind of hawk or eagle which feeds on fish; one of its feathers.

Osteopathy, os-tĕ-op'a-thi, *n.* A system of medical treatment, based on the view that the proper adjustment of the vital mechanism is a more important factor than chemical intake in the maintenance of health.

ostrich, os'trich, *n.* A large running bird of Africa, Arabia, and S. America, the largest of existing birds.

other, uTH'ėr, *a.* and *pron.* Not the same; second of two; not this; opposite; often used reciprocally with each.

ounce, ouns, *n.* The twelfth part of a pound troy, and the sixteenth of a pound avoirdupois; an Asiatic animal like a small leopard.

our, our, *a.* or *pron.* Pertaining or belonging to us. Ours is used when no noun follows.

out, out, *adv.* On or towards the outside, not in or within forth, beyond usual limits; not in proper place; public; exhausted; deficient; not in employment; loudly; in error, at a loss, having taken her place as a woman in society.—*n.* One who is out, a nook or corner.— *vt.* To put out.—*interj.* Away! begone!

outbreak, out'brāk, *n.* A breaking forth; eruption; sudden manifestation as of anger, disease, etc.

outer, out'ėr, *a.* Being on the outside, external.—*n.* That part of a target beyond the circles surrounding the bull's-eye; a shot which hits this part.

outermost, out'ėr-mōst, *a.* Being farthest out; being on the extreme external part.

outgrow, out-grō', *vt.* To surpass in growth; to grow too great or old for anything.

outlaw, out'lä, *n.* A person excluded from the benefit of the law—*vt.* To deprive of the benefit and protection of law; to proscribe.

out-patient, out'pā-shent, *n.* A patient not residing in a hospital, but who receives medical advice, etc., from the institution.

outpost, out'pōst, *n.* A station at a distance from the main body of an army; troops placed at such a station.

outrage, out'rāj, *vt.* (outraging, outraged). To do extreme violence or injury to; to abuse; to commit a rape upon.—*n.* Excessive abuse injurious violence.

outskirt, out'skėrt, *n.* Parts near the edge of an area, border, purlieu; generally in *pl.*

outspoken, out'spō-kn, *a.* Free or bold of speech, candid, frank.

outspread, out-spred', *vt* To spread out, to diffuse.—*a.* Extended; expanded.

outstanding, out-stand'ing, *a.* Projecting outward; prominent; unpaid; undelivered.

oval, ō'val, *a.* Shaped like an egg elliptical.—*n.* A figure shaped like an egg or ellipse.

ovation, ō-vā'shon, *n.* A lesser triumph among the ancient Romans; triumphal reception; public marks of respect.

over, ō'vėr, *prep.* Above; denoting motive, occasion, or superiority; across; throughout; upwards of.— *adv.* From side to side; in width; on all the surface, above the top or edge; in excess, completely, too.— *a.* Upper; covering.—*n.* *(cricket)* The number of balls (six or eight) which the bowler delivers in succession from one end of the pitch before a change is made to the other side.

overcharge, ō'vėr-chärj', *vt.* To charge or burden to excess; to fill too numerously.—*n.* o'ver-charj. An excessive charge.

overflow, ō'vėr-flō', *vt.* (pp. overflowed and overflown). To flow or spread over; to flood; to overwhelm.—*vi.* To be so full that the contents run over; to abound.—*n.* o'ver-flo. An inundation; superabundance.

overhaul, ō'vėr-häl', *vt.* To examine thoroughly with a view to repairs, to re-examine; to gain upon or overtake.—*n.* o'ver-hal. Examination, inspection, repair.

overlook, ō'vėr-lük', *vt.* To oversee to superintend; to view from a higher place; to pass by indulgently.

overnight, ō'vėr-nīt, *adv.* Through or during the night; in the night before.

overpower, ō'vėr-pou'ėr, *vt.* To be too powerful for; to bear down by force; to overcome; to subdue; to crush.

overreach, ō'vėr-rēch', *vt.* To reach over or beyond, to deceive by artifice; to outwit.

overrule, ō'vėr-röl', *vt.* To control; to govern with high authority; to disallow.

overrun, ō'vėr-run', *vt.* To run or spread over; to ravage; to outrun.—*vi.* To overflow, to run over.

oversea, ō'vėr-sē, *a.* Foreign, from beyond sea.—**overseas,** ō'vėr-sēz *adv.* Abroad.

overtake, ō'vėr-tāk', *vt.* To come up with; to catch; to take by surprise.

overthrow, ō'vėr-thrō', *vt.* To throw or turn over, to overset, to defeat to destroy.—*n.* o'ver-thro. Ruin defeat.

overturn, ō'vėr-tėrn', *vt.* To overset or overthrow; to capsize; to subvert; to ruin.

overweening, ō'vėr-wēn'ing, *a* Haughty; arrogant; proud; conceited.

overwork, ō'vėr-wėrk', *vt.* To work beyond strength, to tire with labor.—*n.* o'ver-werk. Work done beyond one's strength or beyond the amount required.

overwrought, ō'vėr-rat', *p.a.* Wrought to excess; excited to excess, tasked beyond strength.

owe, ō, *vt.* (owing, owed). To be indebted in; to be obliged or bound to pay; to be obliged for.

own, ōn, *a.* Belonging to: used, distinctively and emphatically, after a possessive pronoun, or a noun in the possessive.—*vt.* To hold or possess by right; to acknowledge or avow, to concede.

oxygen, oks'i-jen, *n.* A gaseous element, a component of atmospheric air and water, and essential to animal and vegetable life and combustion.

O

P

pabulum, pab'ū-lum, *n.* Food; that which feeds either mind or body.

pace, pās, *n.* A step; space between the two feet in walking; distance of 2-1/2 feet or 5 feet, gait rate of progress.—*vi.* (pacing, paced). To step, to walk slowly; to move by lifting the legs on the same side together; as a horse.—*vt.* To measure by steps; to accompany and set a proper rate of motion; to race.

pacific, pa-sif'ik, *a.* Suited to make peace; pacifying; calm.—**The Pacific Ocean,** the ocean between America, Asia, and Australia.

package, pak'ā j, *n.* A bundle or bale; a packet; charge for packing goods.

pack-horse, pak'hors, *n.* A horse employed in carrying goods and baggage on its back

pack-saddle, pak'sad-l, *n.* The saddle of a pack-horse, made for bearing burdens.

pact, pakt, *n.* A contract; an agreement or covenant.

pad, pad, *n.* An easy-paced horse; a robber who infests the road on foot; a soft saddle; a cushion; a quantity of blotting paper.—*vi.* (padding, padded). To walk or go on foot; to rob on foot.—*vt.* To furnish with padding.

padlock, pad'lok, *n.* A lock with a link to be fastened through a staple.—*vt. To* fasten or provide with a padlock

padre, päd'rā, *n.* A chaplain.

paean, pē'an, *n.* A war-song; song of triumph.

pagan, pā'gan, *n.* A heathen.—*a.* Heathenish; idolatrous.

page, pā j, *n.* A young male attendant on persons of distinction; one side of a leaf of a book, a written record.—*vt.* (paging, paged) To number the pages of

pain, pān, *n.* A penalty, bodily suffering, distress, anguish; *pl.* The throes of childbirth; labor; diligent effort.—*vt.* To cause pain to; to afflict, to distress.

painstaking, pānz'tāk-ing, *a.* Giving close application, laborious and careful.—*n.* The taking of pains; careful labor.

paint, pānt, *vt.* To represent by colors and figures; to cover with color, to portray, to delineate.—*vi.* To practice painting.—*n.* A substance used in painting; a pigment; rouge.

painting, pānt'ing, *n.* Art or employment of laying on colors; art of representing objects by colors; a picture, colors laid on.

pair, pãr, *n.* Two things of like kind suited, or used together; a couple, a man and his wife, two members on opposite sides in parliament, etc., who agree not to vote for a time.—*vi.* To join in pairs, to mate.—*vt.* To unite in pairs.

pajamas, pā-jäm-az, *n.pl.* A sleeping-suit.

palace, pa'lās, *n.* The house in which an emperor, king, bishop etc., resides, a splendid residence.

paleography, pal-ē-og'ra-fi, *n.* The art of deciphering ancient writing.

paleolithic, pal'ē-ō-lith''ik, *a.* Belonging to the earlier stone period, when rude unpolished stone implements were used.

paleontology, pal'ē-on-tol''o-ji, *n.* The science of fossil organic remains.

paleozoic pal'ē-ō-zō''ik, *a.* In *geology,* applied to the lowest division of stratified groups.

palatable, pa'lat-a-bl, *a.* Agreeable to the palate or taste; savory.

palate pa'lāt *n.* The roof of the mouth; taste relish; intellectual taste.

palatial, pa-lā'shal, *a.* Pertaining to a palace; becoming a palace; magnificent.

palaver, pa-la'vè r, *n.* A long or serious conference; idle talk.—*vt.* To flatter or humbug.—*vi.* To talk idly; to engage in a palaver.

pale, pāl, *n.* A pointed stake, an inclosure; sphere or scope.—*vt.* (paling, paled). To inclose with pales to fence in.—*vi.* To turn pale.—*a.* Whitish; wan; deficient in color; not bright, dim.

pall, päl, *n.* An outer mantle of dignity, a cloth thrown over a coffin at a funeral; a linen cloth to cover a chalice; a covering.—*vt.* To cover with a pall, to shroud to make vapid; to cloy.—*vi.* To become vapid or cloying.

palladium, pal-lā'di-um. *n.* A statue of the goddess Pallas; bulwark; safeguard; a grayish-white hard malleable metal.

pallet, pal'et, *n.* A palette; a tool used by potters, etc.; a small rude bed.

palliate, pal'i-āt, *vt.* To extenuate; to mitigate; to lessen, abate, alleviate.

pallid, pal'id, *a.* Pale, wan.

pallor, pal'or, *n.* Paleness.

palm, päm, *n.* The inner part of the hand, a measure of 3 or 4 inches, name of plants constituting an order of endogens; a branch or leaf of such a plant, victory; triumph.—*vt.* To conceal in the palm of the hand, to impose by fraud.

palpitate, pal 'pi-tāt, vi. (palpitating, palpitated). To pulsate rapidly; to throb, to tremble.

palpitation, pal-pi-tā'shon, n. Act of palpitating; violent pulsation of the heart.

palsy, päl'zi, n. Paralysis, especially of a minor kind.—vt. (palsing, palsied). To affect with palsy; to paralyze.

paltry, päl'tri, a. Mean and trivia] trifling; worthless; contemptible.

paludal, pal'ū-dal, a. Pertaining to marshes. Also *paludine, palustral, palustrine.*

pampas, pam'pas, n.pl. The immense grassy treeless plains of South America.

pamper pam'pėr, vt. To gratify to the full; to furnish with that which delights.

pamphlet, pam'flet n. A small book, stitched but not bound; short treatise.

pan, pan, n. A broad and shallow vessel, of metal or earthenware, pond for evaporating salt water to make salt part of a gun-lock hold ing the priming: the skull; the Greek and Roman god of flock and herds.

panacea, pan-a-sē'a, n. A remedy for all diseases; a universal medicine.

pancake, pan'kāk, n. A thin cake fried in a pan or baked on an iron plate.

panel, pa'nel, n. A surface distinct from others adjoining in a piece of work; a sunk portion in a door, etc.; a piece of wood on which a picture is painted, list of Health Insurance doctors for a district; a doctor's list of insured persons; list of those summoned to serve on a jury, in Scotland, the accused.—vt. (paneling, paneled). To form with panels.

pang, pang, n. A sharp and sudden pain; painful spasm; throe.

panic, pan'ik, n. A sudden fright; terror inspired by a trifling cause.—a. Extreme, sudden, or causeless: said of fright.

pant, pant, vi. To breathe quickly, to gasp; to desire ardently.—n. A gasp, a throb.

pantaloons, pan'ta-lönz, n.pl. Tightly fitting trousers; trousers in general.

pantheism, pan'thē-izm, n. The doctrine that the universe is God or that all things are manifestations of God.

Pantheon, pan'thē-on, n. A temple dedicated to all the gods, all the divinities collectively worshiped by a people.

papacy, pā'pa-si, n. The office and dignity of the pope; the popes collectively; papal authority or jurisdiction; popedom.

paper, pā'pėr, n. A substance formed into thin sheets used for writing, printing, etc.; a leaf, or sheet of this; a journal; an essay or article, promissory notes, bills of exchange, etc.—a. Made or consisting of paper; appearing merely in documents without really existing; slight.—vt. To cover with paper; to inclose in paper

par, pär, n. State of equality; equality in condition or value state of shares or stocks when they may be purchased at the original price.

parable, pa'ra-bl, n. An allegorical representation of something real in life or nature, embodying a moral.

parabola, pa-ra'bō-la, n. A conic section, shown when a cone is cut by a plane parallel to one of its sides, the curve described theoretically by a projectile.

parachute, pa'ra-shöt, n. An apparatus like a large umbrella, enabling a safe drop to the ground from an aircraft.

paraclete, pa'ra-klēt, n. One called to aid or support; the Holy Spirit.

parade, pa-rād', n. Ostentation show; military display; place where such display is held.—vt. (parading, paraded). To exhibit in ostentatious manner; to marshal in military order.—vi. To walk about for show; to go about in military procession.

paragraph, pa'ra-graf, n. The character ¶ used as a reference, etc.; a distinct section of a writing, distinguished by a break in the lines; a brief notice.

parallax, pa'ral-laks, n. The apparent change of position of an object when viewed from different points; the difference between the place of a heavenly body as seen from the earth's surface and its center at the same time.

parallel, pa'ral-lel, a. Extended in the same direction, and in all parts equally distant, as lines or surfaces; running in accordance with something, equal in all essential parts.—n. A line which throughout its whole length is equidistant from another line; conformity in all essentials; likeness, comparison, counterpart.— vt. To place so as to be parallel; to correspond to; to compare.

parallelogram, pa-ral-lel'ō-gram, n. A quadrilateral, whose opposite sides are parallel and equal.

parapet, pa'ra-pet n. A wall or rampart breast-high, a wall on the edge of a

P

bridge, quay, etc.

paraphernalia, pa'ra-fér-nā''li-a, *n.pl.* That which a bride brings besides her dowry, as clothing, jewels, etc.; personal attire; trappings.

paraphrase, pa'ra-frāz, *n.* A statement giving the meaning of another statement; a loose or free translation; a sacred song based on a portion of Scripture.—*vt.* To make a paraphrase of; to explain or translate with latitude.

parasite, pa'ra-sīt, *n.* One who frequents the rich, and earns his welcome by flattery; a sycophant: an animal that lives upon or in another; a plant which grows on another.

parasol, pa'ra-sol *n.* A small umbrella used to keep off the sun's rays.

parcel, pär'sel, *n.* A portion of anything, a small bundle or package a collection.—*vt.* (parceling, parceled). To divide into portions, to make up into packages.

parcel-post, pär'sel-pōst, *n.* Depart-ment of a post-office by which parcels are sent.

parch, pärch, *vt.* To dry to extremity; to scorch.—*vi.* To become very dry; to be scorched.

parenthesis, pa-ren'the-sis, *n.;* pl. -theses. A sentence or words inserted in another sentence, usually in brackets. thus, ( ).

parhelion, pär-hē'li-on, *n.*, pl. -lia. A mock sun or meteor, appearing as a bright light near the sun.

park, pärk, *n.* A piece of ground inclosed; ornamental ground adjoining a house; ground in a town for recreation; an assemblage of heavy ordnance.—*vt.* To inclose in a park; to bring together as artillery; to draw up motorcars and leave them for a time in an inclosed space, or at the side of the road.

parody, pa'rod-i, *n.* An adaptation of the words of an author, etc., to a different purpose; a burlesque imitation.—*vt.* (parodying, parodied). To imitate in parody.

parole, pa-rōl', *n.* Words or oral declarations, word of honor, a promise by a prisoner of war not to bear arms against his captors for a certain period, or the like, a military countersign.

paroxysm, pa'roks-izm, *n.* A violent access of feeling (as of rage) convulsion; spasm.

parsimony, pär'si-mō-ni, *n.* The habit of being sparing in expenditure of money; excessive frugality; miserliness; close-ness.

parsley, pärs'li, *n.* A garden vegetable, used for flavoring in cooking.

parsnip, pärs'nip, *n.* An umbelliferous plant with a fleshy esculent root.

parson, pär'sn, *n.* The priest or incumbent of a parish; a clergyman.

part, pärt, *n.* A portion or piece of a whole; a section; a constituent or organic portion; share; lot; party; duty; business; character assigned to an actor in a play; *pl.* faculties, superior endowments, regions' locality.—*vt.* To divide; to sever; to share; to distribute; to separate; to intervene.—*vi.* To become separated, broken, or detached; to quit each other; to depart.

partake, pär-tā k', *vi.* (partaking, pret. partook, pp. partaken). To take or have a part with others; to share, to have something of the nature, claim, or right.—*vt.* To share.

partial, pär'shal, *a.* Belonging to or affecting a part only, not general biased to one party; having a fondness.

partiality, pär'shi-al''i-ti, *n.* Unfair bias; undue favor shown; a liking or fondness.

particularize, pär-tik'ū-lér-īz, *vt.* To make particular mention of; to specify in detail.—*vi.* To be particular to details.

parting, pärt'ing, *p.a.* Serving to part or divide, given at separation departing.— *n.* Division; separation; leave-taking.

partisan, pär'ti-zan, *n.* An adherent of a party or faction; a party man.—*a.* Adhering to a faction.

partition, pär-ti'shon, *n.* Act of parting or dividing; division; a division-wall, part where separation is made.—*vt.* To divide by partitions to divide into shares.

partner, pärt'nér, *n.* One who shares with another; an associate in business, a husband or wife.

partnership, pärt'nér-ship, *n.* Fellowship; the association of two or more persons in any business; joint interest or property

partridge, pär'trij, *n.* A game bird of the grouse family.

parturition, pär-tū-ri'shon, *n.* The act of bringing forth young.

pass, päs, *vi.* (pret. and pp. passed or past). To go by or past, to change; to die; to elapse; to be enacted, to be current, to thrust in fencing or fighting; to go success.

patrol, pa-trōl', *n.* The marching round by

a guard at night to secure the safety of a camp; the guard who go such rounds; on active service, a small party sent out to harass the enemy (fighting patrol), or to get information (reconnaissance patrol).—*vi.* (patrolling, patrolled). To go the rounds as a patrol.—*vt.* To pass round, as a guard.

patron, pā 'tron, *n.* A protector; one who supports or protects a person or a work; one who has the disposition of a church-living, professorship, or other appointment, a guardian saint.

patronize, pat'ron-îz or pā ', *vt.* To act as patron of; to countenance or favor; to assume the air of a superior to.

paunchy, pänsh'i, *a.* Big-bellied.

pauper, pä'pér, *n.* A poor person; one dependent on the public for maintenance.

pause, päz, *n.* A temporary cessation cessation proceeding from doubt; suspense.—*vi.* (pausing, paused). To make a short stop, to delay; to deliberate; to hesitate

pave, pā v, *vt.* (paving, paved). To cover with stone, brick, etc., so as to make a level and solid surface for carriages or foot-passengers.

pavement, pā v'ment, *n.* The solid floor of a street, courtyard, etc. paved part of a road used by footpassengers, material with which anything is paved.

pavilion, pa-vil'yon, *n.* A tent; a small building having a tent-formed roof; a building of ornamental character for entertainments the outer ear.—*vt.* To furnish with pavilions; to shelter with a tent.

pay, pā , *vt.* (paying, paid). To give money, etc., for goods received or service rendered, to reward, to discharge, as a debt; to give, to cover with tar or pitch.—*vi.* To make a payment; to be profitable or remunerative.—*n.* An equivalent for money due, goods, or services; salary, wages; reward.

pea, pē, *n.; pl.* **peas, pease.** A well-known flowering plant cultivated for its seeds; one of the seeds of the plant.

peace, pēs, *n.* A state of quiet; calm; repose; public tranquillity; freedom from war; concord.

peak, pēk, *n.* A projecting point; the top of a mountain ending in a point; the upper corner of a sail extended by a yard, also, the extremity of the yard or gaff.— *vi.* To look sickly; to be emaciated.

peal, pēl, *n.* A series of loud sounds as of bells, thunder, etc.; a set of bells tuned to each other; chime.—*vi.* To give out a peal.—*vt.* To cause to ring or sound.

pear, pār, *n.* A well-known fruit-tree: one of the fruits of the tree.

pearl, pérl, *n.* A smooth lustrous whitish gem produced by certain mollusks' something resembling a pearl; a small printing type; what is choicest and best.—*a.* Relating to or made of pearl or mother-of-pearl.—*vt.* To set or adorn with pearls.

peck, pek, *n.* A dry measure of eight quarts.—*vt.* and *i.* To strike with the beak, or something pointed; to pick up, as food, with the beak.

pectic, pek'tik, *a.* Having the property of forming a jelly.

pectinate, pek'tin-at, *a.* Toothed like a comb.

pectoral, pek'to-ral, *a.* Pertaining to the breast.—*n.* A breastplate, a medicine for the chest and lungs.

peculate, pe'kū-lā t, *vi.* To appropriate money or goods entrusted to one's care.

peculiar, pē-kū'li-èr, *a.* One's own; characteristic; particular; unusual, odd.

peculiarity, pē-kū'li-a''ri-ti, *n.* Quality of being peculiar; something peculiar to a person or thing.

pecuniary, pē-kū'ni-a ri, *a.* Relating to or connected with money; consisting of money.

pedagogue, ped'a-gog, *n.* A teacher of children; a schoolmaster.

pedal, pĕd'al, *a.* Pertaining to a foot or to a pedal.—*n.* pe'dal. A lever to be pressed by the foot; a part of a musical instrument acted on by the feet.

peel, pēl, *vt.* To strip off, as bark or rind; to flay; to pare; to pillage.— *vi.* To lose the skin, bark or rind, to fall off, as bark or skin—*n.* The skin or rind, a baker's wooden shovel.

peep, pēp, *vi.* To chirp as a chicken; to begin to appear, to look through a crevice.—*n.* A chirp, a look through a small opening; first appearance.

pelt, pelt, *n.* A raw hide; a blow; a heavy shower.—*vt.* To strike with something thrown.—*vi.* To throw missiles; to fall in a heavy shower.

pelvis, pel'vis, *n.* The bony cavity forming the framework of the lower part of the abdomen.

pen, pen *n.* An instrument for writing with ink, style or quality of writing; a small inclosure for cows, etc.; a fold.—*vt.* (penning, penned). To write; to com-

P

pose; to coop or shut up.

penal, pē'nal, a. Relating to, enacting, or incurring punishment.

penalty, pen'al-ti, n. Punishment for a crime or offense forfeit for non-fulfillment of conditions; sum to be forfeited; a fine.

penance, pen'ans, n. An ecclesiastical punishment imposed for sin; voluntary suffering as an expression of penitence.

penchant, päng'shäng, n. Strong inclination, bias.

pencil, pen'sil, n. A small brush used by painters; an instrument of black-lead, etc., for writing and drawing, a converging or diverging aggregate of rays of light.—vt. (penciling, penciled). To write or mark with a pencil.

pend, pend, vi. To impend; to wait for settlement.

pendant, pen'dant, n. Anything hanging down by way of ornament, a hanging apparatus for giving light, etc.; an appendix or addition; a flag borne at the masthead.

pendent, pen'dent, a. Hanging; pendulous; projecting.—n. Something hanging.

pendulous, pen'dū-lus, a. Hanging; hanging so as to swing; swinging.

pendulum, pen'dū-lum, n. A body suspended and swinging; the swinging piece in a clock which regulates its motion.

penetrable, pen'e-tra-bl, a. That may be entered or pierced, susceptible of moral or intellectual impression.

penetrate, pen'e-trāt, vt. and i. To enter or pierce, as into another body; to affect, as the mind; to cause to feel; to understand.

penitentiary, pe-ni-ten'sha-ri, a. Relating to penance.—n. One who does penance; an office or official of the R. Catholic church connected with the granting of dispensations, etc.; a house of correction.

penumbra, pen-urn'bra, n. The partial shadow on the margin of the total shadow in an eclipse; the point of a picture where the shade blends with the light.

people, pē'pl, n. The body of persons who compose a community, race, or nation persons indefinitely.—vt. (peopling, peopled). To stock with inhabitants; to populate.

pepper, pep'ėr, n. A plant and its aromatic pungent seed, much used in seasoning, etc.—vt. To sprinkle with pepper; to pelt with shot or missiles; to drub thoroughly.

peppermint, pep'ėr-mint, n. A plant of the mint genus having a penetrating aromatic smell and a strong pungent taste.

per, pėr, prep. A Latin preposition used in the sense of by or for chiefly in certain Latin phrases, as per annum, by or for the year.

perceive, pėr-sēv', vt. (perceiving perceived). To apprehend by the organs of sense or by the mind; to observe, to discern.

percentage, pėr-sent'āj, n. The allowance duty, rate of interest, proportion, etc., reckoned on each hundred.

perception, pėr-sep'shon, n. Act, process, or faculty of perceiving; discernment.

perch, pėrch, n. A spiny fresh-water fish, a roost for fowls, an elevated place or position; 51/2 yards, also called a rod or pole, 301/4 square yards, a square rod.—vi. To sit on a perch; to light, as a bird.—vt. To place on a perch.

perennial, pe-ren'i-al, a. Lasting through the year; perpetual; unceasing.—n. A plant whose root remains alive more years than two.

perfect, pėr'fekt, a. Finished; complete; fully informed; completely skilled; faultless; in grammar, denoting a tense which expresses an act completed.—vt. To accomplish, to make perfect, to make fully skilful.

performance, pėr-form'ans, n. Act of performing, deed; achievement; a literary work; exhibition on the stage; entertainment at a place of amusement.

perfume, pėr'fūm or pėr-fūm', n. A pleasant scent or smell, fragrance. —vt. (perfuming, perfumed). To scent with perfume; to impregnate with a grateful odor.

period, pē'ri-od, n. The time taken up by a heavenly body in revolving round the sun; the time at which anything ends, end, an indefinite portion of any continued state or existence, a complete sentence, the point that marks the end of a sentence, thus (.).

periodical, pē-ri-od'ik-al, n. A magazine, newspaper, etc., published at regular periods.—a. Periodic.

peripatetic, pe'ri-pa-tet''ik, a. Walking about; itinerant; pertaining to Aristotle's system of philosophy, taught while walking.—n. One who walks, a follower of Aristotle.

periscope, pe'ri-skōp, n. An apparatus or

structure rising above the deck of a submarine vessel, giving by means of mirrors, etc., a view of outside surroundings, though the vessel itself remains submerged; a similar device used in trenches.

perish, pe'rish, vi. To die; to wither and decay; to be destroyed; to come to nothing.

peritoneum, pe'ri-tō-nē''um, n. A membrane investing the internal surface of the abdomen, and the viscera contained in it.

perjure, pèr'jŭr, vt. (perjuring, perjured). To forswear, wilfully to make a false oath when administered legally.

permit, pèr-mit' vt. and i. (permitting, permitted). To allow; to grant; to suffer; to concede.—n. per'mit. A written permission or license given by competent authority.

permutation, per-mū-tā 'shon n. Interchange, in *mathematics,* any of the ways in which a set of quantities can be arranged.

pernicious, pèr-ni'shus, a. Having the quality of destroying or injuring; destructive; deadly; noxious.

perpetuity, pèr-pe-tū'i-ti, n. State or quality of being perpetual; endless duration; something of which there will be no end.

perplexity, pèr-pleks'i-ti, n. State of being puzzled, or at a loss; bewilderment; state of being intricate or involved.

persecute, pèr'se-kū t, vt. (persecuting, persecuted). To harass with unjust punishment, to afflict for adherence to a particular creed.

persevere, pèr-se-vèr', vi. (persevering, persevered). To continue steadfastly in any business; to pursue steadily any design.

persist, pèr-sist', vi. To continue steadily in any business or course; to persevere; to continue in a certain state.

personal, pèr'son-al, a. Pertaining to a person; peculiar or proper to him or her, belonging to face and figure; denoting the person in a grammatical sense.

personality, pèr-son-al'i-ti n. State of being personal; that which constitutes an individual a distinct person; disparaging remark on one's conduct and character; in *law,* personal estate.

perspective, pèr-spek'tiv, n. The art of representing objects on a flat surface so that they appear to have their natural dimensions and relations; a representa-

tion of objects in perspective view.—a. Pertaining to the art of perspective.

perspicacious, pèr-spi-kā'shus, a. Quick-sighted; of acute discernment.

persuasive, pèr-swā'siv a. Having the power of persuading; calculated to persuade.—n. That which persuades; an incitement.

pertinent, pèr'ti-nent, a. Related to the subject or matter in hand; opposite; fit.

peruse, pe-rūz', vt. (perusing, perused). To read through to read with attention; to examine carefully.

pervade, pèr-vād', vt. (pervading pervaded). To pass or flow through; to permeate; to be diffused through.

perverse, pèr-vèrs', a. Obstinate in the wrong; stubborn; untractable; petulant.

pervert, pèr-vert', vt. To turn from truth or proper purpose; to corrupt, to misinterpret. to misapply.—n. per'vert. One who has been perverted.

pestilence, pes'ti-lens n. Any contagious disease that is epidemic and fatal; something morally evil or destructive.

pestle, pes'l, n. An instrument for pounding substances in a mortar.—vt. and i. (pestling, pestled). To pound with a pestle.

pet, pet, n. A darling any little animal fondled and indulged; fit of peevishness.—vt. (petting, petted). To fondle, to indulge.

petition, pē-ti'shon, n. An entreaty, supplication, or prayer; a written application in legal proceedings.—vt. To supplicate; to solicit.

petrify, pet-ri-fī, vt. To turn into stone or a fossil; to paralyze or stupefy.—vi. To become stone, or of a stony hardiness.

petulant, pe'tū-lant, a. Irritable; peevish, fretful; saucy; pert; capricious.

pewter, pū'tèr, n. An alloy mainly of tin and lead, a vessel made of pewter.—a. Relating to or made of pewter.

phallus, fal'lus, n. The emblem of the generative power in nature, especially in certain religious usages.

pharmaceutic, pharmaceutical, fär-ma-sū'tik, fär-ma-sū'tik-al, a. Pertaining to the knowledge or art of pharmacy.

pharynx, fā'ringks n. The muscular sac between the mouth and the esophagus.

phase, fāz, n. A particular stage of the moon or a planet in respect to illumination; state of a varying phenomenon, one of the various aspects of a question.

phenomenon, fē-no'me-non, n.; pl. **-mena.** An appearance; anything visi-

P

ble, an appearance whose cause is not immediately obvious; something extraordinary.

philanthropist, fī-lan'throp-ist, *n*. One devoted to philanthropy; one who exerts himself in doing good to his fellowmen.

philosophy, fi-los'o-fi, *n*. The science which tries to account for the phenomena of the universe; metaphysics; the general principles underlying some branch of knowledge; practical wisdom.

phonetics, fō-net'iks, *n.pl*. The doctrine or science of sounds especially of the human voice; the representation of sounds.

phonograph, fō'nō-graf, *n*. An instrument for registering and reproducing sounds; a predecessor of the gramophone.

phosgene, fos'jēn, *n*. A poison gas, carbon oxychloride.

phosphate, fos'fāt, *n*. A salt of phosphoric acid.

photography, fō-tog'ra-fi, *n*. The art or practice of producing representations of scenes and objects by the action of light on chemically prepared surfaces.

photology, fō-tol'o-ji, *n*. The doctrine or science of light.

photometer, fō-tom'et-ėr, *n*. An instrument for measuring the intensity of lights.

phrase, frāz, *n*. A short sentence or expression, an idiom, style, diction.—*vt*. and *i*. (phrasing, phrased). To style, to express.

phraseology, frā-zē-ol'o-ji, *n*. Manner of expression; peculiar words used in a sentence. diction; style.

physics, fi'ziks, *n*. That branch of science which deals with mechanics, dynamics, light, heat, sound, electricity, and magnetism; natural philosophy.

physiognomy, fi-zi-og'no-mi, *n*. The art of perceiving a person's character by his countenance; particular cast or expression of countenance.

physiography, fi-zi-og'ra-fi, *n*. The science of the earth's physical features and phenomena; physical geography.

physiology, fi-zi-ol'o-ji, *n*. The science of the phenomena of life, the study of the functions of living beings.

pick, pik, *vt*. To strike at with something pointed; to peck at, to clean by the teeth, fingers, etc.; to select; to pluck, to gather.—*vi*. To eat slowly; to nibble, to pilfer.—*n*. A pointed tool; a pick-axe; choice; selection.

picket, pik'et, *n*. A pointed stake used in fortification; a pale; an advanced guard or outpost, a game at cards.—*vt*. To fortify with pickets; to post as a guard of observation.

pickle, pik'l, *n*. Brine; a solution of salt and water for preserving flesh, fish, etc., vegetables preserved in vinegar; a state of difficulty or disorder, a troublesome child.—*vt*. (pickling, pickled). To preserve in or treat with pickle.

picture, pik'tūr, *n*. A painting drawing, etc., exhibiting the resemblance of anything; any resemblance or representation, *pl*. the moving photographs shown in cinematography; the cinema.—*vt*. To represent pictorially, to present an ideal likeness of; to describe in a vivid manner.

picturesque, pik-tūr-esk', *a*. Form-ing, or fitted to form, a pleasing picture; abounding with vivid imagery; graphic.

pie, pī, *n*. A paste baked with something in or under it; a mass of types unsorted, the magpie.

piece, pēs, *n*. A portion of anything; a distinct part, a composition or writing of no great length; a separate performance; a picture; a coin; a single firearm.—*vt*. (piecing, pieced). To patch, to join.—*vi*. To unite or join on.

piety, pī'e-ti, *n*. Reverence or veneration towards God, godliness; devotion; religion.

pig, pig, *n*. A young swine; a swine in general, an oblong mass of unforged metal.—*vt*. or *i*. (pigging, pigged). To bring forth pigs; to act like pigs.

pigeon-hole, pi'jon-hōl, *n*. A hole for pigeons to enter their dwelling a division in a desk or case for holding papers.

pigment, pig'ment, *n*. Paint; any preparation used by painters, dyers, etc., to impart colors to bodies, coloring matter.

pill, pil, *n*. A medicine in the form of a little ball, anything nauseous to be accepted.—*vt*. To dose with pills; to form into pills; to rob; to plunder.

pillow, pil'ō, *n*. A long soft cushion; something that bears or supports.—*vt*. To rest or lay on for support.

pilot, pī'lot, *n*. One whose occupation is to steer ships, a guide, a director of one's course.—*vt*. To act as pilot of, to guide through dangers or difficulties.

pimp, pimp, *n*. A man who provides gratifications for others' lusts; a procurer.—*vi*. To pander, to procure women for others.

pin, pin, *n*. A longish piece of metal, wood, etc., used for a fastening, or as a support; a peg; a bolt.—*vt*. (pinning, pinned). To fasten with a pin or pins; to hold fast.—*vt*. To inclose, to pen or pound.

pinch, pinsh, *vt*. To press hard or squeeze, to nip, to afflict.—*vi*. To press painfully; to be sparing.—*n*. A close compression, as with the fingers; a nip; a pang; straits; a strong iron lever; as much as is taken by the finger and thumb; a small quantity.

pinion, pin'yon, *n*. A bird's wing; the joint of a wing remotest from the body; a large wing-feather; a small toothed wheel; a fetter for the arms.—*vt*. To bind the wings of, to cut off, as the first joint of the wing; to fetter.

pink, pingk, *n*. A garden flower; a light rose-color or pigment; the flower or something supremely excellent.—*a*. Of a fine light rose color.—*vt*. To work in eyelet holes; to scallop; to stab.—*vi*. To wink or blink.

pioneer, pī-on-ēr', *n*. One whose business is to prepare the road for an army, make entrenchments etc., one who leads the way.—*vt*. To prepare a way for.—*vi*. To act as pioneer.

pipe, pīp, *n*. A wind-instrument of music; a long tube; a tube with a bowl at one end for tobacco, the windpipe; a call of a bird; a wine measure containing about 105 imperial gallons.—*vi*. (piping, piped). To play on a pipe, to whistle.— *vt*. To utter in a high tone; to call by a pipe or whistle.

piracy, pī'ra-si, *n*. The act or practice of robbing on the high seas; infringement of the law of copyright.

pirate, pī'rat, *n*. A robber on the high seas; a ship engaged in piracy; one who publishes others' writings without permission.—*vi*. (pirating, pirated). To rob on the high-seas.—*vt*. To take without right, as writings.

pistachio, pis-tā'shi-ō, *n*. The nut of a small tree cultivated in S. Europe for its fruit, the tree itself also called *pistacia*.

pistol, pis'tol, *n*. A small firearm fired with one hand.—*vt*. (pistoling, pistolled). To shoot with a pistol.

piston, pis'ton, *n*. a cylindrical piece of metal which fits exactly into a hollow cylinder, and works alternately in two directions.

piston-rod, pis'ton-rod, *n*. A rod which connects a piston to some other piece, and either moved by the piston or moving it.

pit, pit, *n*. A hollow in the earth; the shaft of a mine, a vat in tanning, dyeing, etc.; a concealed hole for catching wild beasts; a small cavity or depression, part of the floor of a theater.—*vt*. (pitting, pitted). To lay in a pit or hole; to mark with little hollows, to set in competition.

pitch, pich, *vt*. To thrust, as a pointed object; to fix; to set; to throw; to set the key-note of; to set in array; to smear or cover with pitch.—*vi*. To settle; to fall headlong, to fix choice, to encamp, to rise and fall, as a ship.—*n*. A throw; degree of elevation; highest rise, descent; elevation of a note; (cricket) prepared ground between wickets, a thick dark resinous substance obtained from tar.

pith, pith, *n*. The spongy substance in the center of exogenous plants the spinal cord or marrow of an animal; strength or force; energy; cogency, essence.

pity, pi'ti, *n*. Sympathy or compassion; ground of pity; thing to be regretted.— *vt*. (pitying, pitied). To feel pain or grief for; to sympathize with.—*vi*. To be compassionate.

pivot, pi'vot, *n*. A pin on which something turns; a turning-point; that on which important results depend.—*vt*. To place on or furnish with a pivot.

placard, plak'ėrd or pla-kärd', *n*. A written or printed bill posted in a public place; a poster.—*vt*. To post placards.

place, plās, *n*. An open space in a town; a locality, spot, or site; position; room; an edifice; quarters; a passage in a book; rank; office; calling; ground or occasion; stead.—*vt*. (placing, placed). To put or set, to locate, to appoint or set in an office, rank, or condition to invest; to lend.

placenta, pla-sen'ta, *n*. The afterbirth; an organ developed in mammals during pregnancy, connecting the mother and fetus, the part of the seed-vessel to which the seeds are attached.

plait, plāt, *n*. A fold; a doubling of cloth, etc., a braid, as of hair, etc.— *vt*. To fold, to double in narrow strips; to braid.

plan, plan, *n*. The representation of anything on a flat surface; sketch; scheme; project; method; process.—*vt*. (planning, planned). To form a plan or repre-

P

sentation of to scheme.—*vi.* To form a scheme.

plane, plane-tree, plān, plān'trē, *n.* A forest tree with a straight smooth stem and palmate leaves a kind of maple.

plant, plant, *n.* One of the living organisms of the vegetable kingdom; a herb; a shoot or slip; the machinery, etc., necessary to carry on a business.—*vt.* To set in the ground for growth; to set firmly; to establish; to furnish with plants, to set and direct, as cannon.—*vi.* To set plants in the ground.

plasma, plas'ma or plaz'ma, *n.* Formless matter; the simplest form of organized matter in the vegetable and animal body.

plaster, pläs'tèr, *n.* An adhesive substance used in medical practice, a mixture of lime, water sand etc., for coating walls; calcined gypsum, used with water for finishing walls, for casts, cement, etc.—*vt.* To overlay with plaster; to lay on coarsely.

plastic, plas'tik, *a.* Having the power to give form to matter; capable of being molded, applied to sculpture, as distinguished from painting, etc.—**plastics,** plas'tiks, *n.* The science or craft of converting various resins into durable materials; the articles so made.

plat, plat, *vt.* (platting, platted). To plait; to weave; to make a groundplan of—*n.* A plot of ground devoted to some special purpose.

plate, plāt, *n.* A flat piece of metal; gold and silver wrought into utensils, a shallow flattish dish for eatables; an engraved piece of metal for printing; a page of stereotype for printing.—*vt.* (plating, plated). To cover with a thin coating of metal, as of silver.

plating, plā t'ing, *n.* The art of covering articles with gold or silver; the coating itself.

plea, plē, *n.* A suit or action at law; that which is alleged in support, justification, or defense; an excuse; a pleading.

plead, plēd, *vi.* (pleading, pleaded or pled). To argue in support of or against a claim, to present an answer to the declaration of a plaintiff; to supplicate with earnestness, to urge.—*vt.* To discuss and defend; to argue; to offer in excuse; to allege in a legal defense.

pleasant, ple'zant, *a.* Pleasing; agreeable; grateful; humorous; sportive.

please, plēz, *vt.* (pleasing, pleased). To excite agreeable sensations or emotions in; to delight, to gratify; to seem good to.—*vi.* To give pleasure; to be kind enough.

pleasurable, ple'zhŭr-a-bl, *a.* Pleasing, giving pleasure; affording gratification.

pleasure, ple'zhŭr, *n.* The gratification of the senses or of the mind; agreeable emotion; delight; joy; approbation; choice; will; purpose; command; arbitrary will or choice.

plebeian, ple-bē'an, *a.* Pertaining to the common people; vulgar; common.—*n.* One of the lower ranks of men, one of the common people of ancient Rome.

plenipotentiary, ple'ni-pō-ten"shia-ri, *n.* A person with full power to act for another, an ambassador with full power.—*a.* Containing or invested with full power.

plight, plīt, *vi.* To pledge, as one's word or honor, to give as a security; never applied to property or goods.—*n.* A pledge, a solemn promise; predicament; risky or dangerous state.

plod, plod, *vi.* (plodding, plodded). To trudge or walk heavily; to toil; to drudge.—*vt.* To accomplish by toilsome exertion.

plot, plot, *n.* A small piece of ground; a plan, as of a field, etc., on paper; a scheme; a conspiracy; the story of a play, novel, etc.—*vt.* (plotting, plotted). To make a plan of; to devise.—*vi.* To conspire; to contrive a plan.

plow, plou, *n.* An instrument for turning up the soil.—*vt.* To turn up with the plow, to make grooves in; to run through, as in sailing.—*vi.* To turn up the soil with a plow; to use a plow.

plum, plum, *n.* A fleshy fruit containing a kernel; the tree producing it, a raisin, a handsome sum or fortune generally.

plumb, plum, *n.* A plummet; a perpendicular position.—*a.* Perpendicular.—*adv.* In a perpendicular direction.—*vt.* To set perpendicularly, to sound with a plummet; to ascertain the capacity of; to sound.

plump, plump, *a.* Fat, stout; chubby.—*vt.* To make plump, to dilate.—*vi.* To plunge or fall like a heavy mass; to fall suddenly; to vote for only one candidate.—*adv.* Suddenly; at once; flatly.

plunder, plun'dèr, *vt.* To deprive of goods or valuables; to pillage; to spoil.—*n.* Robbery; pillage; spoil; booty.

plunge, plunj, *vt.* (plunging, plunged). To thrust into water or other fluid; to immerse; to thrust or push; to cast or involve.—*vi.* To dive or rush into water, etc., to pitch or throw oneself headlong; to throw the body forward and the hind-legs up, as a horse.—*n.* Act of plunging into water, etc.; act of throwing oneself headlong, like an unruly horse.

plutonium, plö-tōn'i-um, *n.* An element got from uranium by bombarding it with neutrons.

ply, plī, *vt.* (plying, plied). To employ with diligence; to work at, to assail briskly; to beset; to press.—*vi.* To work steadily; to go in haste; to run regularly between any two ports, as a vessel.—*n.* A fold; a plait.

pneumatic, nū-mat'ik, *a.* Pertaining to air; moved or played by means of air, filled with or fitted to contain air.

pneumatics, nū-mat'iks, *n.* That branch of physics which treats of the mechanical properties of elastic fluids and particularly of air.

poach, pōch, *vt.* To cook (eggs) by breaking and pouring among boiling water; to pierce; to tread or stamp.—*vt.* To encroach on another's ground to steal game, to kill game contrary to law; to be or become swampy.

poetic, poetical, pō-et'ik, pō-et'ik-al, *a.* Pertaining or suitable to poetry; expressed in poetry or measure; possessing the peculiar beauties of poetry.

poetry, pō'et-ri, *n.* The language of the imagination or emotions expressed rhythmically; the artistic expression of thought in emotional language; whatever appeals to the sense of ideal beauty; verse; poems.

point, point, *n.* The sharp end of anything; a small headland; sting of an epigram; telling force of expression; exact spot; verge; stage; degree; a mark of punctuation; a mark or dot; end or purpose; characteristic; argument; (cricket) fielder square with wicket on off side; *pl.* The movable guiding rails at junctions on railways.—*vt.* To make pointed, to aim, to indicate to punctuate; to fill the joints of with mortar.—*vi.* To direct the finger to an object, to indicate the presence of game, as dogs do; to show distinctly.

poise, poiz, *n.* Weight; balance; that which balances.—*vt.* (poising poised). To balance in weight, to hold in equilibrium.—*vi.* To be balanced or suspended, to depend.

poison, poi'zn, *n.* Any agent capable of producing a morbid effect on anything endowed with life.— *vi.* To infect with poison, to taint, impair, or corrupt.

pole, pōl, *n.* A long piece of wood; a measure of 5-1/2 yards or 30-1/4 square yards; one of the extremities of the axis of the celestial sphere or the earth; the pole-star one of the two points in a magnet in which the power seems concentrated, (with cap.) a native of Poland.—*vt.* (poling, poled). To furnish with poles; to impel by poles.

police, pō-lēs', *n.* The internal government of a community; a body of civil officers for enforcing order, cleanliness, etc.—*vt.* (policing, policed). To guard or regulate by police.

policy, po'li-si, *n.* The governing a city, state, or nation; line of conduct with respect to foreign or internal affairs; dexterity of management; pleasure-grounds around a mansion; contract of insurance.

polytechnic, po-li-tek'nik, *a.* Comprehending many arts; designating a school teaching many branches of art or science.—*n.* A school of instruction in arts.

pomegranate, pōm'gran-āt, *n.* A fruit of the size of an orange, containing numerous seeds, the tree producing the fruit.

pommel, pum'el, *n* A knob or ball the knob on the hilt of a sword; the protuberant part of a saddlebow.—*vt.* (pommeling, pommelled). To beat; to belabor.

pontifical, pon-tif'ik-al, *a.* Belonging to a high-priest or to the pope.—*n.* A book containing rites performable by a bishop; *pl.* the dress of a priest or bishop.

pontoon, pon-tön, *n.* A kind of boat for supporting temporary bridges, a watertight structure to assist in raising submerged vessels.

pop, pop, *n.* A small, smart sound.—*vi.* (popping, popped). To make a small, smart sound; to enter or issue forth suddenly.—*vt.* To offer with a quick sudden motion, to thrust or push suddenly.—*adv.* Suddenly.

popular, po'pū-lėr, *a.* Pertaining to the common people; familiar; plain; liked by people in general; prevalent.

popularize, po'pū-lėr-īz, *vi.* To make popular or suitable to the common mind; to spread among the people.

populate, po'pū-lā t, *vt.* To people; to furnish with inhabitants.

P

population, po-pū-lā 'shon, *n.* Act or process of populating; number of people in a country, etc.; the inhabitants.

porcelain, por'sē-lā n, *n.* The finest species of pottery ware.

porch, pŏrch, *n.* A portico; covered approach at the entrance of buildings.

porcine pŏr'sĭn *a.* Pertaining to swine like a swine; hog-like.

porcupine, por'kū-pîn, *n.* A rodent animal, about 2 feet long, with erectile spines.

pore, pŏr, *n.* A minute opening in the skin, through which the perspirable matter passes, a small interstice.—*vi.* (poring, pored). To look with steady attention; to read or examine with perseverance.

portal, pŏrt'al, *n.* A door or gate; the main entrance of a cathedral, etc.—*a.* Belonging to a vein connected with the liver.

Portuguese, por'tū-gēz, *a.* Pertaining to Portugal.—*n.* The language of Portugal; the people of Portugal.

pose, pŏz, *n.* Attitude or position an artistic posture.—*vi.* (posing posed). To attitudinize; to assume characteristic airs.—*vt.* To cause to assume a certain posture; to state or lay down; to perplex or puzzle.

positive, poz'it-iv, *a.* Definitely laid down explicit, absolute, actual, confident, dogmatic, affirmative noting the simple state of an adjective; applied to the philosophical system of Auguste Comte, which limits itself to human experience, applied to electricity produced by rubbing a vitreous substance.—*n.* That which is positive; the positive degree.

possess, po-zes', *vt.* To have and hold; to own; to affect by some power or influence, to pervade, to put in possession; to furnish or fill.

post, pŏst, *n.* A piece of timber, etc., set upright, a place assigned, a military or other station; office or employment; a carrier of letters, messages, etc., a system for the public conveyance of letters, etc.; a post-office; a size of paper, about 18 or 19 inches by 15.—*vt.* To travel with post-horses; to hasten on.—*vt.* To place, to place in the post-office to transfer (accounts or items) to the ledger; to make master of full details, to fix up in some public place.—*a.* Used in travelling quickly.—*adv.* Travelling as a post, swiftly.

postage, pŏst'āj, *n.* The charge for conveying letters or other articles by post.

posterior, pos-tē'ri-or, *a.* Later or subsequent; hinder.—*n.* A hinder part; *pl.* the hinder parts of an animal.

post-office, pŏst'of-is, *n.* An office where letters are received for transmission, a government department that has the duty of conveying letters, etc.

postpone, pŏst-pōn, *vt.* (postponing postponed). To put off to a later time; to set below something else in value.

pot, pot, *n.* A metallic or earthenware vessel more deep than broad; the quantity contained in a pot; a sort of paper of small-sized sheets.—*vt.* (potting, potted). To put in a pot; to preserve in pots; to plant in a pot of earth.

potter, pot'èr, *n.* One who makes earthenware vessels or crockery.—*vi.* To busy oneself about trifles; to move slowly.

poultice, pōl'tis, *n.* A soft composition applied to sores.—*vt.* (poulticing, poulticed). To apply a poultice to.

pounce, pouns, *n.* A fine powder to prevent ink from spreading on paper; the claw or talon of a bird.—*vt.* (pouncing pounced). To sprinkle or rub with pounce.—*vi.* To fall on and seize with the pounces or talons, to fall on suddenly.

pound, pound, *n.* A standard weight of 12 ounces troy or 16 ounces avoirdupois; a money of account, an inclosure for cattle.— *vt.* To confine in a public pound; to beat, to pulverize.

powder, pou'dèr, *n.* A dry substance of minute particles; dust; gunpowder.—*vt.* To reduce to fine particles, to sprinkle with powder to corn, as meat. vi. To fall to dust; to use powder for the hair or face.

power, pou'èr, *n.* Ability to act or do; strength; influence; talent; command, authority, one who exercises authority; a state or government; warrant; a mechanical ad vantage or effect, product of the multiplication of a number by itself.

practical, prak'ti-kal, *a.* Pertaining to practice, action, or use; not merely theoretical; skilled in actual work.

practice, prak'tis, *n.* A doing or effecting; custom; habit; actual performance, exercise of any profession; medical treatment; training; drill, dexterity.

practice, prak'tis, *vt.* (practicing, practiced). To put in practice; to do or perform frequently or habitually; to exercise, as any profession; to commit;

to teach by practice.— *vi.* To perform certain acts frequently for instruction or amusement; to exercise some profession.

prance, prans, *vt.* (prancing, pranced). To spring, leap, or caper, as a horse; to strut about ostentatiously.

prank, prangk, *vt.* To adorn in a showy manner; to dress up.—*vi.* To have a showy appearance.—*n.* A merry trick; a caper.

prate, prāt, *vi.* (prating, prated). To babble, chatter, tattle.—*vt.* To utter foolishly.—*n.* Trifling talk; unmeaning loquacity.

prattle, prat'l, *vi.* (prattling, prattled). To talk much and idly, like a child; to prate.—*n.* Trifling or puerile talk.

prayer, prā'er, *n.* One who prays; the act of praying; a petition; a solemn petition to G;od; a formula of worship, public or private; that part of a written petition which specifies the thing desired to be granted.

preach, prēch, *vi.* To deliver a sermon, to give earnest advice.—*vt.* To proclaim; to publish in religious discourses; to deliver in public, as a discourse.

precedent, prē-sēd'ent, *a.* Preceding; going before in time; anterior.

precept, prē'sept, *n.* Anything enjoined as an authoritative rule of action; injunction; doctrine; maxim.

precipitate, prē'si'pi-tā t, *vt.* and *i.* To throw or hurl headlong; to has ten excessively; to cause to sink or to fall to the bottom of a vessel, as a substance in solution.—*a.* Headlong, overhasty.—*n.* A substance deposited from a liquid in which it has been dissolved.

precognition, prē -kog-ni'shon, *n.* Previous knowledge; preliminary examination, as of a witness before a trial (*Scots law*).

preconceive, prē-kon-sēv', *vt. To* form a conception or opinion of beforehand.

predicable, pre'di-ka-bl, *a.* That may be attributed to something.— *n.* Anything that may be affirmed of another.

predicate, pre'di-kāt, *vt.* and *i.* To affirm one thing of another; to assert.—*n.* In *logic,* that which is affirmed or denied of the subject; in *grammar,* the word or words which express what is affirmed or denied of the subject.

prefabricate, prē-fab'ri-kāt, *vt.* To manufacture separately parts, of a building, etc., designed to be easily fitted together afterwards.

preface, pre'fās, *n.* Introduction to a discourse or book, etc.—*vt.* (prefacing, prefaced). To introduce by preliminary remarks.

prefect, prē'fekt, *n.* One placed over others, a governor, chief magistrate; a senior pupil entrusted with the maintenance of discipline.

prefer, prē-fėr', *vt.* (preferring, preferred). To bring or lay before; to present, as a petition, etc.; to exalt; to set higher in estimation; to choose rather.

preference, pre'fėr-ens, *n.* Act of preferring; state of being preferred, choice.

prehensible, prē-hen'si-bl, *a.* That may be seized.

prejudice, pre'jū-dis, *n.* An unwarranted bias; prepossession; detriment; injury.—*vt.* To bias the mind of, to do harm to.

preliminary, prē-lim'in-a-ri, *a.* Introductory; preparatory; prefactory.—*n.* Something introductory; preface, prelude.

prelude, prel'ūd or prē-lūd', *vt.* (preluding, preluded). To introduce, to preface.—*vi.* To form a prelude.—*n.* prel'ud or pre'lud. Something preparatory; a musical introduction.

premium, prē'mi-um, *n.* A reward or prize; a bonus; a bounty; sum paid for insurance; increase in value.

preoccupation, prē-ok'kū-pā ''shon, *n.* Act of preoccupying; prior possession; state of being preoccupied.

preoccupy, prē-ok'kū-pī, *vt.* To occupy before another; to engross before another; to engross beforehand.

preparation, pre-pa-rā 'shon, *n.* Act or operation of preparing; that which is prepared; state of being prepared.

prepare, prē-pār', *vt.* and *i.* (preparing, prepared). To make ready; to adjust; to provide; to procure as suitable.

preposterous, prē-pos'tėr-us, *a.* Absurd; irrational; monstrous; utterly ridiculous.

prerogative, prē-ro'ga-tiv, *n.* A prior claim or title; an exclusive privilege; an official and hereditary right.

presage, prē'sā j or pres'a j, *n.* A presentiment; a prognostic, omen, or sign.—*vt.* and *i.* prē-sā j', (presaging, presaged). To betoken; to forebode, to predict.

prescribe, prē-skrib', *vt.* (prescribing, prescribed). To lay down authoritatively for direction; to appoint; to direct to be used as a remedy.—*vi.* To give directions, to give medical directions to become of no validity through lapse of time.

P

prescription, prē-skrip'shon, n. Act of prescribing; that which is prescribed; a claim or title based on long use; the loss of a legal right by lapse of time.

presence, pre'zens, n. State of being present; existence in a certain place; company; sight; port; mien; the person of a great personage; an appearance or apparition; readiness.

present, pre'zent, a. Being at hand, in view, or in a certain place; now existing; ready at hand; quick in emergency.—n. Present time; pl. term used in a legal document for the document itself.

present, prē-zent', vt. To introduce to or bring before a superior; to show, to give or bestow; to nominate to an ecclesiastical benefice; to lay before a public body for consideration, to point or aim, as a weapon.—n. pre'zent. A donation; a gift.

preside, prē-zīd', vi. (presiding, presided). To exercise authority or superintendence; to have the post of chairman.

president, pre'zi-dent, n. One who presides, the head of a province or state; the highest officer of state in a republic.

press, pres, vt. To bear or weigh heavily upon; to squeeze; to urge to enforce; to emphasize, to solicit earnestly; to force into service.— vi. To bear heavily or with force; to crowd; to push with force.—n. A pressing; a crowd; an instrument for squeezing or crushing; a machine for printing, the art or business of printing; periodical literature; an upright cupboard; urgency.

presume, prē-zūm', vt. (presuming, presumed). To take for granted; to take the liberty, to make bold.—vi. To infer, to act in a forward way.

pretend, prē-tend', vt. To feign; to simulate; to assume or profess to feel, use as a pretest.—vi. To assume a false character; to sham; to put in a claim.

prevail, pē-vā l', vi. To gain the victory or superiority; to be in force; to succeed; to gam over by persuasion.

prey, prā, Property taken from an enemy; spoil; booty; a victim.—vi. To take prey or booty; to get food by rapine; to cause to pine away: with on.

price, prīs, n. The value which a seller sets on his goods; cost; value; worthy.—vt. (pricing, priced). To set a price on; to ask the price of.

prick, prik, n. A slender pointed thing that can pierce; a thorn; a puncture by a prick; a sting; tormenting thought.—vt. To pierce with a prick; to erect, as ears; to spur; to sting with remorse, to trace by puncturing.—vi. To spur on; to ride rapidly; to feel a prickly sensation.

prickle, prik'l, n. A small sharppointed shoot; a thorn; a small spine.—vt. To prick, to cause a prickly feeling in.

pride, prīd, n. State or quality of being proud, inordinate self-esteem a cause of pride; glory or delight, highest pitch; splendid show.—vt. To indulge pride, to value (oneself).

priest, prēst, n. A man who officiates in sacred offices; a clergyman above a deacon and below a bishop.

primary, prī'ma-ri, a. First, chief first in time; original; elementary, radical.—n. That which stands first or highest in importance, a large feather of a bird's wing.

prime, prīm, a. Foremost, first, original; first in rank, excellence, or importance; not divisible by any smaller number.— n. The earliest stage; full health; strength; or beauty; the best part.—vt. (priming, primed). To make ready for action; to supply with powder for communicating fire to a charge; to instruct or prepare beforehand to lay on the first color in painting.

priming, prīm'ing, n. The powder used to ignite a charge; a first layer of paint; water carried over with the steam into the cylinder.

primitive, prim'it-iv, a. Being the first or earliest of its kind; original; antiquated, primary radical, not derived.—n. That which is original; an original word.

principal, prin'si-pal, a. First, chief most important or considerable.— n. A chief or head, the president governor, or chief in authority, one primarily engaged; a capital sum lent on interest.

principle, prin'si-pl, n. Cause or origin, a general truth, a fundamental law; a rule of action; uprightness, an element.

print, print, vt. To mark by pressure; to stamp; to form or copy by pressure; as from types, etc.—vi. To use or practice typography, to publish.—n. A mark made by pressure; an engraving, etc.; state of being printed; a newspaper; printed calico.

private, prī'vat, a. Separate from others, solitary, personal, secret not having a public or official character.—**In private**, secretly.—n. A common soldier.

privy, pri'vi, a. Private; assigned to private uses; secret; privately knowing (with *to*).—*n.* A watercloset or necessary house.

prize, prîz, *n.* That which is seized that which is deemed a valuable acquisition; a reward.—*vt.* (prizing, prized). To value highly.

prize-fight, prîz'fît, *n.* A boxing match for a prize.

probability, pro-ba-bil'i-ti, *n.* Likelihood; appearance of truth.

probate, pro⁻'bāt, *n.* The proceeding by which a person's will is established and registered; official proof of a will.

proboscis, prō-bos'is, *n.*, *pl.* **proboscides,** prō-bos'i-dēz. The snout or trunk of an elephant, etc.; the sucking-tube of insects.

proceed, prō-sēd', *vi.* To go forth or forward; to issue, arise, emanate; to prosecute any design; to carry on a legal action; to take a university degree.

procrastinate, prō-kras'ti-nat, *vt.* and i. To put off from day to day; to postpone.

prod, prod, *n.* A pointed instrument, as a goad; a stab.—*vt.* (prodding, prodded). To prick with a pointed instrument; to goad.

prodigal, prod'i-gal, *a.* Lavish; wasteful.—*n.* A waster; a spendthrift.

produce, prō-dūs', *vt.* (producing, produced). To bring forward; to exhibit; to bring forth, bear, yield; to supply, to cause; to extend, as a line.—*n.* prō'dūs, What is produced; outcome; yield; agricultural products.

productive, prō-duk'tiv, *a.* Having the power of producing; fertile; causing to exist; producing commodities of value.

profane, prō-fān', *a.* Not sacred; secular, irreverent, blasphemous; impure.—*vt.* (profaning, profaned). To treat with irreverence; to desecrate.

profanity, prō-fan'i-ti, *n.* Quality of being profane; profane language or conduct.

profess, prō-fes', *vt.* To avow; to acknowledge; to declare belief in; to pretend, to declare oneself versed in.—*vi.* To declare openly.

profession, prō-fe'shon, *n.* Act of professing, declaration; vocation; such as medicine, law; etc.; the body of persons engaged in such calling

professional, prō-fe'shon-al, *a.* Pertaining to a profession.—*n.* A member of any profession; one who makes a living by arts, sports, etc., in which amateurs engage.

profit, pro'fit', *n.* Any advantage, benefit,

or gain, pecuniary gain.— *vt.* To benefit; to advance.—*vi.* To derive profit; to improve; to be made better or wiser.

profitable, pro'fit-a-bl, *a.* Bringing profit or gain; lucrative; beneficial; useful.

profound, prō-found', *a.* Deep; deep in skill or knowledge; far-reaching; bending low; humble.—*n.* The ocean, the abyss.

program, prō'gram, *n.* A plan of proceedings; statement of the order of proceedings in any entertainment.

progress, prō'gres, *n.* A going forward, a journey of state; a circuit; advance; development.—*vi.* progres'. To advance; to improve.

progressive, prō-gres'iv, *a.* Making steady progress; advancing; advocating progress.

prolapse, prolapsus, prō-laps', prō-lap'sus, *n.* A falling down of some internal organ from its proper position.

prolegomenon, prō-le-gom'e-non, *n.; pl.* **-mena.** A preliminary observation, *pl.* an introduction.

prolepsis, prō-lep'sis, *n.* Something of the nature of an anticipation, a rhetorical figure.

proletarian, prō-lē-ta'ri-an, *n.* and *a.* Applied to a member of the poorest class.

promenade, pro-me-näd', *n.* A walk for pleasure, a place set apart for walking.—*vi.* (promenading, promenaded). To walk for pleasure.

promise, pro'mis, *n.* A statement binding the person who makes it; ground or basis of expectation pledge.—*vt.* (promising, pro-mised). To make a promise of; to afford reason to expect.—*vi.* To make a promise; to afford expectations.

promote, prō-mōt', *vt.* (promoting, promoted). To forward or further; to advance; to encourage; to exalt; to form (a company).

pronounce, prō-nouns', *vt.* and *i.* (pronouncing, pronounced). To articulate by the organs of speech; to utter formally; to declare or affirm.

proof, prōf, *n.* Something which tests; trial; what serves to convince; evidence; firmness; a certain standard of strength in spirit; an impression in printing for correction, early impression of an engraving.—*a.* Impenetrable; able to resist.

prop, prop, *n.* A body that supports a weight, a support.—*vt.* (propping, propped). To support by a prop; to sustain generally.

propagate, pro'pa-gāt, *vt.* To multiply by generation or reproduction; to diffuse to increase.—*vi.* To have young or issue; to be multiplied by generation, etc.

prophylactic, prō-fi-lak'tik, *a.* Preventive of disease—*n.* A medicine which preserves against disease.

propitiatory, prō-pi'shi-a-to-ri, *a.* Having the power to make propitious; conciliatory.—*n.* Among the Jews, the mercy-seat.

proportion, pro-pō r'shon, *n.* Comparative relation; relative size and arrangement symmetry, just or equal share, lot, that rule which enables us to find a fourth proportional to three numbers.—*vt.* To adjust in due proportion; to form with symmetry.

prosecute, pro'se-kūt, *vt.* and *i.* (prosecuting, prosecuted). To persist in; to carry on; to pursue at law.

prosecution, pro-se-kū'shon, *n.* Act of prosecuting; the carrying on of a suit at law, the party by whom criminal proceedings are instituted.

proselyte, pro'se-līt, *n.* A convert to the Jewish faith; a new convert.— *vt.* To make a convert of.

prospect, pros'pekt, *n.* A distant view; sight; scene; outlook; exposure, expectation.—*vt.* and *i.* prospekt'. To make search for precious stones or metals.

prostitute, pros'ti-tūt, *vt.* (prostituting, prostituted). To offer publicly for lewd purposes for hire, to devote to anything base.—*a.* Openly devoted to lewdness.—*n.* A female given to indiscriminate lewdness.

prostitution, pros-ti-tū'shon, *n.* Practice of offering the body to indiscriminate intercourse with men, debasement.

prostrate, pros'trāt, *a.* Lying with the body flat; lying at mercy.—*vt.* (prostrating, prostrated). To lay flat or prostrate; to bow in reverence, to overthrow, to ruin.

protect, prō-tekt', *vt.* To shield from danger, injury, etc.; to guard against foreign competition by tariff regulations.

protection, prō-tek'shon, *n.* Act of protecting; shelter; defense; the system of favoring articles of home production by duties on foreign articles.

protest, prō-test', *vi.* To affirm with solemnity, to make a formal declaration of opposition.—*vt.* To assert; to mark for non-payment, as a bill.—*n.* pro'test.

A formal declaration of dissent; a declaration that payment of a bill has been refused.

Protestant, pro'test-ant, *n.* One of the party who adhered to Luther at the Reformation, a member of a reformed church.—*a.* Belonging to the religion of the Protestants.

protocol, prō'tō-kol, *n.* A diplomatic document serving as a preliminary to diplomatic transactions.

protrude, prō-trōd', *vt.* and *i.* (protruding, protruded). To thrust forward, to project.

proud, proud, *a.* Having a high opinion of oneself, haughty; of fearless spirit; ostentatious; magnificent.—**proud flesh,** an excessive granulation in wounds or ulcers.

prove, prōv, *vt.* (proving, proved). To try by experiment; to test; to establish the truth or reality of; to demonstrate, to obtain probate of.—*vi.* To be found by experience or trial, to turn out to be.

province, pro'vins, *n.* A territory at some distance from the metropolis; a large political division; sphere of action, department.

provincial, prō-vin'shal, *a.* Pertaining to or forming a province; characteristic of the people of a province; rustic.—*n.* A person belonging to a province.

provision, prō-vi'zhon, *n.* Act of providing; preparation; stores provided, victuals, stipulation; proviso.—*vt.* To supply with provisions.

provisional, prō-vi'zhon-al, *a.* Provided for present need; temporary.

proviso, prō-vī'zō *n.* An article or clause in any statute or contract; stipulation.

provocative, prō-vok'a-tiv, *a.* Serving to provoke; exciting.—*n.* A stimulant.

provoke, prō-vōk', *vt.* (provoking provoked). To incite; to stimulate, to incense; to irritate.—*vi.* To produce anger.

prowl, proul, *vi.* and *t.* To roam or wander stealthily.—*n.* Act of one who prowls.

prune, prön, *vt.* (pruning, pruned). To trim; to cut or lop off; to clear from superfluities.—*n.* A plum particularly a dried plum.

psychic, psychical, sī'kik, sī'kik-al, *a.* Belonging to the soul, psychological; pertaining to that force by which spiritualists aver they produce "spiritual" phenomena.

psychology, sī-kol'o-ji, *n.* That branch o knowledge which deals with the mind;

mental science.

ptomaine, tō 'mā n, *n*. A name of certain substances generated during putrefaction or morbid conditions prior to death.

public, pub'lik, *a*. Not private, pertaining to a whole community; open or free to all, common, notorious.—*n*. The people, indefinitely.—**In public,** in open view.

publication, pub-li-kā'shon, *n*. Act of publishing; announcement; promulgation; act of offering a book, etc., to the public by sale any book, etc., published.

publish, pub'lish, *vt*. To make public; to proclaim, promulgate, to cause to be printed and offered for sale.

puff, puf, *n*. A sudden emission of breath, a whiff; a short blast of wind; a puffball; piece of light pastry; a consciously exaggerated commendation.—*vi*. To give a quick blast with the mouth; to breathe hard after exertion.—*vt*. To drive with a blast; to inflate; to praise extravagantly.

puff-adder, puf'ad-ér, *n*. A venomous snake which swells out the upper part of its body.

pull, pül, *vt*. To draw towards one; to tug; to rend; to pluck; to gather.—*vi*. To draw; to tug.—*n*. Act of pulling, a twitch, act of rowing a boat; a drink; a struggle.

pulse, puls, *n*. The beating of the heart or an artery; vibration; leguminous plants or their seeds, as beans, etc.—*vi*. (pulsing, pulsed). To beat or throb.

pulverize, pul'vèr-īz, *vt*. To reduce to dust or fine powder.

puma, pü'ma, *n*. A carnivorous quadruped of the cat kind; the cougar.

pumice, pü'mis or pum'is, *n*. A light and spongy stone, used for polishing.

pump, pump, *n*. A machine for raising water or extracting air; a shoe used in dancing.—*vi*. To work a pump.—*vt*. To raise with a pump; to free from liquid by a pump; to put artful questions to extract information.

pun, pun, *n*. A play on words like in sound, but different in meaning; a kind of quibble.—*vi*. (punning, punned) To make a pun or puns.

punch, punsh, *n*. An instrument for driving holes in metal, etc., a blow or thrust, a beverage of spirits, lemon-juice, water, etc.; a buffoon; a short-legged, barrel-bodied horse, a short fat fellow.—*vt*. To stamp or perforate with a punch; to hit with the fist.

punitive, pü-ni-tiv, *a*. Pertaining to, awarding, or involving punishment.

punning, pun'ing, *p.a.* Given to make puns; containing a pun or puns.

pupil, pü'pil, *n*. A young person under the care of a tutor, the aperture in the iris through which the rays of light pass.

pupilary, (or **-ll-**), pü 'pil-a-ri, *a*. Pertaining to a pupil or ward, or to the pupil of the eye.

puppet, pup'et, *n*. A small figure in the human form mechanically worked; a person who is a mere tool.

purchase, pér'chās, *vt*. (purchasing purchased). To buy; to obtain by labor, danger, etc.—*n*. Acquisition of anything by money, what is bought; mechanical advantage.

purify, pü'ri-fī, *vt*. (purifying, purified). To make pure or clear; to free from admixture; to free from guilt.—*vi*. To become pure or clear.

puritan, pür'i-tan, *n*. One very strict in religious matters or in conduct, an early Protestant dissenter from the Church of England. *a*. Pertaining to the Puritans.

purple, pér'pl, *n*. A color produced by mixing red and blue; a purple robe, the badge of the Roman emperors, regal power.—*a*. Of a color made of red and blue, dyed with blood.—*vt*. (purpling, purpled). To make purple.

P

Q

quack, kwak, *vi.* To cry like a duck; to boast; to practice quackery.—*n.* The cry of a duck, a pretender to skill or knowledge, especially medical.—*a.* Pertaining to quackery.

quackery, kwak'è-ri, *n.* Practice or boastful pretenses of a quack, particularly in medicine.

quadragesima, kwod-ra-je'si-ma, *n.* Lent.

quadrangle, kwod-rang-gl, *n.* A plane figure, have four angles and sides; an inner square of a building.

quadrennial, kwod-ren'ni-al, *a.* Comprising four years; occurring once in four years.

quadrilateral, kwod-ri-lat''ér-al, *a.* Having four sides and four angles.—*n.* A plane figure having four sides and angles.

quadrillion, kwod-ril'yon, *n.* The fourth power of a million; a number represented by a unit and 24 ciphers.

quadruped, kwod'rü-ped, *n.* An animal with four legs or feet.

quadruple, kwod'rü-pl, *a.* Fourfold.—*n.* Four times the sum or number.—*vt.* To make fourfold.—*vi.* To become fourfold.

quaff, kwaf, *vt.* and *i.* To drain to the bottom, to drink copiously.

qualification, kwo'li-fi-kā''shon, *n.* Act of qualifying, state of being qualified, suitable quality or characteristic; legal power; ability; modification, restriction.

qualify, kwo'li-fī, *vt.* (qualifying, qualified). To give proper or suitable qualities to, to furnish with the knowledge, skill, etc., necessary; to modify or limit; to soften or moderate, to dilute.—*vi.* To become qualified or fit.

quality, kwo'li-ti, *n.* Sort, kind, or character, a distinguishing property or characteristic; degree of excellence, high rank.

qualm, kwäm *n.* A sudden fit of nausea; a twinge of conscience; compunction.

quandary, kwon-dā'ri or kwon'dari, *n.* A state of perplexity; a predicament.

quarrel, kwo'rel, *n.* An angry dispute; a brawl; cause of dispute; a dart for a crossbow, a glazier's diamond.—*vi.* (quarreling, quarreled). To dispute violently; to disagree.

quarry, kwo'ri, *n.* A place where stones are dug from the earth; any animal pursued for prey, game killed.—*vt.* (quarrying, quarried). To dig or take from a quarry.

quart, kwärt, *n.* The fourth part of a gallon, two pints.

quarter, kwär't'ér, *n.* The fourth part of anything, 28 lbs., 8 bushels; any direction or point of the compass; a district; locality; division of a heraldic shield; proper position; mercy to a beaten foe; *pl.* shelter or lodging; encampment.—*vt.* To divide into four equal parts; to cut to pieces; to furnish with lodgings or shelter, to add to other arms on an heraldic shield.—*vi.* To lodge.

quash, kwosh, *vt.* To subdue or quell; to suppress; to annul or make void.

quasi, kwa'sī, A prefix implying appearance without reality; sort of, sham.

quatercentenary, kwa-t'ér-sen' tena-ri, *n.* A four hundredth anniversary.

quaternary, kwa-t'ér'na-ri, *a.* Consisting of four; arranged in fours; applied to the strata above the tertiary.

quaternion, kwa-t'ér'ni-on, *n.* A set of four; a quantity employed in mathematics.

quaver, kwā'v'ér, *vi.* To have a tremulous motion; to vibrate.—*vt.* To utter with a tremulous sound.—*n.* A shake or rapid vibration of the voice, or on a musical instrument; a musical note equal to half a crotchet.

quay, kē, *n.* A built landing-place for vessels, a wharf.

querimonious, kwe-ri-mō'ni-us, *a.* Apt to complain; complaining; querulous.

quern kw'érn, *n.* A stone hand-mill for grinding grain.

querulous, kwe'rü-lus, *a.* Complaining, murmuring peevish.

query, kwē'ri, *n.* A question; the mark of interrogation (?).—*vi.* (querying, queried). To ask a question or questions.—*vt.* To question; to mark with a query.

quest, kwest, *n.* Act of seeking: search; pursuit; inquiry; solicitation.

question, kwest'yon, *n.* Act of asking; an interrogation; inquiry; discussion, subject of discussion.—*vi.* To ask a question; to doubt.—*vt.* To interrogate; to doubt; to challenge.

quick, kwik, *a.* Alive; brisk; swift; keen, sensitive; irritable.—*n.* A growing plant, usually hawthorn, for hedges, the living flesh; sensitiveness.—*adv.* Quickly, soon.

quicken, kwik'n, *vt.* To revive or resuscitate, to cheer, to increase the speed of, to sharpen, to stimulate.—*vi.* To become alive; to move quickly or more quickly.

quicksand, kwik'sand, *n.* A movable sandbank under water; sand yielding under the feet; something treacherous.

quilt, kwilt, *n.* A padded bedcover.—*vt.* To form into a quilt, to sew pieces of cloth with soft substance between.

quince, kwins, *n.* The fruit of a tree allied to the pear and apple; the tree itself.

quintuple, kwin'tū-pl, *a.* Fivefold.—*vt.* To make fivefold.

quip, kwip, *n.* A sharp sarcastic turn; a severe retort; a gibe.

quirk, kw'ėrk, *n.* An artful turn for evasion a shift; a quibble.

quit, kwit, *a.* Discharged; released free; clear.—*vt.* (quitting, quitted). To discharge; to rid; to acquit; to leave; to abandon.

quite, kwĩt, *adv.* Completely wholly; entirely, altogether, very.

quiver, kwi'v'ėr, *n.* A case or sheath for arrows.—*vi.* To shake with small rapid movements, to tremble, to shiver

quixotic, kwiks-ot'ik, *a.* Chivalrous to extravagance; aiming at visionary ends.

quiz, kwiz, *n.* A hoax a jest, one who quizzes; one liable to be quizzed; a game or test in which two or more persons or teams compete in answering questions.—*vt.* (quizzing, quizzed). To make fun of, as by obscure questions; to look at inquisitively; to tease, to test by questioning.

quote, kwōt, *vt.* (quoting, quoted). To adduce or cite, as from some author; to name as the price of an article.

quotient, kwō'shent, *n.* The number obtained by dividing one number by another.

Q

R

rabbi, rab'bī, *n.* A Jewish teacher or expounder of the law.

rabbit, rab'it, *n.* A burrowing rodent allied to the hare.

rabble, rab'l, *n.* A crowd of vulgar noisy people; the mob, the lower class of people.

rabid, ra'bid, *a.* Raving; furious; mad.

rabies, rā'bi-ēs, *n.* A disease affecting certain animals, especially dogs, from which hydrophobia is communicated.

raccoon, racoon, ra-kön', *n.* An American carnivorous animal.

race, rās, *n.* A body of individuals sprung from a common stock, a breed or stock; a running; a con test in speed a course or career, a rapid current or channel.— *vi.* (racing, raced). To run swiftly; to contend in running.—*vt.* To cause to contend in speed.

radar, rā'där, *n.* A method of finding the position of an object (ship aircraft, etc.) by reflection of radio waves.

radiance, rā'di-ans, *n.* Brightness shooting in rays; luster; brilliancy; splendor.

radiate, rā'di-āt, *vi.* To emit rays of light; to shine; to spread about as in rays.—*vt.* To emit in divergent lines; to enlighten.—*a.* Having rays or lines resembling radii.

radical, ra'di-kal, *a.* Pertaining to the root; original thorough-going; native, underived, relating to radicals in politics.—*n.* A root, a simple, underived word; one who advocates extreme political reform.

radix, rā'diks, *n.* A root, as of a plant or a word; source, origin.

raffle, raf'l, *n.* A kind of lottery.—*vi.* (raffling, raffled). To engage in a raffle.— *vt.* To dispose of by raffle.

raft, räft, *n.* Logs fastened together and floated; a floating structure.

raid, rād, *n.* A hostile incursion, a foray.— *vi.* To engage in a raid.—*vt.* To make a raid on.

rail, rāl, *n.* A horizontal bar of wood or metal, a connected series of posts; a railing; one of the parallel iron bars forming a track for locomotives, etc.; a railway; a grallatorial bird.—*vt.* To inclose with rails; to furnish with rails.—*vi.* To use abusive language; to scold; to inveigh.

rainbow, rān'bō, *n.* An arc of a circle, consisting of all the prismatic colors, appearing in the heavens opposite the sun.

raise, rāz, *vt.* (raising, raised). To cause to rise to lift upward, to excite; to recall from death; to stir up; to construct; to levy; to breed; to originate; to give vent to; to inflate; to cause to be relinquished (a siege).

raisin, rā'zn, *n.* A dried grape.

rake, rāk, *n.* An implement for collecting hay or straw, smoothing earth, etc., a dissolute, lewd man slope.—*vt.* (raking, raked). To apply a rake to, to gather with a rake, to ransack, to enfilade.—*vi.* To use a rake; to search minutely; to incline, to slope, aft, as masts.

rally, ral'i, *vt.* (rallying, rallied). To reunite, as disordered troops, to collect, as things scattered, to attack with raillery; to banter.—*vi.* To recover strength or vigor.—*n.* A stand made by retreating troops; recovery of strength

ram, ram, *n.* The male of the sheep a battering-ram, the loose hammer of a pile-driving machine; a heavy steel beak of a war-vessel; an iron-clad ship with such a beak; one of the signs of the zodiac.—*vt.* (ramming, rammed). To strike with a ram; to batter; to cram.

ramble, ram'bl, *vi.* (rambling, rambled). To roam carelessly about; to talk incoherently; to have parts stretching irregularly.—*n.* An irregular excursion.

rampant, ram'pant, *a.* Rank in growth, exuberant, unrestrained; in *heraldry*, standing up on the hind-legs.

ranch, ranch, *n.* In North America, a farming establishment for rearing cattle and horses.

rancid, ran'sid, *a.* Having a rank or stinking smell; strong-scented; sour; musty.

random, ran'dum, *n.* Action without definite object, chance; caprice.—**At random**, in a haphazard manner.—*a.* Left to chance; done without previous calculation.

range, rānj, *vt.* (ranging, ranged). To set in a row; to dispose systematically; to wander through or scour.—*vt.* To rank; to rove about; to fluctuate.—*n.* A row, a rank; compass or extent; a kitchen grate, distance to which a projectile is carried; a place for gun practice.

rank, rangk, *n.* A row, a line; a social class; comparative station; titled dignity.—*vt.* To place in a line; to classify.— *vi.* To belong to a class; to put in a claim against a bankrupt.—*a.* Luxuriant in growth; strong-scented; utter; coarse, disgusting.

rap, rap, *n.* A quick smart blow; a knock.—*vi.* (rapping, rapped). To strike a quick, sharp blow.—*vt.* To strike with a quick blow.

rapacious, ra-pā'shus, *a.* Greedy of plunder; subsisting on prey; extortionate.

rape, rāp, *n.* A seizing by violence; carnal knowledge of a woman against her will; a plant of the cabbage kind, whose seeds yield an oil.—*vt.* (raping, raped). To carry off violently; to ravish.

rapid, ra'pid, *a.* Very swift; speedy; hurried.—*n.* A swift current in a river.

rash, rash, *a.* Precipitate, hasty; overbold; incautious.—*n.* An eruption on the skin.

ratchet, rach'et, *n.* A catch which abuts against the teeth of a wheel to prevent it running back.

rate, rāt, *n.* Proportion, standard; degree; degree of speed; price; a tax, assessment.—*vt.* (rating, rated). To fix the value, rank, or degree of; to appraise; to reprove; to scold.—*vi.* To be classed in a certain order.

rather, räTH'ėr, *adv.* More readily; preferably; more properly; somewhat.

ratify, ra'ti-fī, *vt.* (ratifying, ratified). To confirm, to approve and sanction.

rattle, rat'l, *vi.* and *t.* (rattling, rattled). To clatter, to chatter fluently.—*n.* A rapid succession of clattering sounds; an instrument or toy which makes a clattering sound; one who talks much and rapidly.

rattlesnake, rat'l-snāk, *n.* A venomous American snake, with horny pieces at the point of the tail which rattle.

raucous, rä'kus, *a.* Hoarse, harsh.

ravage, ra'vāj, *n.* Devastation; havoc.—*vt.* (ravaging, ravaged). To lay waste, to pillage.

rave, rāv, *vi.* (raving, raved). To be delirious, to speak enthusiastically; to dote.

raw, rä, *a.* Not cooked or dressed not manufactured, unfinished; not diluted; bare, as flesh; galled, sensitive; inexperienced; cold and damp

ray, rā, *n.* A line of light; a gleam of intellectual light, one of a number of diverging radii; a flat-fish.—*vt.* and *i.* (raying, rayed). To shine forth, to radiate, to streak.

raze, rāz, *vt.* (razing, razed). To graze; to lay level with the ground; to efface.

reach, rēch, *vt.* To extend, to hand to extend or stretch from a distance; to

arrive at; to gain.—*vi.* To extend, to stretch out the hand in order to touch; to make efforts at attainment.—*n.* Act or power of extending to; straight course of a river; scope.

react, rē-akt', *vi.* To act in return; to return an impulse, to act reciprocally upon each other.—*vt.* To perform anew.

reaction, rē-ak'shon, *n.* A reacting; reciprocal action; tendency to revert to a previous condition, exhaustion consequent on activity and *vice versa.*

read, rēd, *vt.* (reading, read). To peruse; to utter aloud, following something written or printed, to explain.—*vi.* To peruse, to study to stand written or printed; to make sense.—*a.* red, Instructed by reading; learned.

realize, rē'al-īz, *vt.* (realizing, realized). To make real, to convert into money, to impress on the mind as a reality; to render tangible or effective; to acquire; to gain.

realm, relm, *n.* The dominions of a sovereign; a region, sphere, or domain.

realty, rē'al-ti, *n.* The fixed nature of property termed *real;* real property.

ream, rēm, *n.* A package of paper consisting generally of 20 quires or 480 sheets.

reanimate, rē-an'i-māt, *vt.* To animate again; to revive; to infuse new life into.

reap, rēp, *vt.* and *i.* To cut with a scythe, etc., as grain; to gather; to clear of a grain crop; to receive as a reward of labor, etc.

rear, rēr, *n.* The part behind; the part of an army behind the rest; the background.— *vt.* To raise; to bring up, as young; to breed, as cattle, to build up.—*vi.* To rise on the hind-legs, as horse; to become erect.

reasonable, rē'zn-a-bl, *a.* Having the faculty of reason; rational; conformable to reason, moderate fair; tolerable.

reasoning, rē'zn-ing, *n.* The act or process of exercising the faculty of reason; arguments employed.

reassurance, rē-a-shör'ans, *n.* Act of reassuring; a second assurance against loss.

reassure, rē-a-shör', *vt.* To assure anew; to free from fear or terror; to reinsure.

rebuff, rē-buf', *n.* A sudden check; a repulse, refusal.—*vt.* To beat back; to check; to repel the advances of

rebuke, rē-būk', *vt.* (rebuking, rebuked). To reprimand; to reprove sharply.—*n.* A direct and severe reprimand, reproof.

rebus, rē'bus, *n.* A set of words represented by pictures of objects, a kind of puz-

R

zle made up of such pictures.

rebut, rė-but', vt. (rebutting, rebutted). To repel; to refute; in *law*, to oppose by argument, plea, or countervailing proof.

receipt, rē-sēt', n. Act of receiving; that which is received, a written acknowledgment of something received; a recipe.—vt. To give a receipt for; to discharge, as an account.

receive, rė-sēv', vt. (receiving, received). To take, as a thing offered; to admit, to entertain, to contain to be the object of; to take stolen goods.

recess, rē-ses', n. A withdrawing; place or period of retirement, time during which business is suspended; a niche in a wall; an alcove.

recipe, re'si-pē, n. A medical prescription; a statement of ingredients for a mixture.

reciprocal, rē-sip'rō-kal, a. Reciprocating; alternate; done by each to the other; mutual; interchangeable.

reciprocate, rē-sip'rō-kāt, vi. To move backward and forward, to alternate.—vt. To exchange, to give in requital.

reciprocity, re-si-pros'i-ti, n. Reciprocation; interchange; reciprocal obligation, equal commercial rights mutually enjoyed.

reckoning, rek'n-ing, n. Calculation; a statement of accounts with another, landlord's bill, calculation of a ship's position.

reclaim, rē-klā m', vt. To claim back, to reform; to tame; to re cover; to reduce to a state fit for cultivation.

recline, rē-klĭ n', vt. and i. (reclining, reclined). To lean; to rest or repose.

recluse, rē-klös', a. Retired; solitary.—n. A person who lives in seclusion; a hermit.

recognition, re-kog-ni'shon, n. Act of recognizing; avowal; acknowledgment.

recognizance, rē-kog'niz-ans or re-kon'i-zans, n. Recognition, an obligation, as to appear at the assizes, keep the peace, etc.

recognize, re'kog-nĭ z, vt. (recognizing, recognized). To know again: to admit a knowledge of; to acknowledge formally; to indicate one's notice by a bow, etc., to indicate appreciation of.

recoil, rē-koil', vi. To move or start back, to retreat, to shrink, to rebound—n. A starting or falling back, rebound, as of a gun.

recommend, re-kom-mend', vt. To praise to another; to make acceptable; to commit with prayers; to advise.

recompense, re'kom-pens, vt. (recompensing, recompensed). To compensate; to requite; to make amends for.—n. Compensation; reward; amends.

reconcile, re'kon-sĭl, vt. (reconciling, reconciled). To make friendly again; to adjust or settle; to harmonize.

record, rē-kord', vt. To preserve in writing; to register, to chronicle.— n. rek'ord. A written memorial; a register; a public document; memory; one's personal history; best results in contests.

recount, rē-kount', vt. To relate in detail; to count again.—n. A second counting.

recourse, rē-kōrs', n. A going to with a request, as for aid; resort in perplexity.

recover, rē-kuv'ėr, vt. To get back; to regain; to revive; to rescue; to obtain in return for injury or debt.—vi. To grow well; to regain a former condition.

recriminate, rē-krim'in-āt, vi. To return one accusation with another.—vt. To accuse in return.

recruit, rē-kröt', vt. To repair, to supply with new soldiers.—vi. To gain new supplies of anything; to raise new soldiers.—n. A soldier newly enlisted.

rectification, rek'ti-f-kā"shon, n. Act or operation of rectifying; process of refining by repeated distillation.

recur, rē-kėr', vi. (recurring, recurred). To return; to be repeated at a stated interval.

red, red, a. Of a color resembling that of arterial blood.—n. A color resembling that of arterial blood; a red pigment.

redemption, rē-dem'shon, n. The act of redeeming; state of being redeemed; ransom; release; deliverance.

redraw, rē-drä', vt. To draw again.—vi. To draw a new bill of exchange.

redress, rē-dres', vt. To set right; to adjust to repair; to relieve.—n. Relief, deliverance, reparation.

red-tape, red'tāp, n. Excessive official routine and formality.—a. Characterized by excessive routine or formality.

reduce rē-dūs', vt. (reducing, reduced). To bring down; to decrease; to degrade; to subdue; to bring under rules or within categories; to restore to its proper place.

reduction, rē-duk'shon, n. Act of reducing; diminution; conversion into another state or form; subjugation.

redundant, rē-dun'dant, a. Super-fluous; having more words than necessary.

reduplication, rē-dū'pli-kā"shon n. Act of reduplicating; the repetition of a root or initial syllable.

reed, rēd, *n.* A tall broad-leaved grass growing in marshy places, or its hollow stems; a musical instrument; a rustic pipe.

reek, rēk, *n.* Vapor; steam; exhalation; smoke.—*vi.* To smoke; to exhale.

reel, rēl, *n.* A bobbin for thread; a revolving appliance for winding a fishing line; a staggering motion; a lively Scottish dance.—*vt.* To wind upon a reel, to stagger.

refer, rē-fèr', *vt.* (referring, referred). To trace or carry back, to attribute, to appeal; to assign—*vi.* To respect or have relation; to appeal; to apply, to allude.

referendum, ref-èr-en'dum, *n.* The referring of a measure passed by a legislature to the people for final approval.

refine, rē-fīn', *vt.* (refining, refined). To increase the fineness of; to purify; to make elegant; to give culture to.—*vi.* To become purer; to indulge in hair-splitting.

reflection, rē-flek'shon, *n.* Act of reflecting, that which is produced by being reflected; meditation; a censorious remark, reproach.

reflexive, rē-flek'siv, *a.* Reflective; having respect to something past; in *grammar,* having for its object a pronoun which stands for the subject; also applied to such pronouns.

reflux, rē'fluks, *n.* A flowing back; ebb.

reform, rē-form', *vt.* and *i.* To change from worse to better; to amend; to form anew.—*n.* A beneficial change, amendment; a change in the regulations of parliamentary representation.

refrain, rē-frān', *vt.* To restrain; to keep (oneself from action.—*vi.* To forbear, to abstain.—*n.* The burden of a song; part repeated at the end of every stanza.

refuge, re'fūj, *n.* Protection from danger or distress, a retreat, a shelter; a device; contrivance; shift.—*vt.* and *i.* To shelter.

refugee, re-fū-jē', *n.* One who flees for refuge; one who flees to another country or place for safety.

refuse, re-fūz', *vt.* (refusing, refused). To deny, as a request or demand, to decline, to reject.—*vi.* To decline a request or offer.

regale, rē-gāl', *vt.* and *i.* (regaling, regaled). To refresh sumptuously; to feast. *n.* A splendid feast; a treat.

regality, rē-gal'i-ti, *n.* Royalty; kingship.

regard, rē-gärd', *vt.* To notice carefully; to observe; to respect; to heed; to view in the light of; to relate to.—*n.* Look or gaze; respect; notice; heed; esteem; deference; *pl.* good wishes.

regeneration, rē-jen'è-rā"shon, *n.* Act of regenerating; that change by which love to God is implanted in the heart.

regret, rē-gret', *n.* Grief at something done or undone; remorse; penitence.—*vt.* (regretting, regretted). To be sorry for, to lament.

regular, re'gū-lèr, *a.* Conformed to a rule, law, or principle; normal; methodical, uniform; having the parts symmetrical; thorough.—*n.* A monk who has taken the vows in some order; a soldier of a permanent army.

regulate, re'gū-lāt, *vt.* (regulating, regulated). To adjust by rule; to put or keep in good order; to direct.

rehabilitate, rē-ha-bil'i-tāt, *vt.* To restore to a former capacity or position; to reestablish in esteem.

rein, rān, *n.* The strap of a bridle, by which a horse is governed; an instrument for restraining, restraint.—*vt.* To govern by a bridle; to restrain.—*vi.* To obey the reins.

reindeer, rān'dēr, *n.* A deer of northern parts, with broad branched antlers.

reinforce, rē-in-fōrs', *vt.* To strengthen by new assistance, as troops.—*n.* An additional thickness given to an object to strengthen it.

reject, rē-jekt', *vt.* To cast off; to discard, to repel; to forsake; to decline.

relation, rē-lā'shon, *n.* Act of relating; account; reference; connection; kindred; a relative; proportion.

relative, re'lat-iv, *a.* Having relation or reference, not absolute or existing by itself, relevant.—*n.* Something considered in its relation to something else; one allied by blood; a word which relates to or represents another word or sentence.

relax, rē-laks', *vt.* To slacken, to loosen or weaken; to unbend.—*vi.* To become loose, feeble, or languid, to abate in severity.

release, rē-lēs', *vt.* (releasing, released). To liberate; to disengage; to acquit.—*n.* Liberation, discharge; acquittance.

relic, re'lik, *n.* A remaining fragment; the body of a deceased person (usually in *pl.*); a memento or keepsake.

relief, rē-lēf', *n.* Ease or mitigation of pain; succor; remedy; redress; assistance given to a pauper; one who

R

relieves another by taking duty; prominence of figures above a plane surface in sculpture, carving, etc.; prominence or distinctness.

relieve, rē-lēv', vt. (relieving, relieved). To remove or lessen, as anything that pains; to ease; to succor; to release from duty; to give variety to; to set off by contrast; to give the appearance of projection to.

religion, rē-li'jon, n. An acknowledgment of our obligation to God practical piety; devotion; any system of faith and worship.

remain, rē-mān', vi. To continue in a place or condition; to abide; to be left, to last.—n. That which is left pl. a dead body; literary works of one who is dead.

remainder, rē-mān'dėr, n. That which remains; residue; remnant; an estate limited so as to be enjoyed after the death of the present possessor or otherwise.— a. Left over.

remark, rē-märk', n. Notice; an observation in words; a comment.—vt. To observe; to utter by way of comment.

remember, rē-mem'bėr, vt. To have in the memory; to think of; to observe; to give a gratuity for service done.—vi. To have something in remembrance.

remembrance, rē-mem'brans, n. The keeping of a thing in mind; memory; what is remembered; a memorial, a keepsake.

remnant, rem'nant, n. That which is left; a scrap, fragment.—a. Remaining.

remonstrance, rē-mon'strans, n. Act of remonstrating; expostulation, strong representation against something.

remonstrate, rē-mon'strāt, vi. To present strong reasons against an act, to expostulate.

remorse, rē-mors', n. Reproach of conscience, compunction for wrong committed.

remove rē-möv', vt. (removing, removed) To move from its place; to take away; to displace from an office, to banish or destroy.—vi. To be moved from its place; to change the place of residence.—n. A removal; departure.

rend, rend, vt. (rending, rent). To force asunder, to tear away, to sever.—vi. To be or become torn, to split.

render, ren'dėr, vt. To give in return; to give back; to present; to afford; to invest with qualities; to translate; to interpret; to clarify, as tallow.

rendezvous, ren'de-vö, n. A place of meeting.—vi. To meet at a particular place.

renew, rē-nū', vt. To make new again; to repair; to repeat; to grant anew; to transform.—vi. To grow or begin again.

rent, rent, n. Money, etc., payable yearly for the use of lands or tenements, a tear a schism.—vt. To let on lease; to hold on condition of paying rent.—vi. To be leased or let for rent.

renunciation, rē-nun'si-ā"shon, n. Act of renouncing; disavowal; abandonment.

repair, rē-pār', vt. To restore; to refit, to mend to retrieve.—vi. To betake oneself; to resort.—n. Restoration; supply of loss; state as regards repairing; a resorting; abode.

repel, rē-pel', vt. (repelling, repelled). To drive back; to resist successfully.—vi. To cause repugnance, to shock.

repellent, rē-pel'ent, a. Having the effect of repelling; repulsive; deterring.

repent, rē-pent', vi. To feel regret for something done or left undone to be penitent.—vt. To remember with self-reproach or sorrow.

repetition, re-pē-ti'shon, n. Act of repeating; recital; that which is repeated.

replace, rē-plās', vt. (replacing. replaced). To put again in the former place; to put in the place of another, to take the place of.

report, rē-pört', vt. and i. To bring back, as an answer; to relate; to give an official statement of, to take down from the lips of a speaker, etc.; to lay a charge against.—n. An account, rumor repute; noise of explosion; official statement; account of proceedings.

reporter, rē-pört'ėr, n. One who reports; one of a newspaper staff who gives accounts of public meetings, events, etc.

repose rē-pōz', vt. (reposing, reposed). To lay at rest.—vi. To lie at rest; to rely.—n. A lying at rest; tranquillity, composure, absence of show of feeling.

reprehension, re-prē-hen'shon, n. Act of reprehending; reproof; censure, blame. Containing reprehension or reproof.

represent, re-prē-zent', vt. To exhibit by a likeness of; to typify; to act the part of; to describe; to be a substitute for, to exemplify.

reprieve, rē-prēv', vt. (reprieving, reprieved). To grant a respite to; to relieve temporarily.—n. Suspension of the execution of a criminal's sentence, respite.

reprimand, rep'ri-mand, *n*. A severe reproof for a fault.—*vt*. rep-rimand'. To administer a sharp rebuke to.

reprint, rē-print', *vt*. To print again.—*n*. re'print. A second or new edition.

reproach, rē-prōch', *vt*. To charge severely with a fault, to censure.—*n*. Censure; blame; source of blame; disgrace.

reptile, rep'til, *a*. Creeping; grovelling.—*n*. An animal that moves on its belly, or by means of small short legs.

republic, rē-pub'lik, *n*. A common wealth, a state in which the supreme power is vested in elected representatives.

repulse, rē-puls', *n*. Act of repelling, a check or defeat, refusal, denial.—*vt*. (repulsing, repulsed). To repel.

reputation, re-pūt-ā'shon, *n*. Character derived from public opinion; repute; good name; honor; fame.

repute, rē-pūt', *vt*. (reputing, reputed). To estimate; to deem.—*n*. Reputation; character; good character.

request, rē-kwest', *n*. An expressed desire, a petition, thing asked for, a state of being asked for.—*vt*. To ask; to beg.

rescue, res'kū, *vt*. (rescuing, rescued). To deliver from confinement, danger, or evil.—*n*. Act of rescuing; deliverance.

research, rē-sėrch', *n*. A diligent seeking of facts or principles; investigation.—*vt*. To search again.

resemblance, rē-zem'blans, *n*. Likeness; similarity; something similar, similitude.

resemble, rē-zem'bl, *vt*. (resembling, resembled). To be like; to liken, to compare.

reservoir, re'zėr-vwär, *n*. A place where anything is kept in store; an artificial lake to supply a town with water.

reside, rē-zīd', *vi*. (residing, resided). To have one's abode, to dwell; to inhere.

residential, re-zi-den'shal, *a*. Pertaining to or suitable for residence.

resin, re'zin, *n*. An inflammable vegetable substance; the hardened juice of pines.

resistant, resistent, rē-zis'tent, *a*. Making resistance.—*n*. One who or that which resists.

resolute, re'zō-lūt, *a*. Having fixedness of purpose; determined; steadfast.

resolution, re-zō-lū'shon, *n*. Character of being resolute. determination, a formal decision; operation of separating the component parts, solution.

resolve, rē-zolv', *vt*. (resolving, resolved). To separate the component parts of, to analyze, to solve to determine; to decide.—*vi*. To separate into component parts, to melt, to determine; to decide. *n*. Fixed purpose of mind; resolution.

resort, rē-zort', *vi*. To have recourse; to go; to repair frequently.—*n*. Recourse; concourse; a haunt.

resound, rē-zound', *vt*. To give back the sound of; to echo; to praise.—*vi*. To sound again; to echo, to be much praised.

respite, res'pit, *n*. Temporary intermission, interval, a reprieve.—*vt*. (respiting, respited). To grant a respite to; to reprieve.

rest, rest, *n*. Cessation of action peace; sleep; an appliance for support; a pause; remainder; the others.—*vi*. To cease from action to lie for repose; to be supported, to be in a certain state, remain, to be left.—*vt*. To lay at rest; to place, as on a support.

restaurant, res'tō-rong, *n*. An establishment for the sale of refreshments.

restriction, re-strik'shon, *n*. Act of restricting; limitation; a reservation.

result, rē-zult', *vi*. To rise as a consequence; to issue; to ensue; to end.—*n*. Consequence; effect; issue, outcome.

resurrection, re-zėr-rek'shon, *n*. A rising again; the rising of the dead at the general judgment.

retail, rē-tāl', *vt*. To sell in small quantities, to tell to many.—*n*. re' tal. The sale of commodities in small quantities; used also as *adj*.

retainer, rē-tān'ėr, *n*. One who retains, an adherent or dependent; a fee to engage a counsel.

retaliate, rē-ta'li-āt, *vi*. and *t*. To return like for like; to repay; to take revenge.

retire, rē-tīr', *vi*. (retiring, retired). To go back; to withdraw from business or active life; to go to bed.—*vt*. To remove from service, to pay when due, as a bill of exchange.

retiring, rē-tīr'ing, *a*. Reserved; unobtrusive; granted to one who retires from service.

retort, re-tort', *vt*. To retaliate; to throw back.—*vi*. To return an argument or charge.—*n*. A severe reply, a repartee, a chemical vessel for distilling.

retributive, retributory, re-tri'bu-tiv, re-tri'bu-to-ri, *a*. Making retribution; entailing justly deserved punishment.

retrieve, re-trev', *vt*. (retrieving, retrieved). To recover; to regain; to repair.

R

retriever, re-trev'er, *n.* A dog that brings in game which a sportsman has shot.

return, re-tern', *vi.* To come or go back; to recur.—*vt.* To send back; to repay, to report officially to elect, to yield.—*n.* Act of returning; repayment; election of a representative; profit, an official statement; *pl.* tabulated statistics; a light tobacco.

revelation, re-ve-la'shon, *n.* Act of revealing; that which is revealed; divine communication; the Apocalypse.

revenge, re-venj', *vt.* and *i.* (revenging, revenged). To take vengeance for, to avenge.—*n.* Act of revenging; retaliation; deliberate infliction of injury in return for injury; vindictive feeling.

reverence, rev'er-ens, *n.* Awe combined with respect, veneration; an obeisance; a reverend personage; a title of the clergy.—*vt.* To revere; to pay reverence to.

reverse, ra-vèrs', *vt.* (reversing, reversed). To alter to the opposite; to annul.—*n.* A reversal; a complete change or turn; a check; a defeat; the contrary, the back or undersurface.—*a.* Turned backward; opposite.

revert, rē-vèrt', *vt.* To reverse.—*vi.* To return to a former position, habit, statement, etc.; to return to the donor.

review, rē-vū', *vt.* To view again; to reconsider; to write a critical notice of; to inspect.—*vi.* To write reviews.—*n.* A re-examination; a criticism, a periodical containing criticisms; official inspection of troops.

revise, rē-vīz', *vt.* (revising, revised). To go over with care for correction.—*n.* A revision; a second proof-sheet in printing.

revolt, rē-vōlt', *vi.* To renounce allegiance, to rebel, to be disgusted: with at.—*vt.* To shock.—*n.* Rebellion; mutiny.

revolution, re-vō-lū'shon, *n.* Act of revolving, rotation; a turn; circuit; a cycle of time; a radical change; overthrow of existing political institutions.

revue, rē-vū', *n.* A loosely-constructed and spectacular theatrical exhibition, depending on music and scenic and staging effects.

reward, rē-wärd', *n.* What is given in return for good done; recompense; punishment.—*vt.* To repay; to requite.

rhapsody, rap 'so-di, *n.* A short epic poem, or portion of an epic, a confused series of extravagantly enthusiastic statements.

rhetoric, re'to-rik, *n.* The art of using language effectively; the art which teaches oratory; eloquence; flashy oratory declamation.

rhomb, rhombus, rom, rom'bus, *n.* A quadrilateral whose sides are equal, but the angles not right angles.

rhyme, rīm, *n.* A correspondence of sound in the ends of words or verses; a short poem; a word rhyming with another.—*vi.* (rhyming, rhymed). To make verses; to accord in sound.—*vt.* To put into rhyme.

rhythm, rithm, *n.* Periodical emphasis in verse or music; metrical movement; harmony; rhyme; meter, verse.

rib, rib, *n.* One of the curved bones springing from the backbone; something resembling a rib, a long ridge on cloth.—*vt.* (ribbing, ribbed). To furnish with ribs, to inclose with ribs.

ricochet, rik'o-shet, *n.* A rebounding from a flat, horizontal surface.—*vt.* and *i.* rik-o-shet'. To operate upon by ricochet firing; to rebound.

rid, rid, *vt.* (ridding, rid). To make free; to clear; to disencumber—*a.* Free clear.

riddle, rid'l, *n.* A puzzling question; an enigma; a coarse sieve.— *vt.* (riddling, riddled). To solve, to sift, to make many holes in.

ride, rīd, *vi.* (riding, pret. rode, pp. ridden). To be borne on horseback, in a vehicle, etc.; to have ability as an equestrian, to be at anchor.— *vt.* To sit on, so as to be carried; to go over in riding; to domineer over.—*n.* An excursion on horseback, or in a vehicle; a road for the amusement of riding.

ridge, rij, *n.* A long narrow prominence; strip thrown up by a plow; a long crest of hills; upper angle of a roof.—*vt.* (ridging, ridged). To form into ridges.

right, rīt, *a.* Straight; upright; just; suitable, proper real, correct, belonging to that side of the body farther from the heart; to be worn outward perpendicular, formed by one line perpendicular to another.—*adv.* Justly; correctly; very; directly, to the right hand.—*n.* What is right; rectitude; a just claim; authority; side opposite to the left.—*vt.* To put right, to do justice to; to restore to an upright position.—*vi.* To resume a vertical position.

ring, ring, *n.* Anything in the form of a circle; a circle of gold, etc., worn on the finger; an area in which games, etc., are performed; a group of persons, sound of a bell a metallic sound.—*vt.* To encircle to cause to sound, to repeat often or loudly.—*vi*. To sound, to resound; to tingle.

riotous, rī'ot-us, *a*. Indulging in riot or revelry; tumultuous; seditious; excessive.

rip, rip, *vt*. (ripping, ripped). To tear or cut open; to take out by cutting or tearing. —*n*. A rent; a scamp.

ripe, rīp, *a*. Brought to perfection in growth; mature; complete ready for action or effect.—*vt*. and *i*. (riping, riped). To mature.

ripple, rip'l, *vi*. (rippling, rippled). To show a ruffled surface, as water; to make a gentle sound, as running water.—*vt*. To clean the seeds from, as flax.—*n*. A ruffle of the surface of water, a comb for separating the seeds from flax.

rise, rīz, *vi*. (rising pret. rose, pp. risen). To pass to a higher position to stand up; to bring a session to an end, to arise, to swell by fermentation; to slope upwards, to become apparent; to come into existence, to rebel.—*n*. Act of rising ascent, elevation; origin; beginning; appearance above the horizon; increase; advance.

rivet, ri'vet *n*. A metallic bolt whose end is hammered broad after insertion.—*vt*. (riveting, riveted). To fasten with rivets, to clinch, to make firm.

road, rōd, *n*. An open way or public passage; a highway; a means of approach; a roadstead (usually in *plural*).

roast, rōst, *vt*. To cook by exposure to a fire, to parch by heat, to banter severely.—*vi*. To become roasted.—*n*. Roasted meat, part selected for roasting.—*a*. Roasted.

robe, rōb, *n*. A gown, or long, loose garment, worn over other dress an elegant dress.—*vt*. (robing, robed). To put a robe upon; to in vest.

robot, rōb'ot, *n*. Any mechanical contrivance designed to perform work normally requiring the exercise of human intelligence.

rock, rok, *vt*. To move backwards and forwards without displacing to swing.—*vi*. To sway; to reel. *n*. A large mass of stone; defense; source of peril or disaster, a kind of solid sweetmeat.

rod, rod, *n*. A straight slender stick a badge of office; an enchanter's wand; a fishing-rod; a measure of 5-1/2 lineal yards.

rodent, rō'dent, *a*. Gnawing, belonging to the gnawing animals (Rodentia).—*n*. An animal that gnaws, as the squirrel.

roll, rōl, *vt*. To turn on its surface; to wrap on itself by turning; to involve in a bandage or the like; to press with a roller.— *vi*. To turn over and over, to run on wheels, to be tossed about; to sound with a deep prolonged sound.—*n*. Act of rolling, something rolled up; an official document; a catalogue; a cake of bread, a roller, a prolonged deep sound.

roller, rōl'ér, *n*. One who or that which rolls, a cylinder for smoothing, crushing, etc.; that on which something may be rolled up; a long, heavy, swelling wave.

Roman, rō'man, *a*. Pertaining to Rome or its people and to the Roman Catholic religion; applied to the common upright letter in printing.

romance, rō-mans', *n*. A tale in verse in a Romance dialect; a popular epic or tale in prose or verse of some length; a tale of extraordinary adventures, tendency to the wonderful or mysterious; a fiction.—*a*. (with *cap.*). A term applied to the languages sprung from the Latin.— *vi*. To tell fictitious stories.

roost, rōst, *n*. The pole on which birds rest at night, a collection of fowls resting together.—*vi*. To occupy a roost; to settle.

root, rōt, *n*. That part of a plant which fixes itself in the earth; lower part of anything; origin; a form from which words are derived.—*vi*. To fix the root, to be firmly fixed.—*vt*. To plant deeply; to impress durably; to tear up or out, to eradicate.

rope, rōp, *n*. A cord or line of some thickness; a row or string of things united.— *vi*. (roping, roped). To draw out in threads.—*vt*. To pull by a rope; to fasten or inclose with a rope.

rosin, ro'zin, *n*. The resin left after distilling off the volatile oil from turpentine; resin in a solid state.—*vt*. To rub with rosin.

rostrum, ros'trum, *n.*; pl. **-tra**. The beak or bill of a bird; the ram of an ancient ship; pl. a platform or pulpit.

rot, rot, *vi*. (rotting, rotted). To become rotten, to decay.—*vt*. To make rotten.— *n*. Putrid decay; a fatal distemper of sheep; a disease injurious to plants; nonsense.

rouge, rözh, *n*. A cosmetic to impart ruddiness to the complexion.—*vt*. and *i*. (rouging, rouged). To paint with rouge.

R

rough, ruf, *a*. Not smooth; rugged; boisterous, harsh, rude; cruel; vague; hasty.—*vt*. To make rough; to roughhew.—**To rough it,** to submit to hardships.—*n*. State of being rough or unfinished; a rowdy.

roulette, rö-let', *n*. A game of chance; an engraver's tool with a toothed wheel.

round, round, *a*. Circular; spherical; large; open; candid; brisk, as a trot, not minutely accurate, as a number.—*n*. That which is round; rung of a ladder; a circular course or series, circuit made by one on duty; a vocal composition in parts; ammunition for firing once; a turn or bout.—*vt*. To make round; to encircle; to make full and flowing; to pass round.—*vi*. To become round or full, to make a circuit.—*adv*. In a circle; around; not directly.— *prep*. About; around.

rove, röv, *vt*. (roving, roved). To move about aimlessly; to roam; to ramble.—*vt*. To wander over; to card into flakes, as wool.

row, rō, *n*. A series in a line; a rank; a line of houses, an excursion in a boat with oars.—*vt*. To impel by oars, as a boat, to transport by rowing.—*vi*. To work with the oar

rub, rub, *vt*. (rubbing, rubbed). To move something along the surface of with pressure; to scour; to remove by friction; to chafe.—*vi*. To move along with pressure; to fret.—*n*. Act of rubbing; friction; obstruction; difficulty; a gibe.

rubber, rub'ėr, *n*. One who rubs; thing used in polishing or cleaning; india-rubber; obstruction or difficulty; contest of three games in whist.

rudiment, rö'di-ment, *n*. The original of anything; a first principle; an undeveloped organ; *pl* . first elements of a science or art.

rudimentary, rö-di-ment'a-ri, *a*. Pertaining to rudiments; consist ing in first principles; initial; in an undeveloped state.

rue, rö, *vt*. (ruing, rued). To repent of; to regret.—*vi*. To become sorrowful or repentant. *n*. An acrid ill-smelling plant.

ruffle, ruf'l, *vt*. (ruffling, ruffed) To rumple, to derange; to disturb.— *vi*. To bluster.—*n*. A plaited cambric, etc., attached to one's dress; frill, state of being agitated; low vibrating beat of a drum.

rug, rug, *n*. A heavy fabric used to cover a bed, protect a carpet, etc.; a mat

rugby, rug'bi, *n*. One of the two principal varieties of football, played by fifteen men a side, with an oval ball, handling being permitted.

ruin, rö'in, *n*. Destruction; fall; overthrow; anything in a state of decay; that which destroys; *pl*. remains of a city, house, etc.; state of being destroyed.—*vt*. To bring to ruin, to destroy, to impoverish.

rule, röl, *n*. A ruler or measure; a guiding principle or formula; a precept, law, maxim; government; control, regulation, order; method.—*vt*. (ruling, ruled). To govern, to manage; to decide; to mark with lines by a ruler.—*vi*. To exercise supreme authority; to maintain a level, as the market price; to settle, as a rule of court.

rumble, rum'bl, *vi*. (rumbling, rumbled). To make a dull, continued sound.—*n*. A low, heavy, continued sound, a seat for servants behind a carriage.

run, run, *vi*. (running, pret. ran, pp. run). To move by using the legs more quickly than in walking; to take part in a race; to flee; to spread; to ply; to move or pass; to become fluid; to continue in operation, to have a certain direction; to have a certain purport to be current; to continue in time.—*vt*. To cause to run, to pursue, as a course; to incur; to break through (a blockage); to smuggle; to pierce; to melt; to carry on.—*n*. Act of running; course or distance run; a trip; course, tenor, etc.; general demand, as on a back, place where animals may run; generality.

runner, run'ėr, *n*. One who runs; a messenger; a bird of the order Cursores, a stem running along the ground and taking root; that on which something runs or slides.

rustic, rus'tik, *a*. Pertaining to the country; rural; homely; unpolished.—*n*. A country-man, a peasant; a clown.

rustle, rus'l, *vi*. and *t*. (rustling, rustled). To make the noise of things agitated, as straw, leaves, etc.—*n*. The noise of things that rustle; a slight sibilant sound.

rut, rut, *n*. The track of a wheel; a line cut with a spade; line of routine time during which certain animals are under sexual excitement.—*vt*. (rutting, rutted). To cut in ruts.—*vi*. To be in heat, as deer.

S

Sabbath, sa'bath, *n*. The day of rest; Sunday.

saber, sā'bèr, *n*. A sword with one edge, a cavalry sword.—*vt*. (sabering, sabered). To strike or kill with a saber.

sable, sā'bl, *n*. A small animal of the weasel family; the fur of the sable; black.—*a*. Black; dark.

sabotage, sä-bŏ'-täzh, *n*. Malicious destruction of employers, property or national plant by employees on strike or during war-time.

sack, sak, *n*. A bag for flour, wool, etc., that which a sack holds; a sort of jacket; a dry wine; pillage of a town.—*vt*. To put in sacks, to pillage, as a town.

sacrament, sa'kra-ment, *n*. A solemn religious ordinance observed by Christians, as baptism or the Lord's Supper.

sacred, sā'kred, *a*. Set apart for a holy purpose; consecrated; religious; set apart to some one in honor, venerable.

sacrifice, sa'kri-fĭs, *n*. The offering of anything to God; anything offered to a divinity, surrender made in order to gain something else.—*vt*. (sacrificing, sacrificed). To make an offering or sacrifice of.—*vi*. To offer up a sacrifice to some deity.

saddle, sad'l, *n*. A seat for a rider on a horse's back; something like a saddle in shape or use.—*vt*. (saddling, saddled). To put a saddle on; to burden.

Sadducee, sad'ū-sē, *n*. One of a sect among the Jews who denied the resurrection and the existence of angels or spirits.

Sadism, säd'ism, *n*. A form of sexual perversion, in which pleasure is taken in the cruel treatment of the companion.

safe, sāf, *a*. Secure; free from danger; unharmed; no longer dangerous; trustworthy.—*n*. A strong box or chamber for securing valuables, a cool receptacle for meat.

safeguard, sāf'gärd, *n*. One who or that which guards; a defense; protection, a passport.—*vt*. To guard.

sagacity, sa-gas'i-ti, *n*. Quickness of discernment; shrewdness, high intelligence.

sage, sāj, *a*. Wise; sagacious; well-judged; grave.—*n*. A wise man; a man venerable for years, and of sound judgment, a labiate plant.

sailing, sāl'ing, *p.a.* Moved by sails and not by steam.—*n*. Act of setting sail; art or rules of navigation.

saint, sānt, *n*. One eminent for piety and virtue; one of the blessed; a person canonized.—*vt*. To canonize.

saliva, sa-lī'va, *n*. The fluid secreted by certain glands, which moistens the mouth and assists digestion.

salivate, sa'li-vāt, *vt*. To produce an unusual secretion and discharge of saliva.

sallow, sal'ŏ, *a*. Having a pale, sickly, yellowish color.—*n*. A kind of willow.

sally, sal'i, *n*. A leaping forth; a rush of troops from a besieged place, a dart of intellect, fancy etc.; frolic.—*vi*. (sallying, sallied). To leap forth; to issue suddenly.

salon, sä-long, *n*. An apartment for the reception of company; a saloon.

salt, sält, *n*. A substance for seasoning and preserving food; a compound produced by the combination of a base with an acid taste, savor, piquancy, an old sailor.—*a*. Impregnated with salt; pungent.—*vt*. To sprinkle or season with salt.

salute, sa-lūt', *vt*. (saluting, saluted). To greet; to greet by a bow, etc., to kiss, to honor.—*vi*. To perform a salutation; to greet each other.—*n*. Act of saluting; greeting; a kiss; a bow; discharge of artillery, etc.

salvage, sal'väj, *n*. Act of saving a ship or goods from shipwreck, fire, etc.; an allowance for the saving of property; goods thus saved.

salvation, sal-vā'shon, *n*. Act of saving; redemption of man from sin, that which saves.

salve, salv or säv, *n*. A healing ointment; remedy.—*vt*. (salving, salved). To apply salve to; to remedy.

sanatorium, san-a-tŏ'ri-um, *n*. A place to which people go for the sake of health.

sanctify, sangk'ti-fī, *vt*. (sanctifying sanctified). To make holy, to hallow; to make pure from sin.

sanctimonious, sangk-ti-mŏ'ni-us *a*. Making a show of sanctity; hypocritical.

sanction, sangk'shon, *n*. Confirmation; ratification; authority.—*vt*. To ratify; to authorize; to countenance.

sanctity, sangk'ti-ti, *n*. State of being sacred; holiness; inviolability.

sanctuary, sangk'tū-a-ri, *n*. A sacred place; a place of worship; part of a church where the altar is placed, a place of protection to criminals, debtors, etc.; shelter.

sandstone sand'stŏn, *n.* A stone composed of agglutinated grains of sand.

sandwich sand'wich, *n.* Slices of bread, with meat or something savory between.—*vt.* To insert like the meat in a sandwich, to fit between two other pieces

sanguine sang'gwin, *a.* Consisting of blood; full of blood; of the color of blood cheerful, confident.

sanitary san'i-ta-ri, *a.* Pertaining to or designed to secure health; hygienic.

saponify sa-pon'i-fī, *vt.* To convert into soap by combination with an alkali.

Sapphic saf'fik, *a.* Pertaining to *Sappho,* a Grecian poetess, or to a kind of verse invented by her. *n.* A Sapphic verse.

sapphire saf'fīr, *n.* A precious stone of very great hardness, and of various shades of blue; a rich blue color; blue.

sarcastic sär-kas'tik, *a.* Containing sarcasm; scornfully severe; taunting

sarcode sär'kod, *n.* Structureless gelatinous matter forming the bodies of animals belonging to the protozoa.

sash sash, *n.* A long band or scarf worn for ornament; the frame of a window; a frame for a saw.—*vt.* To furnish with sashes or sash windows.

sassafras sas'a-fras, *n.* A kind of laurel, the root of which has medicinal virtues.

Satan sā'tan, *n.* The devil or prince of darkness; the chief of the fallen angels.

satchel sa'chel, *n.* A little sack or bag; a bag for a school-boy's books.

sate sāt, *vt.* (sating, sated). To satiate, to satisfy the appetite of; to glut.

satellite sa'tel-līt, *n.* An attendant; an obsequious dependent; a small planet revolving round another.

satiate sā'shi-āt, *vt.* (satiating, satiated). To fully satisfy the desire of; to surfeit; to glut.—*a.* Filled to satiety.

satisfy sa'tis-fī, *vt.* and *i.* (satisfying, satisfied). To gratify fully; to content; to fulfill the claims of; to answer, to free from doubt.

saturate sa'tūr-āt, *vt.* To imbue till no more can be received; to soak thoroughly.

saunter sän'tèr, *vi.* To stroll about idly; to loiter.—*n.* A stroll; a leisurely pace.

saurian sä'ri-an, *a.* Pertaining to the lizards.—*n.* A scaly reptile, as the lizard.

sausage sä'sāj, *n.* The prepared intestine of an ox, etc., stuffed with minced meat.

savage sa'vāj, *a.* wild uncultivated, barbarous, brutal.—*n.* One who is uncivilized; a barbarian.

savant sä-väng', A man of learning; a man eminent for his scientific acquirements.

save sāv, *vt.* (saving, saved). To preserve; to protect; to rescue; to spare; to keep from doing or suffering, to reserve, to obviate.—*vi.* To be economical.—*prep.* Except.

saving sāv'ing, *a.* Thrifty; that secures from evil; containing some reservation.—*n.* What is saved; sums accumulated by economy: generally *pl.*—*prep.* Excepting.

savior sāv'yėr, *n.* One who saves from evil, destruction, or danger; Christ.

savor sā'vor, *n.* Taste, flavor, odor distinctive quality.—*vi.* To have a particular taste; to partake of some characteristic of something else. *vt.* To taste or smell with pleasure, to like.

say sā, *vt.* (saying, said). To utter in words, to speak, to declare, to assume.—*vi.* To speak; to relate.—*n.* A speech statement.

saying sā'ing, *n.* Something said; speech; an adage; a maxim; a proverb.

scab skab, *n.* An encrusted substance over a sore in healing; a disease of sheep; the mange in horses.

scale skāl, *n.* A thin flake on the skin of an animal, dish of a balance; balance itself (generally *pl.*) anything graduated used as a measure; series of steps or ranks; relative dimensions; succession of notes; gamut.—*vt.* (scaling, scaled). To weigh, as in scales, to strip of scales; to clean, to climb, as by a ladder.—*vi.* To come off in thin layers.

scalene skā'lēn, *a.* A term applied to a triangle of which the three sides are unequal.

scallop skal'op or skol'op, *n.* Edible bivalve of the oyster family; a curving on the edge of anything.—*vt.* To cut the edge of into scallops or segments of circles

scalp skalp, *n.* The skin of the top of the head, with the hair on it.—*vt.* To deprive of the scalp.

scamp skamp, *n.* A knave; swindler; rogue.—*vt.* To do in a perfunctory manner.

scan skan, *vt.* (scanning, scanned). To measure by the metrical feet, as a verse; to scrutinize; to eye.

scandal, skan'dal, *n*. Public reproach; shame; defamatory talk; slander.

scandalize, skan'dal-īz, *vt*. To fend by some action deemed disgraceful, to shock.

scapular, scapulary, skap'ū-lèr, skap'ū-la-ri, *n*. A monastic garment resting on the shoulders, with a flap hanging down in front and another behind.

scar, skär, *n*. The mark of a wound or ulcer, a cicatrix, a cliff, a bare place on the side of a hill.—*vt*. (scarring, scarred). To mark with a scar, to wound.

scarcity, skärs'i-ti, *n*. State or condition of being scarce: deficiency; dearth.

scare, skā r, *vt*. (scaring, scared). To strike with sudden terror; to frighten.—*n*. A sudden fright, a causeless alarm.

scarlet, skär'let, *n*. A bright-red color.—*a*. Of a bright-red color.

scathe, skāth. *n*. Damage, injury.—*vt*. (scathing, scathed). To injure; to harm.

scatter, skat'èr, *vt*. To disperse; to spread; to strew; to disunite.—*vi*. To be dispersed; to straggle apart.

scattered, skat'érd, *p.a*. Thinly spread; loose and irregular in arrangement.

scene, sēn, *n*. A stage; a distinct part of a play, a painted device on the stage; place of action or exhibition; general appearance of any action, a view, display of emotion.

scenery, sēn'è-ri, *n*. The painted representations on the stage, pictorial features, landscape characteristics.

schedule, shed'ūl, sed'ūl, *n*. A paper containing a list, and annexed to a larger writing, as to a will, deed, etc., an inventory.—*vt*. (scheduling, scheduled). To place in a schedule.

scheme, skēm, *n*. A combination of things adjusted by design; a system, project, diagram.—*vt*. and *i*. (scheming, schemed). To plan, contrive, project.

school, skōl, *n*. A place of instruction; a body of pupils; disciples; sect or body; a system or custom; a shoal (of fishes).—*a*. Relating to a school; scholastic.—*vt*. To instruct; to reprove.

schooner, skōn'èr, *n*. A vessel with two or more masts, her chief sails fore-and-aft.

sciatic, sciatical, sī-at'ik, sī-at'ik-al *a*. Pertaining to the hip or to sciatica.

sciatica, sī-at'i-ka, *n*. Neuralgia or inflammation of the sciatic nerve or great nerve of the thigh.

science, sī'ens, *n*. Knowledge reduced to a system; the facts pertaining to any department of mind or matter in their due connections; skill resulting from training.

scientific, sī-en-tif'ik, *a*. Pertaining to science; versed in science; according to the rules or principles of science.

scleroma, sclerosis, sklē-rō'ma skle-ro'sis, *n*. Induration of the cellular tissue.

scoff, skof, *n*. An expression of derision or scorn; a gibe.—*vi*. To utter contemptuous language; to jeer, to mock.—*vt*. To mock at.

scold, skōld, *vi*. To find fault with rude clamor; to utter harsh, rude rebuke.—*vt*. To reprimand loudly: to chide.—*n*. A clamorous, foul mouthed woman.

scorch, skorch, *vt*. To burn superficially, to singe, to parch.—*vi*. To be as hot as to burn a surface; to be dried up; to ride a cycle at excessive speed.

score, skōr, *n*. A notch; a long scratch or mark, an account or reckoning, the number twenty; a debt; the number of points made in certain games, motive, ground draft of a musical composition.— *vt*. (scoring, scored). To make scores or scratches on; to record; to get for oneself, as points, etc., in games.

scoria, skō'ri-a, *n*.; pl. **-ae**. Dross; cinder; the cellular, slaggy lavas of a volcano.

scorn, skorn, *n*. Extreme contempt; subject of contempt. *vt*. To hold in extreme contempt, to despise.—*vi*. To feel or show scorn.

scorpion, skor'pi-on, *n*. An animal of the class Arachnida, with a jointed tail terminating with a venomous sting; a sign of the zodiac.

Scottish, skot'ish, *a* Pertaining to Scotland, its inhabitants, or language.

scoundrel, skoun'drel, *n*. A mean, worthless fellow; a rascal.—*a*. Base, unprincipled.

scout, skout, *n*. A person sent to obtain intelligence regarding an enemy; a college servant.—*vi*. To act as a scout.—*vt*. To watch closely, to treat with disdain.

scowl, skoul, *vi*. To wrinkle the brows, as in displeasure, to frown.—*n*. A deep angry frown; gloom.

scrape, skrāp, *vt*. (scraping, scraped). To rub with something hard; to clean by a sharp edge; to act on with a grating noise; to erase; to collect laboriously.— *vi*. To roughen or remove a surface by rubbing; to make a grating noise.—*n*. Act of scraping; an awkward bow; an

S

awkward predicament.

scraper, skrāp'ėr, n. One who or that which scrapes; an instrument for scraping or cleaning.

scratch, skrach, vt. and i. To mark or wound with something sharp; to tear with the nails; to withdraw from the list of competitors.—n. A score in a surface; a slight wound; a line from which runners start etc.; one most heavily handicapped in a contest.—a. Taken at random, hastily collected.

scrawl, skräl, vt. and i. To write or draw carelessly or awkwardly.—n. Inelegant or hasty writing.

scream, skrēm, vi. To shriek; to utter a shrill cry.—n. A sharp, shrill cry.

screw, skrö, n. A cylinder with a spiral ridge which enables it when turned to enter another body, a screw-propeller; a twist or turn; a niggard.—vt. To fasten by a screw; to twist; to oppress.

screw-propeller, skrö'prö-pel-ėr, n. An apparatus on the principle of the common screw, for propelling boats and ships.

scribble, skrib'l, vt. and i. (scribbling, scribbled). To write with haste or without care; to tease coarsely, as cotton or wool.—n. Careless writing; a scrawl.

scribe, skrīb, n. A writer, notary copyist; doctor of the law among the Jews.

scrimmage, skrim'āj, n. A tussle; a confused, close struggle in football.

scrimp, skrimp, vt. To make too small or short; to scant; to limit.— a. Scanty.

scrofula, skro'fū-la, n. A disease, a variety of consumption, often showing itself by glandular tumors in the neck which suppurate.

scroll, skrōl, n. A roll of paper or parchment, a draft or first copy, a spiral ornament; a flourish added to a person's name.

scrub, skrub, vt. (scrubbing scrubbed). To rub hard with something rough, to make clean or bright.—vi. To be diligent and penurious.—n. One who labors hard and lives sparingly; a mean fellow; a worn-out brush; low underwood.—a. Mean.

scruple, skrö'pl, n. A weight of 20 grains; doubt, hesitation, backwardness.—vi. (scrupling, scrupled). To doubt, to hesitate.

scuffle, skuf'l, n. A confused struggle.—vi. (scuffling, scuffled). To strive confusedly at close quarters.

scull, skul, n. A short oar, used in pairs.—vt. To propel by sculls, or by moving an oar at the stern.

sculptor, skulp'tor, n. One who works in sculpture; an artist who carves or models figures.

sculpture, skulp'tūr, n. The art of carving wood or stone into images; an image in stone, etc.— vt. (sculpturing, sculptured). To carve; to form, as images on stone, etc.

scum, skum, n. Impurities which rise to the surface of liquors refuse.—vt. (scumming scummed). To take the scum from.—vi. To throw up scum.

scurvy, skėr'vi, n. A disease caused by insufficiency of vegetable food.—a. Vile; mean; malicious.

scuttle, skut'l, n. A broad basket; a pail for coals; a hatchway in a ship's deck, a short run, a quick pace.—vt. (scuttling, scuttled). To sink by making holes in (a ship).— vi. To scurry.

scythe, sīTH, n. An implement for mowing grass, etc.—vt. To cut with a scythe.

sea, sē, n. The mass of salt water covering most of the earth, some portion of this, a name of certain lakes; a large wave; a surge; a flood.

sea-anemone, sē'a-nem'o-nē, n. A beautiful sea-shore, plant-like animal.

sea-breeze, sē'brēz, n. A wind or current of air blowing from the sea upon land.

seal, sēl, n. A hard substance bearing some device, used to make impressions, the wax stamped with a seal; assurance; that which makes fast, a carnivorous marine mammal.—vt. To set a seal to; to confirm; to fasten; to shut or keep close.

seamanship, sē'man-ship, n. The art or skill of a seaman; art of managing a ship.

seamstress, sēm'stres, n. A woman whose occupation is sewing, a sempstress.

seamy, sēm'i, a. Having a seam; showing seams; showing the worst side. disagreeable.

seance, sā-ängs, n. A session, as of some public body; a sitting with the view of evoking spiritual manifestations.

sea-port, sē'pōrt, n. A harbor on the seacoast; a town on or near the sea.

sear, sēr, n. A catch in the mechanism of a rifle which holds back the cockingpiece.

search, sėrch, vt. To look through to find something; to examine.—vi. To seek diligently, to inquire.—n. Act of searching; examination; inquiry.

sea-shore, sē'shŏr, n. The shore of the sea; ground between high and low water mark.

sea-sick, sē'sik, *a.* Affected with sickness caused by the motion of a vessel at sea.

season, sē'zn, *n.* A division of the year, a suitable time a time, time of the year marked by special activity; seasoning.—*vt.* To accustom, to acclimatize, to flavor.—*vi.* To become suitable by time.

seasonable, sē'zn-a-bl, *a.* Natural to the season, opportune, timely.

seasoning, sē'zn-ing, *n.* Something added to food to give it relish, relish, condiment.

seat, sēt, *n.* That on which one sits a chair, stool, etc., place of sitting a right to sit, residence; station— *vt.* To place on a seat; to settle; to locate; to assign seats to; to fit up with seats.

secessionist, sē-se'shon-ist, *n.* One who advocates or engages in a secession.

seclude sē-klöd', *vt.* (secluding, secluded). To shut up apart; to separate; *refl.* to withdraw into solitude.

seclusion, sē-klö'zhon, *n.* Act of secluding: retired mode of life; privacy.

second, se'kund, *a.* Next after the first; repeated again; inferior; other.—*n.* One who or that which comes next a first, one who supports another; attendant in a duel; sixtieth part of a minute; a lower part in music, *pl.* a coarse kind of flour.—*vt.* To follow in the next place; to support; to join with in proposing some measure.

secret, sē'kret, *a.* Hidden; concealed, private; unseen.—*n.* Something hidden or not to be revealed; a mystery

secretary, se'krē-ta-ri, *n.* A person employed to write orders, letters, etc., an escritoire, one who manages the affairs of a department of government.

secrete, sē-krēt', *vt.* (secreting, secreted). To hide, to separate from the blood in animals or from the sap in vegetables.

section, sek'shon, *n.* Act of cutting; a distinct part, subdivision of a chapter, etc., representation of an object as if cut asunder by an intersecting plane, a quarter of a platoon of infantry, the normal fire-unit.

sector, sek'tor, *n.* A part of a circle between two radii; a mathematical instrument useful in making diagrams.

secular, se'kū-lėr, *a.* Pertaining to things not spiritual or sacred worldly; temporal; coming once in a century.

secularism, sek'ū-lėr-izm, *n.* The elimination of the religious element from life.

secure, sē-kūr', *a.* Free from care or dan-ger; heedless; undisturbed; safe; confident.—*vt.* (securing, secured). To make safe or certain, to seize and confine; to guarantee, to fasten.

security, sē-kū'ri-ti, *n.* Safety; confidence; protection; a guarantee; a surety, an evidence of property, as a bond, a certificate of stock, etc.

sedate, sē-dāt', *a.* Composed in manner; staid; placid; sober; serious.

sedition, sē-di'shon, *n.* A commotion in a state, insurrection, civic discord.

seduce, sē-dūs', *vt.* (seducing, seduced).To lead astray; to corrupt; to entice to a surrender of chastity.

seduction, sē-duk'shon, *n.* Act of seducing; allurement; the persuading of a female to surrender her chastity.

see, sē, *vt.* (seeing, pret, saw, pp. seen). To perceive by the eye; to notice; to discover; to understand; to receive, to experience, to attend.—*vi.* To have the power of sight; to understand, to consider.—*interj.* Lo! look!—*n.* A seat of episcopal power; a diocese.

seed, sēd, *n.* That product of a plant which may produce a similar plant; seeds collectively; the semen, first principle, offspring.— *vi.* To produce seed; to shed the seed.—*vt.* To sow; to supply with seed.

seeming, sēm'ing, *p.a.* Appearing; specious.—*n.* Appearance; semblance.

seemly, sēm'li, *a.* Becoming, suitable; decorous.—*adv.* In a suitable manner.

see-saw, sē'sä, *n.* A swinging movement up and down; a game in which children swing up and down on the two ends of a balanced piece of timber.—*vi.* and *t.* To move up and down or to and fro.

seethe, sēTH, *vt.* (seething, seethed). To boil, to soak.—*vi.* To be in a state of ebullition, to be hot.

segment, seg'ment, *n.* A part cut off, a section; a natural division of a body (as an orange).

seize, sēz, *vt.* (seizing, seized). To lay hold of suddenly; to take by force or legal authority; to attack, as a disease, fear, etc.; to comprehend to put in possession.—*vi.* To take hold or possession.

select, sē-lekt', *vt.* To choose; to pick out; to cull.—*a.* Chosen; choice, exclusive.

selection, sē-lek'shon, *n.* Act of selecting; a collection of things selected.

selenium, se-lē'ni-um, *n.* A non-metallic element akin to sulphur and tellurium.

selenology, sel-ē-nol'o-ji, *n.* That branch of astronomy which treats of the moon.

self, self, *n.;* pl. **selves,** selvz. One's individual person; personal interest; a blossom of a uniform color (with *pl.* selfs).—*a.* or *pron.* Same. Affixed to pronouns and adjectives to express emphasis or distinction, or reflexive usage.

self-control, self-kon-trōl', *n.* Control exercised over oneself; self-command.

self-denial, self-dĕ-nī'al, *n.* The forebearing to gratify one's own desires.

self-denying, self-dĕ-nī'ing, *a.* Denying oneself; forbearing to indulge one's own desires.

self-esteem, self-es-tēm', *n.* The esteem or good opinion of oneself; vanity.

self-evident, self-ev'i-dent, *a.* Evident in its own nature; evident without proof.

self-government, self-gu'vėrn-ment, *n.* The government of oneself, government by rulers appointed by the people.

self-important, self-im-pōrt'ant, *a.* Important in one's own esteem; pompous.

self-imposed, self'im-pōzd, *a.* Imposed or voluntarily taken on oneself.

selfish, self'ish, *a.* Devoted unduly to self, influenced by a view to private advantage.

self-sufficient, self-suf-fi'shent, *a.* Having too much confidence in oneself; conceited; assuming; overbearing.

sell, sel, *vt.* (selling, sold). To give in exchange for money, etc., to betray.—*vi.* To practice selling; to be sold.

selvedge, selvage, sel'vej, sel'vāj, *n.* The edge of cloth; border of close work.

semaphore, se'ma-för, *n.* An apparatus for signalling at a distance, usually a pole supporting a movable arm.

seminary, se'min-a-ri, *n.* A school or academy; a place for educating for the priesthood.

semination, se-min-ā'shon, *n.* Act of sowing; the natural dispersion of seeds.

Semite, sem'īt, *n.* A descendant of Shem; one of the Semitic race, a Shemite.

semi-vowel, se'mi-vou-el, *n.* A sound partaking of the nature of both a vowel and a consonant, as *l, m, r.*

senile, sē'nīl, *a.* Pertaining to old age; characterized by the failings of old age.

senior, sē'ni-or, sēn'yor, *a.* Older; older or more advanced in office.—*n.* One older in age or office.

senna, sen'na, *n.* The dried leaves of certain plants used as a purgative; the plant itself.

sensation, sen-sā'shon, *n.* Impression made through the senses feeling; power of feeling; what produces excited interest.

sensational, sen-sā'shon-al, *a.* Relating to sensation; producing excited interest.

sense, sens, *n.* The faculty of receiving impressions; a separate faculty of perception; sight; hearing, taste, smell, or touch, consciousness; discernment; understanding; good judgment; meaning.

sensorium, sen-sō'ri-um, *n.* The common center at which all the impressions of sense are received; the brain.

sensual, sens'ū-al *a.* Pertaining to the senses, as distinct from the mind; carnal; voluptuous; indulging in lust.

sentient, sen'shi-ent, *a.* Having the capacity of sensation; perceptive; sensible.

sentiment, sen'ti-ment, *n.* Thought prompted by emotion; tenderness of feeling; sensibility; a thought or opinion.

sentimental, sen-ti-men'tal, *a.* Having sentiment, apt to be swayed by emotional feelings; mawkishly tender.

sentinel, sen'ti-nel, *n.* One who is set to keep watch; a sentry (now archaic or poetical).

sentry, sen'tri, *n.* A soldier placed on guard; guard; watch; sentinel's duty.

separate, se'pa-rāt, *vt.* (separating, separated). To put or set apart, to disjoin.—*vi.* To go apart, to cleave or split.—*a.* Detached; distinct; individual.

separation, se-pa-rā'shon, *n.* Act of separating; disunion; incomplete one's abode, to subside, to become calm; to adjust differences or accounts.

settlement, set'l-ment, *n.* Act of settling, establishment in life; colonization; a colony; adjustment; liquidation; arrangement; settling of property on a wife.

severalty, se'vėr-al-ti, *n.* A state of separation from the rest, or from all others

severe, sē-vēr', *a.* Serious; grave; harsh; stern; austere; rigidly exact, keen.

severity, sē-ve 'ri-ti, *n.* State or quality of being severe; rigor; intensity; austerity.

Sevres, sā-vr, *n.* A kind of beautiful porcelain, made of *Sevres,* near Paris.

sewer, sū'ėr, *n.* A subterranean drain, as in a city, to carry off water, filth, etc.

sewing, sō'ing, *n.* Act of using a needle, that which is sewed; stitches made.

sexual, seks'ū-al, *a.* Pertaining to, proceeding from, characterized by sex.

shabby, shab'i, *a.* Poor in appearance;

threadbare; mean; paltry; stingy.

shackle, shak'l, *n*. A fetter; a manacle; that which obstructs free action.—*vt*. (shackling, shackled). To bind with shackles; to hamper.

shade, shād, *n*. Obscurity caused by the interception of light; obscure retreat; twilight dimness; a screen; darker part of a picture; gradation of light; a scarcely perceptible degree or amount; a ghost.—*vt*. (shading, shaded). To screen from light, to obscure; to protect; to darken; to mark with gradations of color

shadow, sha'dō, *n*. A figure projected by the interception of light; shade; an inseparable companion, an imperfect representation; a spirit; protection.—*vt*. To shade; to cloud, to screen, to represent faintly, to follow closely.

shake, shāk, *vt*. (shaking, pret, shook, pp. shaken). To cause to move with quick vibrations; to agitate, to move from firmness; to cause to waver; to trill.—*vi*. To tremble; to shiver; to quake.—*n*. A wavering or rapid motion, tremor; shock; a trill in music; a crack in timber.

shallow, shal'ō, *a*. Not deep; superficial; simple, silly.—*n*. A place where the water is not deep; a shoal.

sham, sham, *n*. That which appears to be what it is not; imposture, humbug.—*a*. False; counterfeit.—*vt*. and *i*. (shamming, shammed). To feign, pretend.

shame, shām, *n*. A painful sensation excited by guilt, disgrace, etc.; reproach; disgrace.—*vt*. (shaming, shamed). To make ashamed; to disgrace.

shamefaced, shām'fāst, *a*. Easily put out of countenance; modest; bashful.

shameful, shām'ful, *a*. Full of shame; disgraceful; scandalous; infamous.

shampoo, sham-pö', *vt*. (shampooing, shampooed). To press and rub the body after a hot bath; to wash and rub thoroughly the head.

shamrock, sham'rok, *n*. A trefoil plant, the national emblem of Ireland.

shank, shangk, *n*. The leg; the shinbone, the part of a tool connecting the acting part with a handle; the stem of an anchor.

shanty, shan'ti, *n*. A hut or mean dwelling; song sung by sailors working together.

shape, shāp, *vt*. (shaping, shaped). To form; to mold; to adjust.—*vi*. To suit.— *n*. Form or figure; make; a model; a dish of blancmange, etc.

shard, shärd, *n*. A fragment of an earthen

vessel; the wing-case of a beetle.

share, shār, *n*. A part bestowed or contributed; lot or portion; a plowshare.— *vt*. (sharing, shared). To part among two or more, to participate in.—*vi*. To have part.

shareholder, shār'hōld-èr, *n*. One who holds shares in a joint property.

shark, shärk, *n*. A voracious seafish; an unscrupulous person; a sharper.

shave, shāv, *vt*. (shaving, shaved). To cut off the hair from the skin with a razor; to cut off thin slices from, to skim along, to fleece.—*vi*. To cut off the beard with a razor.—*n*. A cutting off of the beard; a thin slice; an exceedingly narrow escape.

sheath, shēth, *n*. A case for a sword, etc.; a scabbard; wing-case of an insect.

sheathe, shēTH, *vt*. (sheathing, sheathed). To put into a sheath, to protect by a casing.

shed, shed, *vt*. (shedding, shed). To cast or throw off; to emit or diffuse; to let fall in drops; to spill.— *vi*. To let fall seed, a covering, etc.—*n*. A watershed; the opening between threads in a loom through which the shuttle passes; a penthouse; a hut; a large open structure.

sheep, shēp, *sing*. and *pl*. A ruminant animal valued for its wool and flesh; a silly or timid fellow— **sheep's eye**, a loving or wistful glance.

sheet, shēt, *n*. A broad, thin piece of anything broad expanse, piece of linen or cotton spread on a bed; piece of paper, a rope fastened to the lower corner of a sail.—*vt*. To furnish with sheets; to shroud.

shelf, shelf, *n*. pl. **shelves**, shelvz. A board fixed along a wail to support articles; a ledge; a ledge of rocks in the sea.

shell, shel, *n*. A hard outside covering, an outside crust, framework any slight hollow structure; a projectile containing a bursting charge.—*vt*. To strip off the shell of, to throw bomb-shells into or among.—*vi*. To cast the exterior covering.

sherbet, sher'bet, *n*. An Eastern drink of water, the juice of fruits, and sugar.

sheriff, she'rif, *n*. An officer in each county to whom is entrusted the administration of the law; in Scotland, the chief judge of a county.

shibboleth, shib'bō-leth. *n*. The watchword of a party; a cry or motto.

shield, shēld, *n*. A broad piece of armor carried on the arm protection, an escutcheon with a coat of arms.—*vt.* To cover, as with a shield; to protect.

shift, shift, *vi.* To change; to change place or direction; to manage; to practice indirect methods.—*vt.* To remove, to alter to dress in fresh clothes.—*n.* A change; expedient; evasion, an under garment; a squad of workmen; the working time of a relay of men; the spell of work.

shingle, shing'gl, *n.* A thin piece of wood used in covering roofs, loose gravel and pebbles.—*vt.* To cover with shingles; to hammer so as to expel slag or scoriae from in puddling iron.

shingles, shing'glz, *n.* An eruptive disease which spreads around the body.

shiny, shīn'i, *a.* Bright; brilliant; clear.

ship, ship, *n.* A vessel of some size adapted to navigation, a three-masted, square-rigged vessel.—*vt.* (shipping, shipped). To put on board of a ship; to transport in a ship, to hire for service in a ship; to fix in its place.—*vi.* To engage for service on a ship; to embark.

shipwreck, ship'rek, *n.* The wreck or loss of a ship; destruction; ruin.—*vt.* To wreck; to cast away; to ruin.

shipwright, ship'rīt, *n.* A builder of ships or other vessels; a ship-carpenter.

shirt, shėrt, *n.* A man's loose under garment of linen etc., a lady's blouse.—*vt.* To clothe with a shirt.

shiver, shi'vėr, *vt.* To shatter.—*vi.* To fall into many small pieces; to tremble, as from cold, to shudder.—*n.* A small fragment, a shaking fit, shudder.

shoal, shōl, *n.* A multitude; a crowd, a sandbank or bar, a shallow.—*vi.* To become more shallow.—*a.* Shallow.

shock, shok, *n.* A violent striking against; violent onset; a sudden disturbing emotion; a stook; a thick mass of hair.—*vt.* To give a shock to; to encounter violently; to disgust; to make up into shocks or stooks.

shook, shúk, pret. and pp. of *shake.*—*n.* The staves for a single barrel made into a package.

shoot, shöt, *vt.* (shooting shot). To cause to fly forth; to discharge; to hit or kill with a missile, to empty out suddenly, to thrust forward; to pass rapidly under, over, etc.—*vi.* To charge a missile; to dart along; to sprout; to project.—*n.* A shooting; a young branch; a sloping trough; a place for shooting rubbish.

shooting, shöt'ing, *n.* Sport of killing game with firearms; tract over which game is shot, sensation of a darting

pain.—*a.* Pertaining to one who shoots.

shop, shop *n.* A place where goods are sold by retail; a building in which mechanics work; one's special business.—*vi.* (shopping, shopped) To visit shops for purchasing goods.

shot, shot, *n.* Act of shooting; a projectile; a bullet; bullets collectively; range or reach; a marksman; the number of fish caught in one haul; a reckoning.—*vt.* (shotting, shotted). To load with shot.—*a.* Having a changeable color, as silk, interwoven.

should, shúd, the pret. of *shall,* denoting present or past duty or obligation, or expressing a hypothetical case.

shoulder, shō l'dė r, *n.* The joint by which the arm or the fore-leg is connected with the body; a projection; support.—*vt.* To push with the shoulder, to put upon the shoulder.—*vi.* To push forward.

shoulder-strap, shōl'dėr-strap, *n.* A strap worn on the shoulder, either to support dress, or as a badge of distinction.

shout shout, *vi.* To utter a loud and sudden cry.—*vt.* To utter with a shout.—*n.* A loud sudden cry.

shove, shuv, *vt.* and *i.* (shoving, shoved). To push forward; to press against; to jostle.—*n.* Act of shoving, a push.

shovel, shu'vel, *n.* An instrument with a broad shallow blade for lifting earth, etc.—*vt.* (shoveling, shoveled). To throw with a shovel.

show, shō, *vt.* (pret. showed, pp. (shown or showed). To display to the view of others: to let be seen; to make known; to prove; to bestow, afford.—*vi.* To appear—*n.* Act of showing; exhibition; appearance; pretense; pageant; things exhibited for money.

shrew, shrö, *n.* A peevish, ill-tempered woman; a scold; a shrew-mouse.

shrine, shrīn, *n.* A case, as for sacred relics, a tomb altar, a place hallowed from its associations.— *vt.* (shrining, shrined). To enshrine.

shrink, shringk, *vi.* (pret. shrank or shrunk, pp. shrunk or shrunken). To contact spontaneously, to shrivel; to withdraw, as from danger; to flinch.—*vt.* To cause to contract.—*n.* contraction.

shrub, shrub, *n.* A woody plant less than a tree, a plant with several woody stems from the same root a beverage containing the juice of fruit, etc.

shrubbery, shrub'ér-i, *n*. An ornamental plantation of shrubs shrubs collectively.

shrug, shrug, *vt*. and *i*. (shrugging, shrugged) To draw up or to contract as the shoulders.—*n*. A drawing up of the shoulders.

shudder, shud'ér, *vi*. To tremble with fear, horror, etc.; to quake.—*n*. A tremor.

shuffle, shuf'l, *vt*. (shuffling; shuffled). To shove one way and the other, to confuse, to change the position of cards.—*vi*. To change position, to quibble, to move with a dragging gait; to scrape the floor in dancing.—*n*. An evasion; mixing cards; scraping movement in dancing.

shunt, shunt, *vi*. and *t*. In railways; to turn from one line of rails into another, to free oneself of.

shut, shut, *vt*. (shutting, shut). To close or stop up, to bar, to preclude, to exclude, to confine.—*vi*. To close itself; to be closed.—*a*. Made close, closed, not resonant.

shutter, shut'ér, *n*. One who shuts; a moveable covering for a window or aperture.

shuttle, shut'l, *n*. An instrument used by weavers for shooting the thread of the woof between the threads of the warp.

shuttle-cock, shut'l-kok, *n*. A cork stuck with feathers, and struck by a battledore.—*vt*. To throw backwards and forwards.

sick, sik, *a*. Affected with disease of any kind; ill; inclined to vomit; disgusted or weary; pertaining to those who are sick.

sicken, sik'n, *vt*. To make sick; to disgust.—vi. To become sick, to be disgusted; to languish.

sickle, sik'l, *n*. An instrument for cutting grain, used with one hand; a reaping-hook.

side, sīd, *n*. The broad or long surface of a body, edge, border, right or left half of the body; part between the top and bottom; any party or interest opposed to another.—*a*. Being on, from, or toward the side, indirect.—*vi*. (siding, sided). To embrace the opinions of one party.

sienna, sē-en'na, *n*. An earth of a fine yellow color, used as a pigment.

sieve, siv, *n*. A utensil for separating the smaller particles of a loose substance.

sift, sift, *vt*. To separate by a sieve to examine minutely.—*vi*. To pass as if through a sieve.

sigh, sī, *vi*. To make a long breath audibly, as from grief; to make a melancholy sound.—*n*. A long breath made audibly, as in grief.

signal, sig'nal, *n*. A sign to communicate intelligence, orders, etc., at a distance. *a*. Worthy of note; remarkable.—*vt*. or *i*. (signalling, signalled). To communicate by signals.

signet, sig'net, *n*. A seal; seal used by the sovereign in sealing private letters.

significant, sig-ni'fi-kant, *a*. Signifying something; indicative; important.

signification, sig'ni-fi-kā"shon, *n*. Act of signifying; meaning; import; sense.

signify, sig'ni-fī, *vt*. (signifying, signified). To make known either by signs or words; to betoken; to mean; to imply; to import.

silent, sī'lent, *a*. Not speaking; mute; dumb; taciturn; making no noise.

sill, sil, *n*. The timber or stone at the foot of a door or window; the threshold; the floor of a gallery in a mine.

silo, sī'lō, *n*. The pit in which green fodder is preserved in the method of ensilage.

silurian, sī-lū'ri-an, *a*. Applied to the lowest division of the paleozoic strata.

silver, sil'vèr, *n*. A precious metal of a white color, money: plate made of silver.—*a*. Made of silver; silvery.—*vt*. and *i*. To cover with a coat of silver, to tinge with gray.

silversmith, sil'vèr-smith, *n*. One whose occupation is to work in silver.

simper, sim'pér, *vi*. To smile in a silly manner.—*n*. A silly or affected smile.

simple, sim'pl, *a*. Not complex single; not involved; clear; artless; mere, plain, sincere, silly.—*n*. Something not mixed, a medicinal herb.

simpleton, sim'pl-ton, *n*. A simple or silly person; one easily deceived.

simplicity, sim-plis'i-ti, *n*. State or quality of being simple; singleness; artlessness; sincerity; plainness, foolishness.

since, sins, *adv*. From that time; from then till now; ago.—*prep*. Ever from the time of; after.—*conj*. From the time when; because that.

sincere, sin-sēr', *a*. Pure, unmixed; real; genuine; guileless; frank; true.

sincerity, sin-se'ri-ti, *n*. Honesty of mind or intention; freedom from hypocrisy.

sinful, sin'fùl, *a*. Full of sin; wicked; iniquitous; wrong.

singe, sinj, *vt*. (singeing, singed). To burn slightly; to burn the surface of—*n*. A burning of the surface.

single, sing'gl, *a*. Being one or a unit; individual; unmarried; performed by one person simple, sincere.—*vt.* (singling, singled). To select individually; with out.

singular, sing'gū-lėr, *a.* That is single, expressing one person or thing; remarkable; rare; odd.—*n.* The singular number

sip, sip, *vt.* (sipping, sipped). To drink in small quantities; to drink out of.—*vi.* To take a fluid with the lips.—*n.* A small quantity of liquid taken with the lips.

siren, sī'ren, *n.* A sea-nymph who enticed seamen by songs, and then slew them; a woman dangerous from her fascinations; a fog-signal; a signal used as an air-raid warning.—*a.* Bewitching.

size, sīz, *n.* Comparative magnitude; bigness; bulk; a glutinous substance used by painters, etc.—*vt.* (sizing, sized). To arrange according to size; to take the size of; to cover with size.

skeleton, ske'le-ton, *n.* The bony framework of an animal; general structure or frame; outline.—*a.* Resembling a skeleton.

sketch, skech, *n.* An outline or general delineation; a first rough draft.—*vt.* To draw a sketch of; to give the chief points of; to plan.—*vi.* To practice sketching.

skim, skim, *vt.* (skimming, skimmed). To remove the scum from; to take off from a surface; to pass lightly over; to glance over superficially.—*vi.* To glide along.

skirmish, skėr'mish, *n.* A slight battle; a brief contest.—*vi.* To fight in short contests or in small parties.

slack, slak, *a.* Not tight or tense; loose; remiss; backward; not busy.—*adv.* In a slack manner; partially; insufficiently.—*n.* The part of a rope that hangs loose; small broken coal.—*vt.* and *i.* To slacken; to slake.

slake, slāk, *vt.* (slaking, slaked). To quench, as thirst or rage; to extinguish.*vi.* To abate; to become extinct.—*n.* A muddy tract adjoining the sea.

slang, slang, *n.* and *a.* A class of expressions not generally approved of, as being inelegant or undignified.—*vt.* To address with slang; to abuse vulgarly.

slant, slant, *a.* Sloping.—*vt.* and *i.* To turn from a direct line, to slope to incline.—*n.* A slope

slaughter, slä'tėr, *n.* A slaying; carnage, massacre, a killing of beasts for market.—*vt.* To slay; to kill for the market.

slavish, slāv'ish, *a.* Pertaining to slaves; servile, mean; oppressively laborious.

sleazy, slē'zi, *a.* Thin, flimsy, want-ing firmness of texture, as silk. Also *sleezy.*

sled, sled, *n.* A sledge.—*vt.* (sledding, sledded). To convey on a sled.

sledge, sledge-hammer, slej, slej' ham-ėr, *n.* A large, heavy hammer, used by iron-workers.

sleep, slēp, *vi.* (sleeping, slept). To take rest by a suspension of voluntary exercise of the powers of body and mind; to be dormant or inactive.—*vt.* To pass in sleeping; to get rid of by sleeping, with *off*—*n.* That state in which volition is suspended; slumber; death; dormant state.

sleight, slīt, *n.* A sly artifice; an artful trick, dexterity.

slice, slīs *vt.* (slicing, sliced). To cut into thin pieces; to divide.—*n.* A thin, broad piece cut off; a broad flat utensil.

slide, slīd, *vi.* (sliding, pret. slid, pp. slid, slidden). To move along a surface by slipping: to pass smoothly or gradually.—*vt.* To thrust smoothly along a surface.—*n.* A smooth and easy passage, that part of an apparatus which slides into place.

slime, slīm, *n.* A soft or glutinous substance moist earth or mud; viscous substance exuded by certain animals.—*vt.* (sliming, slimed). To cover with slime, to make slimy.

sling, sling, *vt.* (slinging, slung). To throw, to hang so as to swing, to place in a sling.—*n.* An instrument for throwing stones, a bandage to support a wounded limb; a rope for raising heavy articles.

slink, slingk, *vi.* (slinking, slunk). To sneak; to steal away.—*vt.* To cast prematurely.—*n.* A premature calf.

slip, slip, *vi.* (slipping, slipped). To move smoothly along; to glide; to depart secretly; to have the feet slide; to err; to escape insensibly.—*vt.* To put or thrust secretly. to omit; to disengage oneself from; to make a slip of for planting.—*n.* A sliding of the feet, an unintentional error; a twig cut for planting or grafting; a long narrow piece, a leash by which a dog is held; a long strip of printed matter, a loose covering, an inclined plane upon which a ship is built.

slipper, slip'ėr, *n.* One who slips or lets slip; a loose light shoe for household wear.

slipshod, slip'shod, *a.* Shod with slippers; having shoes down at heel; slovenly.

slope, slōp, *n.* An oblique direction; a declivity.—*vt.* and *i.* (sloping sloped). To form with a slope; to incline.

slot, slot, *n.* A bolt or bar; an oblong hole; track of a deer.—*vt.* (slotting, slotted). To make a slot in

sloth, slōth or sloth, *n.* Indolence: laziness; idleness; a South American mammal.

slouch, slouch. *n.* A stoop in walking; an ungainly gait: a droop.—*vi.* To hang down; to have a drooping gait.—*vt.* To cause to hang down.

slue, slö, *vt.* (sluing, slued). To turn or swing round (as the yard of a ship).

slump, slump, *n.* The whole number taken in one lot; a sudden fall in prices or values.—*vt.* To throw into one lot.—*vi.* To sink in walking, as in snow.

slur, slėr, *vt.* (slurring, slurred). To soil; to traduce; to pass lightly over, to pronounce in a careless indistinct manner.—*n.* A slight reproach; a stain or stigma.

smack, smak, *vi.* To make a sharp noise with the lips; to taste; to savor.—*vt.* To make a sharp noise with, to slap.—*n.* A loud kiss, a sharp noise; a smart blow; a slap; a slight taste; a smattering; a fishing-vessel.

small, smäl, *a.* Little; petty; short; weak, gentle, not loud, narrow-minded; mean.—*n.* The small part of a thing; *pl.* small-clothes.

smart, smärt, *n.* A quick, keen pain, pungent grief.—*a.* Keen; quick; sharp; brisk; witty; spruce; well dressed.—*vt.* To feel a sharp pain, to be acutely painful; to be punished.

smell, smel, *vt.* (smelling, smelled). To perceive by the nose; to perceive the scent of, to detect.—*vi.* To give out an odor.—*n.* The faculty by which odors are perceived; scent, perfume.

smelt, smelt, *vt.* To melt, as ore, to separate the metal.—*n.* A small fish allied to the salmon.

smile, smīl, *vi.* (smiling, smiled). To show pleasure, sarcasm, pity, etc., by a look, to appear propitious.— *vt.* To express by a smile; to affect by smiling.—*n.* A set of the features expressing pleasure, scorn, etc.; favor.

smock, smok, *n.* A chemise; a smock; frock.—*vt.* To clothe with a smock; to pucker diagonally.

smocking, smok'ing, *n.* An ornamental diagonal puckering, in form of a honeycomb, and capable of being expanded.

smoke, smōk, *n.* The exhalation from a burning substance; vapor; idle talk; nothingness; a drawing in and puffing out of tobacco fumes.—*vi.* (smoking, smoked). To emit smoke, to use tobacco.—*vt.* To apply smoke to; to befoul by smoke; to fumigate; to use in smoking.

smooth, smōTH, *a.* Even on the surface; glossy; moving equably; not harsh, bland.—*n.* Smooth part of anything.— *vt.* To make smooth; to level; to make easy; to pallitate; to soothe.

smother, smuTH'ėr, *n.* Stifling smoke; suffocating dust.—*vt.* To stifle, to suffocate to suppress.— *vi.* To be suffocated or suppressed; to smoulder.

smoulder, smōl'dėr, *vi.* To burn and smoke without flame; to exist in a suppressed state.

snaffle, snaf'l, *n.* A bridle consisting of a slender bitmouth without a curb.—*vt.* To bridle, to manage with a snaffle.

snag, snag, *n.* A short projecting stump, a shoot; the tine of a deer's antler; a tree in a river dangerous to vessels.

snail, snāl, *n.* A slimy, slow-creeping mollusk; a slug; a sluggard.

snap, snap, *vt.* (snapping, snapped). To bite or seize suddenly, to break with a sharp sound, to break short.—*vi.* To try to seize with the teeth, to break suddenly or without bending.—*n.* A quick eager bite; a sudden breaking; a sharp noise; a kind of biscuit.

snare, snār, *n.* A line with a noose for catching animals; anything that entraps.—*vt.* (snaring, snared). To catch with a snare; to ensnare.

snarl, snärl, *vi.* To growl, as an angry dog, to talk in rude murmuring terms.—*vt.* To entangle.—*n.* A sharp angry growl; a knot; embarrassment.

snatch, snach, *vt.* To seize hastily or abruptly.—*vi.* To make a grasp.—*n.* A hasty catch; a short fit or turn; a small portion; a snack.

sneak, snēk, *vt.* To creep privately; to go furtively; to crouch.—*n.* A mean fellow, one guilty of under hand work.

snip, snip, *vt.* (snipping, snipped). To cut off at a stroke with shears; to clip.—*n.* A single cut with shears; a bit cut off.

snore, snōr, *vi.* (snoring, snored). To breathe with a rough, hoarse noise in sleep.—*n.* A breathing with a hoarse noise in sleep.

snort, snort, *vi.* To force air with violence through the nose.—*n.* A loud sound produced by forcing the air through the nostrils.

S

snow, snō, *n.* Watery particles congealed in the air, and falling in flakes.—*vi.* To fall in snow; used impersonally.—*vt.* To scatter like snow.

snow-plow, snō'plou, *n.* An implement for clearing away the snow from roads, etc.

snub, snub, *vt.* (snubbing, snubbed). To stop or rebuke with a tart, sarcastic remark, to slight designedly.—*n.* A check; a rebuke.

snuff, snuf, *vt.* To draw up through the nose; to smell; to crop, as the snuff of a candle.—*vi.* To draw up air or tobacco through the nose; to take offense.—*n.* A drawing up through the nose; resentment; burned wick of a candle; pulverized tobacco.

so, sō, *adv.* In this or that manner; to that degree; thus; extremely; very; the case being such; thereby.—*conj.* Provided that in case that, therefore; accordingly.

soak, sōk, *vt.* To let lie in a fluid till the substance has imbibed all that it can; to steep; to wet thoroughly.—*vi.* To steep; to enter by pores; to tipple.

soap, sōp, *n.* A compound of oil or fat with an alkali, used in washing.—*vt.* To rub or cover with soap.

soar, sōr, *vi.* To mount upon the wing, to rise high; to tower.—*n.* A towering flight; a lofty ascent.

sob, sob, *vi.* (sobbing, sobbed). To sigh or weep convulsively; to make a similar sound.—*n.* A convulsive catching of the breath in weeping or sorrow.

sober, sō'bėr, *a.* Temperate; not drunk; calm; cool; staid; grave; dull-looking.—*vt.* To make sober.—*vi.* To become sober

society, sō-sī'e-ti, *n.* Fellowship; company; a body of persons united for some object; persons living in the same circle, those who take the lead in social life.

sociology, sō-shi-ol'o-ji, *n.* The science which treats of society, its development, the progress of civilization, etc.

sock, sok, *n.* The shoe of the ancient actors of comedy; a short woven covering for the foot.

sod, sod, *n.* That layer of earth which is covered with grass; piece of turf

soda, sō'da, *n.* The alkali carbonate of sodium used in washing, glass-making, etc., and extensively made from salt.

soft, soft, *a.* Easily yielding to pressure, delicate, mild, effeminate not loud or harsh; not strong or glaring.—*adv.* Softly.—*interj.* Be soft, stop, not so fast.

soften, sof'n, *vt.* To make soft or more soft; to mollify; to alleviate; to tone down.—*vi.* To become soft; to relent; to become milder.

soil, soil, *vt.* To sully; to tarnish; to manure; to feed (cattle) indoors with green fodder.—*vi.* To tarnish.—*n.* Dirt; ordure; tarnish; the upper stratum of the earth; mould; loam; earth; land; country.

solder, sol'dėr, *vt.* To unite metals by a fused metallic substance, to patch up.—*n.* A metallic cement.

soldier, sōl'jėr, *n.* A man in military service; a man of distinguished valor

sole, sōl, *n.* The under side of the foot; the bottom of a shoe, a marine fish allied to the flounder.—*vt.* (soling, soled). To furnish with a sole, as a shoe.—*a.* Single; individual, only, alone.

solid, so'lid, *a.* Resisting pressure not liquid or gaseous; not hollow, cubic, sound, not frivolous.—*n.* A body that naturally retains the same shape.

soliloquy, sō-lil'ō-kwi, *n.* A speaking to oneself; discourse of a person alone.

solitaire, so'li-tār, *n.* A solitary, an article of jewelry in which a single gem is set; a game for a single person.

soluble, so'lū-bl, *a.* Susceptible of being dissolved in a fluid, capable of being solved, as a problem.

solution, so-lū'shon, *n.* A dissolving; preparation made by dissolving a solid in a liquid; act of solving; explanation; termination or crisis of a disease.

solvent, sol'vent, *a.* Having the power of dissolving; able to pay all debts. *n.* A fluid that dissolves any substance.

somehow, sum'hou, *adv.* In some way not yet known; one way or another.

somersault, somerset, sum'ėr-sält sum'ėr-set, *n.* A leap in which the heels turn over the head; a turn of the body in the air.

something, sum'thing, *n.* A thing quantity, or degree indefinitely; a person or thing of importance.— *adv.* somewhat.

somewhat, sum'whot, *n.* Something, more or less.—*adv.* In some degree; a little.

sonorous, sō-nō'rus, *a.* Giving sound when struck, resonant high-sounding.

soon, sön, *adv.* In a short time; shortly; early; quickly; promptly; readily; gladly.

soot, söt, *n.* A black substance formed from burning matter.—*vt.* To cover or foul with soot.

soothe, sŏTH, *vt.* (soothing, soothed). To

please with soft words; to flatter, to pacify; to assuage, to soften.

soporiferous, sō-pō-rif'ik, *a.* Causing sleep.—*n.* A drug or anything that induces sleep.

soprano, sō-prä'nō, *n.* The highest female voice; a singer with such a voice.

sore, sōr, *a.* Painful; severe; distressing, tender, galled.—*n.* An ulcer; wound, etc.—*adv.* Severely; sorely.

sorrel, so'rel, *n.* A plant allied to the locks, a reddish or yellow-brown color.—*a.* Of a reddish color.

sorrow, so'rō, *n.* Affliction or distress of mind; grief; regret.—*vi.* To feel sorrow; to grieve.

sort, sort, *n.* Nature or character kind; species; manner; a set.—*vt.* To assort; to arrange; to reduce to order.—*vi.* To consort; to agree.

soul, sōl, *n.* The spiritual principle in man the moral and emotional part of man's nature; elevation of mind; fervor; essence; an inspirer or leader; a person.

sound, sound, *a.* Not in any way defective healthy valid, free from error; orthodox; just; heavy.—*n.* A narrow channel of water; a strait; air-bladder of a fish, that which is heard; noise.—*vt.* To measure the depth of; to examine medically; to try to discover the opinion, etc., of to cause to give out a sound, to pronounce.—*vi.* To give out a sound; to appear on narration, to be spread or published.

soundings, sound'ingz, *n.pl.* The depths of water in rivers, harbors, etc.

soundness sound'nes, *n.* Healthiness; solidity; validity, orthodoxy.

sour, sour, *a.* Acid or sharp to the taste; tart; peevish; morose.—*vt.* To make sour; to make cross or discontented; to embitter.—*vi.* To become sour or peevish.

source, sōrs, *n.* That from which anything rises; the spring, etc., from which a stream proceeds first cause; origin.

Soviet, sov'i-et, *n.* The method of government in Russia since the Revolution, local soviets (elected councils) sending delegates to larger bodies, and these, in their turn, to the Supreme Congress, which elects the Supreme Council.

sow, sō, *vt.* (pret. sowed, pp. sowed or sown). To scatter seed over, to spread abroad.—*vi.* To scatter seed for growth.

spa, spä, *n.* A place to which people go on account of a spring of mineral water

space, spās, *n.* Extension; room; interval between points or objects quantity of time; a while.—*vt.* (spacing, spaced). To arrange at proper intervals; to arrange the spaces in.

spade, spād, *n.* An instrument for digging; a playing card of a black suit.—*vt.* (spading, spaded). To dig with a spade; to use a spade on.

span, span, *n.* Reach or extent in general; space between the thumb and little finger, nine inches; a short space of time; the stretch of an arch; a yoke of animals.—*vt.* (spanning, spanned). To extend across; to measure with the hand with the fingers extended.

spar, spär, *n.* A long piece of timber; a pole, a crystalline mineral, boxing-match; flourish of the fists.— *vi.* (sparring, sparred). To fight in show; to box; to bandy words.

spare, spär, *a.* Scanty; thin; sparing or chary; superfluous; held in reserve.—*vt.* (sparing, spared). To use frugally; to dispense with; to omit, to use tenderly, to withhold from.—*vi.* To be frugal; to use mercy or forbearance.

spark, spärk, *n.* A particle of ignited substance, which flies off from burning bodies; a small transient light; a gay man; a lover.—*vi.* To emit particles of fire, to sparkle.

sparkle, spär'kl, *n.* A little spark; luster.— *vi.* (sparkling, sparkled). To emit sparks; to glitter; to be animated.

speak, spēk, *vi.* (pret. spoke, spake, pp. spoken). To utter words; to talk; to deliver a speech; to argue; to plead to be expressive.—*vt.* To utter with the mouth, to pronounce; to accost; to express.

spear, spēr, *n.* A long, pointed weapon; a lance.—*vt.* To pierce or kill with a spear.

special, spe'shal, *a.* Pertaining to a species; particular; distinctive; having a particular purpose or scope.

specialize, spe-shal-īz, *vt.* To assign a specific use to.—*vi.* To apply oneself to a particular subject.

specific, spe-sif'ik, *a.* Pertaining to, designating or constituting a species; definite; precise.—*n.* A remedy which exerts a special action in the cure of a disease, an infallible remedy.

specification, spe'si-fi-kā''shon, *n.* The act of specifying, details of particulars; particular mention; statement.

specify, spe'si-fī, *vt.* (specifying, specified). To make specific; to state in

S

detail.

speckle, spek'l, *n.* A speck; a small colored marking.—*vt.* (speckling, speckled). To mark with small specks.

spectacle, spek'ta-kl, *n.* A show; a sight, an exhibition, a pageant, *pl.* glasses to assist or correct defective vision.

speculate, spek'ū-lāt, *vi.* (speculating, speculated). To meditate, to engage in risky financial transactions with a view to profit.

speculator, spek'ū-lāt-or, *n.* A theorizer; one who speculates in business.

speech, spēch, *n.* The faculty of speaking; language; talk; a formal discourse, oration.

speed, spēd, *n.* Success; velocity; haste.—*vi.* (speeding, sped). To make haste; to prosper.—*vt.* To dispatch in haste; to help forward; to dismiss with good wishes.

sphere, sfēr, *n.* An orb, a ball, a globe; a sun, star, or planet; circuit of motion, action, etc.; range; province, rank.—*vt.* (sphering, sphered). To place in a sphere or among the spheres.

sphincter, sfingk'tėr, *n.* A ring-like muscle closing the external orifices of organs, as the mouth or anus.

spice, spīs, *n.* A vegetable production, aromatic to the smell and pungent to the taste; something piquant, flavor, smack.—*vt.* (spicing, spiced). To season with spice; to flavor.

spill, spil, *vt.* (pret. and pp. spilled or split). To suffer to fall, flow over, etc., to shed.—*vi.* To be shed, to be suffered to fall, be lost, or wasted.—*n.* A spigot; piece of wood or paper used to light a lamp, etc.; a fall.

spin, spin, *vt.* (spinning, spun). To draw out and twist into threads to protract; to whirl; to make threads, as a spider.—*vi.* To work at drawing and twisting threads; to rotate; to go quickly.—*n.* Act of spinning; a rapid run.

spindle, spin'dl, *n.* A pin carrying a bobbin in a spinning machine; a small axis; a long, slender stalk; a measure of yarn.—*vi.* To grow in a long slender stalk.

spine, spīn, *n.* A prickle a thorn a thin, pointed spike in animals; the backbone or spinal column.

spire, spīr, *n.* A winding line like a screw; a spiral; a wreath; a convolution, a steeple, a stalk or blade of grass, etc.—*vi.* (spiring, spired). To taper up.

spirit, spi'rit, *n.* The breath of life; the

soul; a spectre; vivacity; courage; mood; essence; real meaning; intent, a liquid obtained by distillation, *pl.* alcoholic liquor.—*vt.* To infuse spirit into; to encourage.

spirt, spėrt, *vt.* To force out in a jet; to squirt.—*vi.* To gush out in a jet.—*n.* A jet of fluid.

spit, spit, *n.* A prong on which meat is roasted; low land running into the sea.—*vt.* (spitting, spitted). To put on a spit: to pierce.

spit, spit, *vt.* and *i.* (spitting, spat). To eject from the mouth, as saliva.—*n.* What is ejected from the mouth; spittle.

spite, spīt, *n.* A feeling of ill-will; malice rancor—**In spite of**, notwithstanding.—*vt.* (spiting, spited). To mortify or chagrin; to thwart.

splash, splash, *vt.* and *i.* To bespatter with liquid matter.—*n.* A quantity of wet matter thrown on anything; a noise from water dashed about; a spot of dirt.

splice, splīs, *vt.* (splicing, spliced). To unite, as two ropes, by interweaving the strands; to unite by overlapping, as timber.—*n.* Union of ropes by interweaving; piece added by splicing.

splinter, splint'ėr, *n.* A piece of wood, or other solid substance, split off.—*vt.* To split into splinters, to shiver.

split, split, *vt.* (splitting, split). To divide lengthwise; to cleave; to rend; to burst.—*vi.* To part asunder; to burst; to crack; to differ in opinion.—*n.* A rent; fissure, breach or separation.—*a.* Divided; rent. deeply cleft

splutter, splut'ėr, *n.* A bustle, a stir.—*vi.* To speak confusedly; to sputter

spode, spōd, *n.* A material composed of calcined ivory, of which vases, etc., are made.

spoil, spoil, *n.* Pillage; booty; plunder.—*vt.* To plunder; to impair; to ruin; to injure by over-indulgence.—*vi.* To grow useless; to decay.

spoke, spōk, *n.* A bar of a wheel, the round of a ladder, a bar.—*vt.* (spoking, spoked). To furnish with spokes. Pret. of *speak.*

sponge, spunj, *n.* A soft porous marine substance which readily imbibes liquids, a mean parasite.—*vt.* (sponging, sponged). To wipe with a sponge; to wipe out completely, to harass by extortion to get by mean arts.—*vi.* To imbibe; to act as a hanger-on

sport, spōrt, *n.* A game; a merrymaking; out-of-door recreation, as shooting, horse-racing, etc.; jest; object of mockery; a plant or animal that differs from the normal type.—*vt.* To divert (oneself), to wear in public.—*vi.* To play, to frolic, to practice the diversions of the field.

spot, spot, *n.* A place discolored; a speck; a blemish; a flaw; a locality.—*vt.* (spotting, spotted). To make a spot on, to stain, to catch with the eye.—*vi.* To act as observer of enemy's position, of effect of gunfire, or of approach of hostile aircraft.

sprain, sprān, *vt.* To overstrain, as the muscles or ligaments of a joint.—*n.* A violent strain of a joint without dislocation.

sprawl, spräl, *vi.* To struggle or show convulsive motions; to lie or crawl with the limbs stretched.

spray, sprā, *n.* A twig; collection of small branches; water or any liquid flying in small drops or particles.—*vt.* To cause to take the form of spray; to treat with spray.

spring, spring, *vi.* (pret. sprang or sprung, pp. sprung). To leap; to start up; to dart; to warp, to become cracked; to originate.—*vt.* To start or rouse, to propose on a sudden; to crack, to jump over.—*n.* A leap; resilience, an elastic body made of various materials, especially steel; cause; an issue of water, source of supply, season of the year when plants begin to grow; a crack in timber.

sprinkle, spring'kl, *vt.* and *i.* (sprinkling, sprinkled). To scatter in small drops, to bedew.—*n.* A small quantity scattered in drops.

spur, spėr, *n.* An instrument with sharp points, worn on horsemen's heels, incitement; stimulus; a sharp outgrowth; a mountain mass that shoots from another.— *vt.* (spurring, spurred). To prick with a spur; to incite; to put spurs on.—*vi.* To travel with great expedition.

spurn, spėrn, *vt.* To drive away, as with the foot, to reject with disdain to treat with contempt.—*vi.* To kick up the heels; to manifest disdain.

spy, spī, *vt.* (spying, spied). To gain sight of; to gain knowledge of by artifice, to explore.—*vi.* To pry.—*n.* One who keeps watch on the actions of others; a secret emissary.

squall, skwäl, *vi.* To cry out; to scream violently.—*n.* A loud scream; a violent gust of wind; a brief storm of wind.

square, skwär, *a.* Having four equal sides and four right angles forming a right angle; just; honest, even; suitable.—*n.* A figure having four equal sides and right angles any similar figure or area; an instrument having one edge at right angles to another, product of a number multiplied by itself; level; equality.—*vt.* (squaring, squared). To make square; to form to right angles; to adjust; to fit; to settle (accounts), to multiply a number by itself.—*vi.* To suit; to spar (colloq.).

squeeze, skwēz, *vt.* (squeezing, squeezed). To subject to pressure; to harass by extortion; to hug.—*vi.* To press; to crowd.—*n.* An application of pressure; compression.

squint, skwint, *a.* Looking obliquely or different ways.—*n.* An oblique look, an affection in which the optic axes do not coincide.—*vi.* To look obliquely.

stable, stā'bl, *a.* Firm; firmly established; steadfast.—*n.* A house for horses, etc.—*vt.* (stabling stabled). To put or keep in a stable.—*vi.* To dwell in a stable.

stack, stak, *n.* A large, regularly built pile of hay, grain, etc.; a number of chimneys standing together; a single tall chimney; a high rock detached.—*vt.* To build into a stack, to pile together.

staff, stäf, *n.*; pl. **staves** or **staffs,** stavz, stafs. A stick or rod; a prop or support; a baton; the five parallel lines on which musical characters are written, a body of officers attached to an army as a whole (pl. *staffs);* a body of persons assisting in any undertaking.

stage, stāj, *n.* An elevated platform; the platform on which theatrical performances are exhibited place of action; a halting-place, distance between two stopping places, degree of progression point reached—*vt.* To put upon the theatrical stage.

stagger, stag'ėr, *vi.* To reel; to totter; to waver.—*vt.* To cause to waver; to amaze; to arrange working hours so that employees enter and leave their place of work at intervals in batches, instead of simultaneously.—*n.* A sudden swaying of the body; *pl.* a disease of cattle, etc., attended with giddiness.

stalk, stäk, *n.* The stem of a plant; part that supports a flower, leaf, fruit, etc., a stately step or walk.—*vi.* To walk in a dignified manner.—*vt.* To watch and follow warily, as game, for the purpose of killing.

stall, stäl, *n.* A place where a horse or ox is kept and fed, division of a stable; a

S

bench or shed where anything is exposed to sale, etc., the seat of a clerical dignitary in the choir; a seat in a theatre.—*vt.* To put into a stall; to plunge into mire.

stamina, sta'mi-na, *n.pl.* Whatever constitutes the principal strength; robustness, power of endurance.

stammer, stam'ėr, *vt.* and *t.* To make involuntary breaks in utterance; to stutter.—*n.* Defective utterance, a stutter.

stamp, stamp, *vt.* To strike by thrusting the foot down; to impress; to imprint; to affix a postage-stamp to, to coin, to form.—*vi.* To strike the foot forcibly downward.—*n.* Act of stamping, an instrument for crushing or for making impressions; mark imprinted; a postage-stamp, character, sort.

stand, stand, *vi.* (standing, stood). To be upon the feet in an upright position, to be on end; to have locality; to stop; to endure; to persevere; to be as regards circumstances, to be equivalent to become a candidate; to hold a certain course, to be valid.—*vt.* To set on end, to endure.—*n.* Act of standing; a stop; a halt; a station; a small table or frame; platform for spectators at gatherings.

standard, stan'därd, *n.* A nag of war, a banner; a rule or measure criterion, test, a certain grade in schools; an upright support.—*a.* Serving as a standard, satisfying certain legal conditions; not trained on a wall, etc., but standing by itself.

star, stär, *n.* Any celestial body except the sun and moon, a heavenly body similar to our sun; a figure with radiating points; a badge of honor; an asterisk, thus *; a brilliant theatrical performer.—*vt.* (starring, starred). To adorn with stars; to bespangle.—*vi.* To shine as a star, to appear as an eminent actor among inferior players.

start, stärt, *vi.* To move with sudden quickness, to wince, to deviate, to set out; to begin; to move from its place.—*vt.* To rouse suddenly; to startle, to originate, to dislocate.— *n.* A sudden motion; a twitch; outset; a handicap.

startle, stärt'l, *vi.* (startling, startled). To move suddenly.—*vt.* To cause to start; to frighten.—*n.* A start, as from fear.

starve, stärv, *vi.* (starving, starved). To perish with cold, to suffer from hunger, to be very indigent.—*vt.* To kill or distress with hunger or cold; to make inefficient through insufficient expenditure.

state, stāt, *n.* Condition; situation; rank; pomp; grandeur; an estate (of the realm), a commonwealth, a nation, civil power.—*a.* National public, governmental.—*vt.* (stating, stated). To express the particulars of, to narrate.

stately, stāt'li, *a.* Such as pertains to state; august; grand; lofty; dignified.

statistics, sta-tist'iks, *n.* A collection of facts, tabulated numerically; the science of subjects as elucidated by facts.

stay, stā, *vt.* (pret. & pp. stayed or staid). To prop; to stop; to delay; to await.—*vi.* To remain; to reside; to delay; to forbear to act; to stop.—*n.* Sojourn; stop; obstacle; a prop, a rope to support a mast; *pl.* a stiffened bodice worn by females a corset.—**To miss stays,** to fail in the attempt to tack about.

stead sted, *n.* Place or room which another had or might have; assistance: preceded by *in.*—*vt.* To be of use to.

steady, sted'i, *a.* Firm; stable; constant; regular; equable.—*vt.* (steadying, steadied). To make or keep firm.

steal, stēl, *vt.* (pret. stole, pp. stolen). To take feloniously; to pilfer; to gain by address or imperceptibly; to perform secretly.—*vi.* To pass silently or privily; to practice theft.

steam, stēm, *n.* The vapor of water; aeriform fluid generated by the boiling of water.—*vi.* To give out steam: to rise in vaporous form; to sail by means of steam.—*vt.* To expose to steam; to apply steam to.

steel, stēl, *n.* A very hard form or iron, produced by addition of carbon; weapons, swords, etc.; a knife-sharpener, sternness; rigor.—*a.* Made of or like steel; unfeeling; rigorous.—*vt.* To furnish with steel; to harden.

steep, stēp, *a.* Sloping greatly; precipitous.—*n.* A precipitous place; a cliff; process of steeping; liquid in which something is steeped.— *vt.* To soak, to imbue.

stem, stem, *n.* The principal body of a tree, shrub, etc., the stalk stock or branch of a family; the prow of a vessel.—*vt.* (stemming, stemmed). To make way against to press forward through; to dam up; to check.

step, step, *vi.* (stepping, stepped). To move the leg and foot in walking; to walk.—*vt.* To set (the foot); to fix the foot of, as of a mast.—*n.* A pace, a small space; a grade; a rise; footprint; gait; footfall; action adopted something to support the feet in ascending; round of a ladder; *pl.* a step-ladder.

sterile, ste'ril, *a.* Barren unfruitful incapable of reproduction; barren of ideas.

sterling, ster'ling, *a.* An epithet distinctive of English money; genuine; of excellent quality.

stern, stern, *a* Austere, harsh; rigid, stringent.—*n.* The hind part of a ship.

stick, stik, *vt.* (sticking, stuck). To pierce or stab; to fasten by piercing, gluing, etc.; to fix; to set.—*vi.* To adhere, to abide firmly; to be brought to a stop; to scruple.—*n.* A rod or wand; a staff; a stiff, awkward person.

stickler, stik'ler, *n.* One who stickles an obstinate contender about trifles.

stiff, stif, *a.* Rigid; tense; not moving easily; thick; not natural and easy; formal in manner, stubborn difficult; strong.

stiffness, stif'nes *n.* Want of pliancy; rigidity; viscidness; stubbornness; formality.

stifle, sti'fl, *vt.* and *i.* (stifling, stifled). To suffocate; to smother; to suppress.—*n.* The joint of a horse next to the buttock.

stigma, stig'ma, *n.; pl.* **-mas** or **-mata.** A brand made with a redhot iron; any mark of infamy, part of a flower pistil which receives the pollen, pl. *stigmata.* bodily marks like Christ's wounds impressed supernaturally.

stigmatize, stig'mat-īz, *vt. To* characterize by some opprobrious epithet.

still, stil, *a.* At rest; calm, silent, not loud; soft; not effervescing.—*vt. To* make still; to check; to appease or allay.— *adv. To* this time, always nevertheless; yet.—*n.* A vessel or apparatus for distilling; a distillery

sting, sting, *vt.* (stinging, stung). To pierce, as wasps, etc.; to prick, as a nettle, to pain acutely.—*n.* A sharp-pointed defensive organ of certain animals, the thrust of a sting into the flesh; something that gives acute pain; the biting effect of words.

stingily, stin'ji-li, *adv* In a stringy or niggardly manner; meanly; shabbily.

stink, stingk, *vi.* (stinking, stunk). To emit a strong offensive smell; to be in disrepute.—*n.* A strong offensive smell.

stitch, stich, *n.* A sharp pain, one complete movement of a needle in sewing; a complete turn or link in knitting, netting, etc.—*vt.* and *i.* To sew by making stitches in, to unite by stitches.

stock, stok, *a.* A post; a lifeless mass; stem of a tree; wooden piece of a rifle; a

stiff cravat; an original progenitor; lineage; capital invested in any business; money funded in government securities store, animals belonging to a farm; liquor used to form a foundation for soups and gravies, a sweet-smelling garden-plant, *pl.* an instrument of punishment confining the offender's ankles or wrists; timbers on which a ship is supported while building.—*vt.* To provide with a stock, to lay up in store.—*a.* Kept in stock; standing; permanent.

stocking, stok'ing, *n.* A close-fitting knitted covering for the foot and leg.

stone, stōn, *n.* A hard mass of earthy or mineral matter, a pebble; a precious stone; concretion in the kidneys or bladder, a testicle; the nut of a fruit a measure of 14 lbs. avoirdupois.—*a.* Made of stone like stone.—*vt.* (stoning stoned). To pelt with stones; to free from stones; to provide with stones.

stop, stop, *vt.* (stopping, stopped). To stuff up; to close; to arrest the progress of; to put an end to; to regulate the sounds of musical strings by the fingers, etc.—*vi.* To cease from any motion, to come to an end; to stay; to remain.—*n.* Obstruction; interruption; pause; a series of pipes in an organ giving distinctive sounds; a point in writing.

store, stōr, *n.* A large quantity for supply; abundance; a place where goods are kept; a shop; *pl.* necessary articles laid up for use.—*a.* Pertaining to a store; kept in store.—*vt.* (storing, stored). To amass; to supply; to reposit in a store for preservation.

storm, storm, *n.* A violent disturbance of the atmosphere; a tempest; an outbreak; assault on a strong position.—*vt.* To take by assault; to attack.—*vi.* To be in violent agitation; to rage.

straight, strāt, *a.* Stretched tight; direct, correct; upright.—*n.* A straight part or piece; straight direction.—*adv.* Immediately, directly.—*vt.* To straighten.

straightforward, strāt'for-werd, *a.* Proceeding in a straight course; candid; honest; frank; open.—*adv.* Directly forward.

strain, strān, *vt.* To stretch tightly; to exert to the utmost; to overtask; to sprain; to carry too far; to wrest, to filter.—*vi.* To exert oneself; to filter.—*n.* Violent effort; excessive stretching or exertion; tenor; theme; a lay; tune; race; family blood: tendency

strangle, strang'gl, *vt.* (strangling, strangled). To choke; to throttle; to suppress or stifle.

strap, strap, *n.* A long narrow slip of leather, etc.; a plate or strip of metal.—*vt.* (strapping, strapped). To beat with a strap; to fasten with a strap.

strategic, strategical, stra-tej'ik, stra-tej'ik-al, *a.* Pertaining to strategy; effected by strategy.

stray, strā, *vi.* To go astray; to err; to roam.—*a.* Having gone astray; straggling.—*n.* Any domestic animal that wanders at large, or is lost.

streak, strēk, *n.* A long mark; a stripe, appearance of a mineral when scratched.—*vt.* To form streaks in.

stream, strēm, *n.* A river or brook; a current; drift.—*vi.* and *t.* To move in a stream, to stretch in a long line, to float at full length in the air.

strength, strength. *n.* Property of being strong; force or energy; power; support; vigor; intensity; amount or numbers of an army fleet, or the like.—**On the strength of**, in reliance upon, on the faith of.

stress, stres, *vt.* To put in difficulties, to subject to emphasis.—*n.* Constraint; pressure; weight; violence. as of weather, emphasis.

stride, strīd, *vi.* (striding, pret. strode, pp. stridden). To walk with long steps; to straddle.—*vt.* To pass over at a step.—*n.* A long step, a measured tread.

strike, strīk, *vi.* (striking, pret. struck, pp. struck, stricken). To move or turn aside rapidly, to light (upon), to make a blow, to hit, to be stranded; to yield; to quit work to compel better terms.—*vt.* To smite to mint; to thrust in; to notify by sound; to occur to; to impress strongly, to effect at once, to lower as the flag or sails of a vessel.—*n.* Act of workmen who quit work to force their employer to give better terms; a strickle.

string, string, *n.* A small cord; a piece of twine; a line with the things on it; chord of a musical instrument, a series.—*vt.* (stringing strung). To furnish with string, to put on a string; to make tense.

stroke, strōk, *n.* A blow, calamity attack, striking of a clock, touch, a masterly effort; a dash in writing or printing a touch of the pen, a line; a gentle rub; the sweep of an oar, a stroke-oar.—*vt.* (stroking stroked). To rub gently with the hand.

strong, strong, *a.* Having power or force; robust, not easily broken firm; effectual; earnest, containing much alcohol; glaring; forcible, tending upwards in price, effecting inflection by internal vowel change.

strut, strut, *vi.* (strutting strutted). To walk with affected dignity.—*n.* A lofty, proud step or walk; a strengthening piece placed diagonally in a framework.

strychnia, strychnine, strik'ni-a, strik' nīn. *n.* A vegetable alkaloid poison obtained from the seeds of nux-vomica.

stubble, stub'l, *n.* The stumps of a grain crop left in the ground after reaping.

stubborn, stub'orn, *a.* Not to be moved or persuaded; obstinate; intractable.

studied, stu'did, *a.* Made the object of study; qualified by study; premeditated.

study, stu'di, *n.* Earnest endeavor application to books, etc.; subject which one studies, apartment devoted to study; a reverie; a preparatory sketch.—*vt.* and *i.* (studying, studied). To apply the mind to, to investigate; to have careful regard to.

stuff, stuf, *n.* Substance indefinitely; material; cloth; a light woolen fabric goods, trash.—*vt.* To pack, to thrust in, to fill, as meat with seasoning; to fill, as an animal's skin to preserve the form— *vi.* To cram; to feed gluttonously.

stump, stump, *n.* The part of a tree, limb, etc., left after the rest is cut off or destroyed; a worn-down tooth; a wicket in cricket.—*vt.* To lop as trees, to make a tour through, delivering speeches, to put out of play in cricket by knocking down a stump.—*vi.* To walk stiffly or noisily.

stun, stun, *vt.* (stunning, stunned). To overpower the sense of hearing of; to stupefy; to make senseless with a blow, to surprise completely.

stupendous, stū-pen'dus, *a.* Of astonishing magnitude; grand or awe-inspiring.

style, stīl, *n.* A burin; pin of a sundial, manner of writing with regard to language; a characteristic mode in the fine arts, type; external manner, mode, or fashion; title; in *botany,* a slender prolongation of the ovary supporting the stigma.—*vt.* (styling, styled). To term, to designate.

subject, sub'jekt, *a.* Ruled by another; liable; prone; submissive.— *n.* One who owes allegiance to a ruler or government; matter dealt with, theme, topic, the nominative of a verb; the thinking agent or principle.—*vt.* sub-jekt'. To subdue; to make liable; to cause to undergo.

subjective, sub-jekt'iv or sub'jek-tiv, *a.* Relating to the subject; belonging to ourselves, the conscious subject; exhibiting strongly the personality of the author

subjunctive, sub-jungk'tiv, *a.* and *n.* Applied to a mood of verbs that expresses condition, hypothesis, or contingency.

sublimate, sub'li-māt, *vt.* To raise by heat into vapor, as a solid, which, on cooling, returns again to the solid state. to refine; to elevate.—*n.* The product of sublimation.

sublimation, sub-li-mā'shon, *n.* The process or operation of sublimating; exaltation; a highly refined product.

sublime, sub-līm', *a.* High in place or excellence, affecting the mind with a sense of grandeur; noble; majestic.— **The sublime**, the grand in the works of nature or of art; grandeur of style; highest degree.—*vt.* (subliming, sublimed). To render sublime to sublimate.— *vi.* To be susceptible of sublimation.

submit, sub-mit', *vt.* (submitting, submitted). To yield or surrender; to refer, to state, as a claim.—*vi.* To surrender, to acquiesce; to suffer without complaint.

subordinate, sub-or'din-āt, *a.* Inferior, occupying a lower position.—*n.* One who stands in rank, power, etc., below another.—*vt.* To place in a lower order or rank.

subpoena, sub-pē'na, *n.* A writ summoning a witness under a penalty.—*vt.* (subpoenaing, subpoenaed). To serve with a writ of subpoena.

subscribe, sub-skrīb', *vt.* and *i.* (subscribing, subscribed). To append one's own signature to; to promise to contribute (money) by writing one's name; to assent.

subsidize, sub'si-dīz, *vt.* (subsidizing, subsidized). To furnish with a subsidy; to purchase the assistance of another by a subsidy.

subsidy, sub'si-di, *n.* A sum of money granted for a purpose; a sum given by a government to meet expenses.

substance, sub'stans, *n.* That of which a thing consists; material; a body; essence; purport; means and resources.

substantive, sub'stan-tiv, *a.* Expressing existence; independent; real; of the nature of a noun.—*n.* A noun.

substitute, sub'sti-tūt, *vt.* (substituting,

substituted). To put in the place of another; to exchange.—*n.* A person or thing in the place of another, a deputy.

subterfuge, sub'tėr-fūj, *n.* An artifice to escape or justify; evasion; a dishonest shift.

subterranean, subterraneous, sub-te-rā'nē-an, sub-te-rā'nē-us *a.* Being under the surface of the earth.

succeed, suk-sēd', *vt.* To follow in order; to take the place of, to come after.—*vi.* To follow in order; to ensue; to become heir, to obtain the end or object desired; to prosper.

succession suk-se'shon, *n.* A following of things in order, series of things; lineage; right of inheriting act or right of succeeding to an office, rank, etc.

successor, suk-ses'or, *n.* One who succeeds or follows another.

suck, suk, *vt.* and *i.* To draw with the mouth, to draw milk from with the mouth, to imbibe, to absorb.— *n.* Act of sucking; milk drawn from the breast.

sucker, suk'ėr, *n.* One who or that which sucks, an organ in animals for sucking; piston of a pump shoot of a plant; the sucking-fish.

suffer, suf'ėr, *vt.* To endure; to undergo; to be affected by, to permit.—*vi.* To undergo pain; to be injured.

sufferance, suf'ėr-ans, *n.* Endurance; pain endured; passive consent, allowance.

sugar, shü'gėr, *n.* A sweet granular substance, manufactured from sugar-cane, maple, beet, etc.; something sweet like sugar—*a.* Belonging to or made of sugar.— *vt.* To season, mix, etc., with sugar; to sweeten.

suggest, su-jest' or sug-jest', *vt.* To hint; to insinuate; to propose; to intimate.

suggestion, su-jest 'yon, *n.* A hint, a tentative proposal; insinuation; intimation.

suit, sūt, *n.* Act of suing; a request; courtship; a suing at law, a set of things.—*vt.* and *i.* To adapt; to fit; to be agreeable to, to agree.

sully, sul'i, *vt.* (sullying, sullied). To soil; to tarnish; to stain or pollute.—*vi.* To be soiled.—*n.* Soil; tarnish, spot.

sulphur, sul'fėr, *n.* Brimstone, a simple mineral substance of a yellow color which burns with a pale blue flame.

Summer, sum'ėr, *n.* The warmest season of the year; a lintel, a girder.—*a.* Relating to summer.—*vi.* To pass the summer.—*vt.* To keep or carry through the summer.

summon, sum'un, *vt.* To call by authority to appear at a place, especially a court of justice; to send for; to call up.

sumptuary, sump'tū-a-ri, *a.* Relating to expense; regulating expenditure.

sumptuous, sump'tū-us, *a.* Very expensive or costly; splendid; magnificent.

sun, sun, *n.* The self-luminous orb which gives light and heat to all the planets, sunshine or sunlight; sunny position; chief source of light, glory, etc.; a year.—*vt.* (sunning, sunned). To expose to the sun's rays.

sunburn, sun'bern, *vt.* To discolor or scorch by the sun; to tan.

sunstroke, sun'strŏk, *n.* A bodily affection produced by exposure to the sun.

supererogation, sū-pèr-e'rŏ-gā'' shon, *n.* Giving more than enough; performance of more than duty requires.

superficial, sū-pèr-fi'shal, *a.* Being on the surface; shallow; not thorough.

superfluous, sū-pèr'flü-us, *a.* Being more than is wanted; redundant; unnecessary.

superhuman, sū-pèr-hū'man, *a.* Above or beyond what is human; divine.

superintendent, sū-pèr-in-tend''ent, *n.* One who manages and directs; an overseer.—*a.* Overlooking others with authority.

superior, sū-pē'ri-or, *a.* Higher; higher in rank or dignity; greater in excellence.—*n.* One who is superior to another; chief of a monastery, convent, or abbey.

superlative, sū-pèr'lat-iv, *a.* Highest in degree; supreme.—*n.* That which is superlative; the highest degree of adjectives or adverbs.

superscription, sū-pèr-skrip'shon, *n.* Act of superscribing; that which is written or engraved above or on the outside; address on a letter, etc.

supersede, sū-pèr-sēd', *vt.* (superseding, superseded). To set aside; to take the place of; to supplant.

supersonic, sū-pèr-son'ik, *a.* Faster than sound, above the audible limit.

superstition, sū-pèr-sti'shon, *n.* Groundless belief in supernatural agencies; a popular belief held without reason.

superstructure, sū-pèr-struk'tūr, *n.* Any structure raised on something else.

supervene, sū-pèr-vēn', *vi.* (supervening, supervened). To come, as something extraneous; to happen.

supervise, sū-pèr-vīz', *vt.* (supervising, supervised). To oversee and direct, to superintend; to inspect.

supplicate, sup'li-kāt, *vt.* (supplicating, supplicated). To beg humbly for; to entreat; to address in prayer.—*vi.* To beg; to petition; to beseech.

supply, sup-plī', *vt.* (supplying, sup plied). To furnish, to provide; to satisfy.—*n.* Act of supplying; quantity supplied; store; *pl.* stores or articles necessary; money provided for government expenses.

support, sup-pŏrt', *vt.* To rest under and bear, to prop, to endure; to assist; to second; to maintain; to provide for—*n.* Act of supporting; a prop; help; sustenance; maintenance.

suppress, sup-pres', *vt.* To pull down; to crush; to quell, to check; to conceal.

surf, sèrf, *n.* The swell of the sea which breaks on the shore, rocks, etc.

surface, sèr'fās, *n.* The exterior part of anything that has length and breadth; outside; external appearance.—*a.* Pertaining to the surface; superficial.

surfeit, sèr'fit, *n.* An overloading of the stomach, disgust caused by excess; satiety.—*vt.* and *i.* To feed to excess; to nauseate; to cloy.

surmise, sèr-mīz', *n.* A supposition conjecture; speculation.—*vt.* (surmising, surmised). To guess; to imagine; to suspect.

survey, sèr-vā', *vt.* To oversee; to examine; to measure and value, as land, etc.; to determine the boundaries, natural features, etc., of.—*n.* ser'va or ser-va'. A general view examination; determination or account of topographical particulars.

survive, sèr-vīv', *vt.* (surviving, survived). To outlive, to live beyond the life of; to outlast.—*vi.* To live after another or after anything else.

suspense, sus-pens', *n.* State of being uncertain; indecision; cessation for a time.

suspension, sus-pen'shon, *n.* Act of suspending; intermission; abeyance; deprivation of office or privileges for a time.

suspicion, sus-pi'shon, *n.* Act of suspecting; fear of something wrong; mistrust.

suspicious, sus-pi'shus, *a.* Mistrustful; inclined to suspect; apt to raise suspicion; doubtful.

sustain, sus-tān', *vt.* To rest under and bear up; to support, to aid effectually; to undergo; to endure, to hold valid; to confirm; to continue.

swallow, swol'ŏ, *vt.* To receive through the gullet into the stomach, to engulf, to absorb to believe readily, to put up with.—*n.* The gullet; voracity; capacity of swallowing; a small migratory bird.

swamp, swomp, *n.* A piece of wet spongy land; a fen; a bog.—*vt.* To sink in a swamp, to overwhelm, to overset or fill, as a boat in water.

swarm, swärm, *n.* A large body of small insects, a multitude.—*vi.* To depart from a hive in a body, to crowd; to abound; to climb a tree, pole, etc., by clasping it with the arms and legs.

sway, swā, *vi.* To swing or vibrate; to incline, to govern.—*vt.* To swing to wield; to bias; to influence; to rule.—*n.* Swing or sweep; preponderance; power; rule; ascendency.

swear, swār, *vt.* and *t.* (swearing, pret. swore, pp. sworn). To make a solemn declaration, with an appeal to God for its truth; to make promise upon oath; to cause to take an oath, to curse.

swell, swel, *vi.* (pp. swelled or swollen). To grow larger, to heave, to bulge out; to increase.—*vt.* To expand or increase, to puff up.—*n.* Act of swelling; gradual increase; a rise of ground; a wave or surge; an arrangement in an organ for regulating the intensity of the sound; an important person; a dandy.

swim, swim, *vi.* (swimming, pret. swam, swum, pp. swum). To float; to move through water by the motion of the limbs or fins; to be flooded; to be dizzy.—*vt.* To pass by swimming.—*n.* Act of swimming; distance swum; air-bladder of fishes.

switch, swich, *n.* A small flexible twig or rod; a movable rail at unctions; a device for changing the course of an electric current.—*vt.* To strike with a switch; to shunt.

swivel, swi-vel, *n.* A link in a chain partly consisting of a pivot turning in a hole in the next link; a fastening that allows the thing fastened to turn round freely.—*vi.* (swivelling, swivelled). To turn on a swivel.

sword, sörd, *n.* A military weapon consisting of a long steel blade and a hilt, used for thrusting or cutting; the emblem of justice, authority, war, or destruction; the military profession.

sworn, swŏrn, *p.a.* Bound by oath; having taken an oath; closely bound.

syllable, sil'la-bl, *n.* A sound or combination of sounds uttered with one effort; the smallest expressive element of language.—*vt.* To articulate.

symbol, sim'bol, *n.* A sign; an emblem; a type; a figure; an attribute; a creed or summary of articles or religion.

symbolize, sim'bol-īz, *vt.* To represent by a symbol; to typify; to treat as symbolic.—*vi.* To express or represent in symbols.

sympathy, sim'pa-thi, *n.* Fellow-feeling; compassion; agreement of inclinations; correspondence of sensations or affections.

syndicate, sin'di-kāt, *n.* A body of syndics; office of a syndic; body of persons associated to promote some enterprise. —*vt.* To form a syndicate or body for the use of.

synthesis, sin'the-sis, *n.*; pl. -ses. The putting of things together to form a whole; composition or combination.

syringe, si'rinj, *n.* A tube and piston serving to draw in and expel fluid.—*vt.* (syringing, syringed). To inject by a syringe; to cleanse by injections from a syringe.

S

T

tabby, tab'i, *n.* A rich watered silk or other stuff; a cat of a brindled color, a female cat.—*vt.* To water or cause to look wavy.

tabernacle, tab'ér-na-kl, *n.* A booth, a temporary habitation, a place of worship, a repository for holy things.—*vi.* To sojourn.

table, tā'bl, *n.* A thing with a flat surface; an article of furniture having a flat surface, fare or eatables; persons sitting at a table; a syllabus; index; list.—*vt.* (tabling, tabled). To tabulate, to lay on the table.—*a.* Appertaining to a table.

tabular, ta'bū-lèr, *a.* In form of a table; having a flat surface; set in columns.

tabulate, ta'bū-lāt, *vt.* (tabulating, tabulated). To set down in a table of items.—*a.* tabular.

taciturn, ta'si-tèrn, *a.* Habitually silent, not apt to talk or speak.

tack, tak, *n.* A small nail, a slight fastening; a rope for certain sails; course of a ship as regards the wind; in *Scots law,* a lease.—*vt.* To fasten by tacks; to attach slightly; to append.—*vi.* To change the course of a ship so as to have the wind acting from the other side.

tackle, tak'l, *n.* Gear or apparatus pulleys and ropes for moving weights; ropes and rigging, etc., of a ship.—*vt.* (tackling, tackled). To supply with tackle; to set vigorously to work upon; to seize.

tact, takt, *n.* Touch; nice perception or discernment; adroitness in words or actions.

tail, tāl, *n.* The projecting termination of an animal behind, the hinder or inferior part, the reverse of a coin; limited ownership.

taint, tānt, *vt.* To defile, to infect, to vitiate.—*vi.* To be infected or corrupted.— *n.* Infection; corruption; a stain; a blemish on reputation.

take, tāk, *vt.* (taking, pret. took, pp. taken). To receive or accept, to capture, to captivate, to understand; to feel concerning; to employ; to need; to form or adopt; to assume; to note down; to be infected or seized with, to bear, to conduct, carry, to leap over.—*vi.* To direct one's course; to please; to have the intended effect, to admit of being made a portrait of.

talc, talk, *n.* A magnesian mineral, unctuous to the touch.—*vt.* To rub with talc.

talent, ta'lent, *n.* An ancient weight and denomination of money, a special faculty; general mental power; people of high abilities collectively.

tally, tal'i, *n.* A piece of wood on which notches are cut to keep accounts, anything made to suit another.—*vt.* (tallying, tallied). To record on a tally, to make to correspond.—*vi.* To correspond or agree exactly.

tame, tām, *a.* Having lost its natural wildness; domesticated; spiritless; insipid.— *vt.* (taming, tamed). To make tame; to subdue; to depress.

tandem, tan'dem, *adv.* With two horses harnessed singly one before the other.—*n.* A wheeled carriage so drawn; a cycle for two persons, one behind the other.

tangent, tan'jent, *n.* A straight line which touches a circle or curve, but which, when produced, does not cut it.

tantalize, tan'ta-līz, *vt.* (tantalizing, tantalized). To torment by presenting something desirable which cannot be attained to excite by hopes that are never realized.

tantrum, tan'trum, *n.* A fit of ill-humor; display of temper; chiefly in pl.

tape, tāp, *n.* A narrow strip of woven work, used for strings and the like.

tapioca, tap-i-ō'ka, *n.* A farinaceous substance prepared from cassava meal.

tar, tär, *n.* A thick, dark, viscid substance obtained from pine or fir, coal, shale etc., a sailor.—*vt.* (tarring, tarred). To smear with tar.

tart, tärt, *a.* Sharp to the taste; sour; acid; severe; snappish.—*n.* A species of pastry, consisting of fruit baked in paste.

task, täsk, *n.* A piece of work imposed by another or requiring to be done; burdensome employment; toil.—*vt.* To impose a task upon.

tassel, tas'el, *n.* An ornament consisting of a knob with hanging threads.—*vi.* (tasseling, tasseled). To put forth a tassel or flower, as maize.—*vt.* To adorn with tassels.

taste, tāst, *vt.* (tasting, tasted). To test by the tongue and palate; to perceive the flavor of, to experience, to partake of.— *vi.* To make trial by the tongue and palate; to have a flavor, to have experience.—*n.* Act of lasting; sense of tasting; flavor; intellectual relish or discernment, manner or style.

taunt, tänt, *vt.* To reproach with severe or sarcastic words, to upbraid.—*n.* A bitter or sarcastic reproach.

tax, taks, *n.* A contribution levied by authority; a rate, duty, or impost charged on income or property; a burdensome duty; an exaction.—*vt.* To impose a tax on; to put to a certain effort; to accuse.

tea, tē, *n.* The dried leaves of plants cultivated in China, Assam, Ceylon, etc.; the plant itself; a decoction of tea leaves in boiling water; any decoction of vegetables.—*vi.* (teaing, teaed). To take tea.

teach, tēch, *vt.* (teaching, taught) To instruct; to inform; to make familiar with.—*vi.* To practice giving instruction.

teak, tēk, *n.* An E. Indian tree which furnishes hard and valuable timber.

team, tēm, *n.* A brood; horses or other beasts harnessed together a side in a game, match, etc.

tear, tār, *vt.* (pret. tore, pp. torn). To pull in pieces to rend; to wound; to drag; to pull with violence; to make by rending.—*vi.* To be rent or torn, to rage.—*n.* A rent.

tease, tēz, *vt.* (teasing, teased) To pull apart the fibers of; to annoy; to torment.

tedious, tē'di-us, *a.* Tiresome; wearisome; irksome; fatiguing; dilatory, tardy.

telegraph, tel'e-graf, *n.* Any apparatus for transmitting messages to a distance; an apparatus for transmitting messages along a wire by electricity, but now also wireless.—*vt.* To convey or announce by telegraph.

telepathy, te-lep'a-thi or tel'e-pathi, *n.* Occult communication between persons at some distance.

telescope, tel'e-skōp, *n.* An optical instrument for viewing distant objects.—*vt.* (telescoping. telescoped). To drive the parts of into each other, like the joints of a telescope.

tell, tel, *vt.* (telling, told). To number; to relate, to disclose, to explain; to distinguish; to inform; to bid.—*vi.* To give an account; to take effect

temerity, tē-me'ri-ti, *n.* Contempt of danger, extreme boldness; rashness.

temper, tem'pė r, *vt.* To proportion duly; to moderate, to form to a proper hardness.—*n.* Due mixture; disposition of the mind, temperament; irritation; state of a metal as to its hardness; medium.

temperament, tem'pėr-a-mėnt, *n.* Due mixture of qualities; combined mental and physical constitution; disposition.

temperance, tem'pėr-ans, *n.* Moderation in indulgence of the natural appetites; sobriety; abstinence from intoxicants.

temperature, tem'pėr-a-tūr, *n.* State with regard to heat or cold climatic heat.

templet, template, tem'plet, tem' plāt, *n.* A board whose edge is shaped so as to serve as a guide in making an article with a corresponding contour.

temporal, tem'pō-ral, *a.* Pertaining to time; pertaining to this life, not spiritual or ecclesiastical, secular; pertaining to the temples of the head.—*n.* Anything temporal or secular; a temporality.

tenant, te'nant, *n.* One who occupies lands or houses for which he pays rent.—*vt.* To hold as a tenant.—*vi.* To live as a tenant, to dwell.

tend, tend, *vi.* To move in or have a certain direction; to conduce; to attend.—*vt.* To attend; to guard, to take care of

tender, ten'dėr, *n.* One who attends; a small vessel employed to attend on a larger one a carriage with fuel, etc., attached to a locomotive; an offer of money or service an estimate; thing offered.—*vt.* To present for acceptance.—*a.* Fragile; delicate; compassionate, kind.

tendon, ten'don, *n.* A sinew; a hard, insensible cord or bundle of fibers by which a muscle is attached to a bone.

tennis, ten'is, *n.* A game in which a ball is driven against a wall, and caused to rebound; in ordinary use, lawn-tennis

tenor, ten'or, *n.* A prevailing course or direction; purport; substance, as of a discourse, the highest of the male adult chest voices; one who sings a tenor part.—*a.* Adapted for singing or playing the tenor.

tense, tens, *n.* Inflection of a verb to express time.—*a.* Stretched; tight; strained to stiffness, rigid, not lax.

tension, ten'shon, *n.* Act of stretching; state of being stretched; tightness; strain; intensity; elastic force.

tensor, ten'sor, *n.* A muscle that extends or stretches the part to which it is fixed.

tentacle, ten'ta-kl, *n. sing.* and *pl.* A filiform organ of various animals used for prehension or as a feeler.

tentative, ten'ta-tiv, *a.* Experimental; empirical.—*n.* An essay; a trial.

tenure, ten'ūr, *n.* A holding or manner of holding real estate, condition of occupancy; manner of possessing in general.

term, tėrm, *n.* A limit; boundary time for

T

which anything lasts; period of session, etc.; day on which rent or interest is paid; a word; a word having a technical meaning; *pl.* conditions; relative position or footing.—*vt.* To name; to call.

terminal, tėr'min-al, *a.* Pertaining to or forming the end; terminating.—*n.* An extremity, the clamping screw at each end of a voltaic battery.

terminate, tėr'min-āt, *vt.* and *i.* (terminating, terminated). To bound; to limit to end.—*a.* Limited.

terminology, tėr-min-ol'o-ji, *n.* The science or theory of technical or other terms; terms used in any art, science, etc.

terminus, tėr'mi-nus, *n.; pl.* -ni. A boundary, a limit, station at the end of a railway, etc.

terrace, te'räs, *n.* A raised level bank of earth, a raised flat area, a row of houses; flat roof of a house.—*vt.* (terracing, terraced). To form into or furnish with a terrace.

territory, te'ri-to-ri, *n.* A definite piece of' land under any distinct administration; a dominion; region, country.

terror, te'ror, *n.* Such fear as agitates body and mind, dread alarm, cause of fear.

terrorism, te'ror-izm, *n.* A system of government by terror; intimidation.

tertiary, tėr'shi-a-ri, *a.* Third, applied to the third great division of stratified rocks, resting on the chalk.—*n.* The tertiary system of rocks.

tessera, tes'e-ra, *n., pl.* -rae. A small cube of marble, ivory, etc. used for mosaic work.

test, test, *n.* A vessel used in trying or refining gold, etc.; a cupel; examination; means of trial; a standard, oath taken before admission to privileges, a hard outer covering.—*vt.* To put to a trial; to refine; to examine; to prove; to attest.

testify, tes'ti-fī, *vi.* (testifying, testified). To bear witness; to give evidence.—*vt.* To bear witness to.

tether, teTH'ėr, *n.* A rope confining a grazing animal with certain limits, scope allowed.—*vt.* To confine with a tether.

tetrahedron, te-tra-hē'dron, *n.* A solid body having four equal triangles as its faces.

text, tekst, *n.* An author's own work as distinct from annotations, a passage of Scripture selected as the subject of a discourse; a topic; a large kind of handwriting, particular kind of lettering.

textile, teks'tīl, *a.* Woven; capable of being woven.—*n.* A fabric made by weaving.

texture, teks'tūr, *n.* A web, that which is woven; a fabric; manner in which constituent parts are connected; the grain or peculiar character of a solid.

thallus, thal'us, *n.* A solid mass of cells, forming the substance of the thallogens.

than, THan, *conj.* A particle used after certain adjectives and adverbs expressing comparison or diversity, as *more, other;* etc.

Thanksgiving, thangks'giv-ing, *n.* Act of giving thanks; public celebration of divine goodness.

that, THat, *a.* and *pron.; pl.* **those,** THōz. A pronominal adjective pointing to a person or thing mentioned or understood; a demonstrative pronoun; a relative pronoun equivalent to *who* or *which.*—*conj.* Introducing a reason, purpose, or result, a noun clause, or a wish.

theater, thē 'a-tėr, *n.* A house for the exhibition of dramatic performances, a place of action, a room for anatomical demonstrations, etc.

theft, theft, *n.* Act of stealing, unlawful taking of another's goods; thing stolen.

their, THār, *pronominal* or *possessive adj.* Pertaining or belonging to them.— **theirs,** possessive case of they, used without a noun.

theme, thēm, *n.* A subject or topic short dissertation by a student leading subject in a musical composition.

then, THen, *adv.* At that time, past or future, soon afterwards.—*conj.* In that case, therefore.

theory, thē'ō-ri, *n.* Speculation; hypothesis to explain something rules or knowledge of an art as distinguished from practice.

thermal, thermic, thėr'mal, thėr' mik, *a.* Pertaining to heat; warm; hot.

they, THā, *pron. pl.* The plural of *he, she,* or *it;* sometimes used indefinitely.

thick, thik, *a.* Having extent measured through; dense; foggy; crowded; close; stupid; gross.—*n.* The thickest part.— *adv.* In close succession; fast or close together.

thicket, thik'et, *n.* A wood or collection of trees or shrubs closely set.

thin-skinned, thin'skind, *a.* Having a thin skin, unduly sensitive irritable.

thirst, thẻrst, *n.* The desire or distress occasioned by want of water; eager desire after anything.—*vi.* To feel thirst; to desire vehemently.

thistle, this'l, *n.* A prickly composite plant, the national emblem of Scotland.

thorax, thō raks, *n.; pl.* **-races.** That part of the human body which contains the lungs, heart, etc.; the chest.

thorough-bred, thu'rō-bred, *a.* Bred from pure and unmixed blood, as horses completely bred or accomplished, high-spirited.— *n.* An animal of pure blood.

thoroughfare, thu'rō-fär, *n.* A passage through, unobstructed way; power of passing.

those, THŏz, *a.* and *pron.* Pl. of *that.*

though, THŏ, *conj.* Granting it to be the fact that; notwithstanding that; if.—*adv.* However.

thread, thred, *n.* A fine cord; any fine filament, prominent spiral part of a screw, continued course or tenor; general purpose.—*vt.* To pass a thread through; to pass or pierce through.

threadbare, thred'bār, *a.* Having the nap worn off, worn out, trite hackneyed.

threaten, thret'n, *vt.* To use threats towards; to menace; to show to be impending.—*vi.* To use threats.

threshold, thresh'ōld, *n.* The stone or piece of timber which lies under a door; a doorsill, entrance, outset.

thrill, thril, *vt.* To send a quiver through; to affect with a keen tingling.—*vi.* To quiver, to move trem*ulously.*—*n.* A warbling; thrilling sensation.

throe, thrō, *n.* Extreme pain, anguish of travail in childbirth.—*vi.* (throeing, throed). To struggle in extreme pain.

throne, thrōn, *n.* The seat of a king or ruler, sovereign power and dignity.—*vt.* (throning, throned). To place on a royal seat; to enthrone; to exalt.

throttle, throt'l, *n.* The windpipe or trachea, the throat, the gullet.—*vt.* (throttling, throttled). To choke; to strangle.

through, thrö, *prep.* From end to end of; by means of; on account of; throughout.—*adv.* From end to end, to completion.—*a.* Going with little or no interruption from one place to another.

thumb, thum, *n.* The short thick finger of the hand.—*vt.* To soil or handle awkwardly with the fingers.

thump, thump, *n.* A dull, heavy blow; sound made by such a blow.—*vt. and i.* To strike with something thick or heavy.

thwart, thwärt, *a.* Transverse; being across.—*vt.* To cross; to frustrate or defeat.—*n.* The bench on which the rowers sit, athwart the boat.

ticket, tik'et *n.* A label; a card or paper enabling one to enter a place, travel in a railway, etc.—*vt.* To put a ticket on to label.

tickle, tik'l, *vt.* (tickling, tickled). To touch and cause a peculiar thrilling sensation in; to please; to flutter; to puzzle.

ticklish, tik'lish, *a.* Easily tickled; touchy, liable to be overthrown; difficult, critical.

tide, tīd, *n.* Time; season; the rising and falling of the sea; flow; current.—*vt.* or *i.* (tiding, tided). To drive with the tide.—**To tide over,** to surmount.

tidy, tī'di, *a.* Clean and orderly; neat, trim, moderately large.—*vt.* (tidying, tidied). To make tidy.—*n.* A piece of fancy work to throw over a chair, etc.

tie, ti, *vt.* (tying, tied). To bind, to fasten; to oblige; to constrain.—*n.* That which binds or fastens together, a fastening, a neck-tie; bond; obligation; an equality in numbers.

tile, tīl, *n.* A slab of baked clay for covering roofs floors, walls, etc.— *vt.* (tiling, tiled) To cover with tiles; to guard against the entrance of the uninitiated.

till, til, *n.* A money box or drawer for money in a shop, etc.—*prep.* To the time of; until.—*vt.* To cultivate; to plow and prepare for seed.

tilt, tilt, *vi.* To run or ride and thrust with a lance; to joust; to lean or slope; to heel over.—*vt.* To set in a sloping position; to cover with an awning.—*n.* Inclination forward; a military contest with lances on horseback; a tilt-hammer; an awning.

timber, tim'bẻr, *n.* Wood suitable for building purposes; trees yielding such wood, one of the main beams of a fabric.—*vt.* To furnish with timber.

time, tīm, *n.* The measure of duration; a particular part or point of duration; occasion; season; epoch; present life; leisure; rhythm rate of movement.—*vt.* (timing, timed). To adapt to the time or occasion; to regulate or measure as to time.

tincture, tingk'tūr, *n.* A tinge, tint, or shade; slight quality added to anything; flavor; extract or solution of the active principles of some substance.—*vt.* (tincturing, tinctured). To tinge, to imbue.

tinsel, tin'sel, *n.* Thin, glittering metallic

sheets; cloth overlaid with foil; something superficially showy.—*a.* Consisting of tinsel showy to excess.—*vt.* (tinselling, tinselled). To adorn with tinsel.

tissue, ti'shū, *n.* Any woven stuff; a textile fabric; a primary layer of organic substance, a fabrication.

tissue-paper, ti'shū-pā-pėr, *n.* A very thin paper, used for protecting or wrapping.

tithe, tīTH, *n.* The tenth part of anything, tenth part allotted to the clergy; any small part.—*vt.* (tithing, tithed). To levy a tithe on.—*vi.* To pay tithes.

to, tū or tō, *prep.* Denoting motion towards; indicating a point reached, destination, addition, ratio, opposition, or contrast; marking an object; the sign of the infinitive mood.—*adv.* Forward; on.

toad, tōd, *n.* A reptile resembling the frog, but not adapted for leaping.

toddle, tod'l, *vi.* (toddling, toddled). To walk with short tottering steps. *n.* A little toddling walk.

toe, tō, *n.* One of the small members forming the extremity of the foot.—*vt.* (toeing, toed). To touch or reach with the toes.

together, tü-geTH'ėr, *adv.* In company; in concert; without intermission.

toilet, toi'let, *n.* A cloth over a table in a dressing room; a dressing-table; act or mode of dressing; attire.

token, tō'kn, *n.* A mark; sign; indication, souvenir, keepsake a piece of money current by sufferance, not coined by authority.

tolerate, tol'ė-rāt, *vt.* (tolerating, tolerated). To allow or permit; to treat with forbearance, to put up with to allow religious freedom to.

tombstone, töm'stōn, *n.* A stone erected over a grave; a sepulchral monument.

tone, tōn, *n.* Any sound in relation to its pitch, quality, or strength; sound as expressive of sentiment timbre; healthy activity of animal organs; mood; tenor; prevailing character.—*vt.* (toning, toned). To give a certain tone to.—**To tone down,** to soften.

tongue, tung, *n.* The fleshy movable organ in the mouth, of taste, speech, etc., speech, a language strip of land, a tapering flame; pin of a buckle.—*vt.* To utter, to scold; to modify with the tongue in playing, as in the flute.

too, tö, *adv.* Over, more than sufficiently; very; likewise; also; besides.

tool, töl, *n.* Any instrument to be used by the hands; a person used as an instrument by another.—*vt.* To shape or mark with a tool.

toot, töt, *vi.* To make a noise like that of a pipe or horn.—*vt.* To sound, as a horn.—*n.* A sound blown on a horn.

tooth, toth, *n.*; pl. **teeth,** tēth. A bony growth in the jaws for chewing; any projection resembling a tooth.—*vt.* To furnish with teeth, to indent.

top, top, *n.* The highest part of anything, highest rank: platform in ships surrounding the head of the lower masts; a whirling toy.—*a.* Being on the top; highest.—*vi.* (topping, topped). To rise aloft; to be eminent.—*vt.* To cap, to surmount to rise to the top of

topography, to-pog'ra-fi, *n.* The description of a particular place tract of land, etc.

topple, top'l, *vi.* (toppling, toppled). To fall, as with the top first.—*vt.* To throw forward.

toss, tos, *vt.* To pitch, to fling, to jerk, as the head; to agitate.—*vi.* To roll and tumble, to be in violent commotion.—*n.* A throw; pitch throw of the head.

tot, tot, *n.* Anything small or insignificant.—*vt.* (totting, totted). To sum (with up).

total, tō'tal, *a.* Pertaining to the whole; complete.—*n.* The whole; an aggregate.

touch, tuch, *vt.* To perceive by the sense of feeling; to come in contact with, to taste; to reach or arrive at; to refer to; to affect.—*vi.* To be in contact, to take effect, to make mention; to call when on a voyage.—*n.* Act of touching; contact, sense of feeling a trait, a little; a stroke; distinctive handling; in football, etc., part of the field beyond the flags.

toupee, toupet, tö-pē', tö'pē, *n.* A curl or artificial lock of hair; a small wig or upper part of wig.

tournament, tör'na-ment, *n.* A martial sport performed by knights on horseback; contest in which a number take part.

tourniquet, tör'ni-ket, *n.* A bandage tightened by a screw to check a how of blood.

tout, tout, *vi.* To ply or seek for customers.—*n.* One who plies for customers.

tow, to, *vt.* To drag, as a boat, by a rope.—*n.* Act of towing; state of being towed; coarse part of flax or hemp.

toward, towards, to'erd, to'erdz, *prep.* In the direction of, regarding; in aid of; for; about.—*adv.* At hand, going on.

towel, tou'el, *n.* A cloth for drying the skin after washing, or for domestic purposes.

tower, tou'ėr, *n.* A lofty narrow building, a citadel, a fortress.—*vi.* To soar; to be lofty; to stand sublime.

trace, trās, *n.* A mark left by anything; footstep; vestige; track; one of the straps by which a carriage, etc., is drawn.—*vt.* (tracing traced). To track out; to follow by marks left; to draw or copy with lines or marks.

trade, trād, *n.* Employment; commerce; traffic; those engaged in any trade.—*a.* Pertaining to trade.—*vi.* (trading, traded). To traffic; to carry on commerce; to have dealings.—*vt.* To sell or exchange in commerce.

tradition, tra-di'shon, *n.* The handing down of opinions, stories, etc., from father to son, by oral communication; a statement so handed down.

tragedy, tra'je-di, *n.* A drama representing an important event generally having a fatal issue, a fatal and mournful event; a murderous or bloody deed.

tragic, tragical, tra'jik, tra'jik-al *a.* Pertaining to tragedy; murderous; calamitous.

trail, trāl, *n.* Something dragged behind; a train; the end of a field gun-carriage that rests on the ground in firing; a path; track followed by a hunter; the position of a rifle when carried horizontally at the full extent of the right arm.—*vt.* To draw behind or along the ground; to drag.—*vi.* To be dragged along a surface; to hang down loosely; to grow along the ground.

trailer, trāl'ėr, *n.* One who trails, a plant which cannot grow upward without support; a carriage dragged by a motor vehicle; a series of excerpts advertising coming attractions at the cinema.

train, trān *vt.* To draw, to entice; to rear and instruct, to drill; to bring into proper bodily condition; to shape, to bring to bear as a gun.— *vi.* To undergo special drill.—*n.* A trail; that part of a gown which trails; tail; a series; course; retinue; line of carriages and an engine on a railway; line to conduct fire to a charge or mine.

trance, trans, *n.* A state of insensibility; ecstasy, catalepsy.—*vt.* (trancing, tranced). To entrance; to enchant.

transcribe, tran-skrī b', *vt.* (transcribing, transcribed). To write over again or in the same words; to copy.

transfer, trans-fėr', *vt.* (transferring, transferred). To convey from one place or person to another, to make over.—*n.* trans'fer. Act of transferring; removal of a thing from one place or person to another; something transferred.

transfuse, trans-fūz', *vt.* (transfusing, transfused). To transfer by pouring; to cause to pass from one to another.

transition, tran-zi'shon, *n.* Passage from one place, state, or topic to another.—*a.* Pertaining to passage from one state, etc., to another.

translate, trans-lāt', *vt.* (translating, translated). To remove from one place to another; to transfer; to render into another language.

transmigration, trans-mi-grā' shon, *n.* Act of transmigrating; the passing of a soul into another body after death.

transmission, trans-mi'shon, *n.* Act of transmitting, transference, a passing through any body, as of light through glass, the gear box of an automobile by which engine power is transmitted to the wheels.

transmit, trans-mit', *vt.* (transmitting, transmitted). To send from one person or place to another, to hand down; to allow to pass through.

transparent, trans-pā'rent, *a.* That can be seen through distinctly; not sufficient to hide underlying feelings.

transpire, trans-pīr, *vt.* (transpiring, transpired). To emit through the pores of the skin; to send off in vapor.—*vi.* To exhale; to escape from secrecy, to become public.

transport, trans-pōrt', *vt.* To carry from one place to another, to carry into banishment; to carry away by violence of passion, to ravish with pleasure.—*n.* trans' port. Transportation a ship employed to carry soldiers, warlike stores, etc.; passion; ecstasy.

trap, trap, *n.* A contrivance for catching unawares; an ambush; a contrivance in drains to prevent effluvia rising; a carriage of any kind, on springs; a kind of movable ladder; an igneous rock.—*vt.* (trapping, trapped). To catch in a trap; to ensnare; to adorn.—*vi.* To set traps for game.

trapeze, tra-pēz', *n.* A sort of swing, consisting of a cross-bar suspended by cords, for gymnastic exercises.

traumatic, trä-mat'ik, *a.* Pertaining to wounds.—*n.* A medicine useful in the cure of wounds.

travel, tra'vel, *n.* Act of journeying; journey to a distant country; *pl.* account of occurrences during a journey.—*vi.* (travelling, travelled). To journey; to go to a distant country; to pass; to move.

travelling, tra'vel-ing, *p.a.* Pertaining to, used in, or incurred by travel.

traverse, tra'vérs, *a.* Transverse.— *n.* Something that is transverse; something that thwarts, a denial.—*vt.* (traversing, traversed). To cross; to thwart; to cross in travelling; to deny.—*adv.* Athwart; crosswise.

travesty, tra'ves-ti, *vt.* (travestying travestied) To transform so as to have a ludicrous effect, to burlesque.—*n.* A burlesque treatment; parody.

tread, tred, *vi.* (pret. trod, pp. trod trodden). To set the foot on the ground; to step; to walk with a measured step, to copulate, as fowls.—*vt.* To plant the foot on; to trample, to dance; to walk on in a formal manner; to copulate with as a bird.—*n.* A step; gait; horizontal part of the step of a stair.

treasure, tre'zhür, *n.* Wealth accumulated; great abundance; something very much valued.—*vt.* (treasuring, treasured). To lay up or collect; to prize.

treatise, trē'tiz, *n.* A written composition on some particular subject; a dissertation.

treatment, trēt'ment, *n.* Act or manner of treating; management; usage.

treaty, trē'ti, *n.* Negotiation; agreement between two or more nations.

tremendous, trē-men'dus, *a.* Such as may cause trembling; terrible; extraordinary.

trench, trensh, *vt.* To dig a ditch into turn over and mix, as soil.—*vi.* To cut a trench or trenches; to encroach (with *on* or upon).—*n.* A long narrow excavation; a deep ditch cut for defense.

trepidation, tre-pid-ā'shon, *n.* Confused alarm; perturbation; involuntary trembling.

trespass, tres'pas, *vi.* To enter unlawfully upon the land of another; to do wrong; to offend.—*n.* An offense; a sin; wrong done by entering on the land of another.

tribune, trī'būn, *n.* Among the ancient Romans, a magistrate chosen by the people, to protect them from the patricians; a platform; tribunal, throne of a bishop.

tributary, tri'bū-ta-ri, *a.* Paying tribute to another; subject; contributing.—*n.* One that pays tribute; a stream which falls into another.

tribute, tri'būt, *n.* A sum paid by one prince or nation to another; personal contribution.

trick, trik, *n.* An artifice; a crafty device; fraud; a knack or art; a personal practice or habit, a prank; all the cards played in one round.—*vt.* To deceive; to impose on, to cheat, to draw in outline; to dress; to adorn (often with out).

trident, trī'dent, *n.* Any instrument of the form of a fork with three prongs.

trifle, trī'fl, *n.* Something of no moment or value, a kind of fancy confection.— *vi.* (trifling, trifled). To act with levity; to play or toy; to finger lightly.—*vt.* To waste.

trilith, trilithon, trī'lith, trī'lith-on *n.* Three large blocks of stone placed together like door-posts and a lintel, and standing by themselves, as in sundry ancient monuments.

trill, tril, *n.* A shake of the voice in singing; a quavering sound.—*vt.* To sing with a quavering voice, to sing sweetly or clearly.—*vi.* To sound with tremulous vibrations; to pipe; to trickle.

trillion, tril 'yon, *n.* The product of a million multiplied twice by itself.

trilogy, tril'o-ji, *n.* A series of three connected dramas, each complete in itself

trim, trim, *vt.* (trimming, trimmed). To put in order; to embellish, to clip or pare; to adjust.—*vi.* To hold a middle course between parties.—*a.* Set in good order; properly adjusted, neat, tidy.—*n.* Condition; order; mood, dress.

trio, trī'o or trē'o, *n.* Three united; musical composition for three voices or instruments, performers of a trio.

trip, trip, *vi.* (tripping, tripped). To run or step lightly, to skip, to stumble; to err.—*vt.* To cause to fall or stumble; to loose an anchor.—*n.* A stumble, a light short step; an excursion or jaunt, a mistake.

triplicate, tri'pli-kāt, *a.* Threefold. *n.* A third thing corresponding to two others.

Trojan, trō'jan, *a.* Pertaining to ancient Troy.—*n.* An inhabitant of ancient Troy; a jolly fellow; a plucky determined fellow.

troop, tröp, *n.* A collection of people; a company; a body of soldiers; *pl.* soldiers in general, a troupe.—*vi.* To collect in numbers; to march in a body.

trophy, trō'fi, *n.* A memorial of some victory, an architectural ornament representing the stem of a tree, hung with military weapons.

Tropic, tro'pik, n. Either of two circles on the celestial sphere, limiting the sun's apparent annual path; either of two corresponding parallels of latitude including the torrid zone, pl. the regions between or near these.—a. Pertaining to the tropics

trot, trot, vi. (trotting, trotted). To run with small steps; to move fast.—vt. To cause to trot.—n. Pace of a horse more rapid than a walk

troubadour, trö'ba-dör, n. one of a class of poets who flourished in S. Europe, especially in Provence, from the eleventh to the end of the thirteenth century.

trouble, tru'bl, vt. (troubling, troubled). To disturb, to distress to busy.—n. Distress, agitation; affliction; labor.

trowel, trou'el, n. A hand-tool for lifting and dressing mortar and plaster etc., a gardener's tool.—vt. (troweliing, trowelled) To dress or form with a trowel

troy, troy-weight, troi, troi'wāt, n. A weight used for gold and silver divided into 12 ounces, each of 20 pennyweights, each of 24 grains, so that a pound troy = 5760 grains.

truant, trö'ant, n. One who shirks duty, one who stays from school without leave.—a. Idle; wilfully absenting oneself.

truck, truk, vi. and t. To barter.—n. Exchange of commodities; barter; payment of workmen's wages partly in goods, a small wheel, a barrow with two low wheels; an open railway wagon for goods, a motor driven vehicle used to carry heavy loads or general freight; the cap at the end of a flagstaff or topmast.

true, trö, a. Conformable to fact; truthful, genuine, constant, faithful; loyal; honest; exact; correct; right.

trump, trump, n. A winning card one of a suit for the time being superior to the others; a person upon whom one can depend, a trumpet.—vt. To take with a trump card; to concoct or forge.

trunk, trungk, n. The woody stem of a tree; body of an animal without the limbs, main body, chest for containing clothes, etc.; a long wooden tube.

truss, trus, n. A bundle, as of hay or straw; a bandage used in cases of rupture, a combination of timbers constitut-ing an unyielding frame.—vt. To put in a bundle; to make tight or fast, to skewer.

trust, trust, n. Reliance; confidence; hope; credit; that which is entrusted; safekeeping; care; management.—vt. To rely on; to believe, to intrust, to sell to upon credit, to be confident.—vi. To have reliance; to confide readily.—a. Held in trust.

trustee, trus-tē', n. One appointed to hold property for the benefit of those entitled to it.

trustworthy, trust'wèr-THi, a. Worthy of trust or confidence, faithful reliable.

try, trī, vt. (trying, tried). To test; to make trial of, to afflict; to examine judicially; to attempt.—vi. To endeavor.—n. The act of trying; a trial, experiment, in Rugby *football,* the right of trying to kick a goal obtained by carrying the ball behind the opponents' goal line and touching it down.

tub, tub, n. An open wooden vessel a small cask, a clumsy boat, a vessel used as a bath.—vt. (tubbing, tubbed). To set in a tub.—vi. To make use of a bathing-tub.

tunic, tū'nik, n. A garment of various kinds; an ecclesiastical vestment worn over the alb; a full-dress military coat; a covering membrane; an integument.

turbine, tèr'bĭn, n. A kind of waterwheel, usually horizontal, made to revolve under the influence of pressure derived from a fall of water; a similar contrivance driven by steam.

turmeric, tèr'mer-ik, n. An E. Indian plant of the ginger family yielding a condiment, a yellow dye, and a test for alkalies.

turn, tèrn, vt. To cause to move round; to shape by a lathe; to direct; to alter in course; to blunt; to reverse; to change.—vi. To revolve; to depend; to change position or course; to return; to have recourse; to become; to become sour; to reel; to become nauseated; to result.—n. Act of turning; a revolution; bend; a short walk; an alteration of course; occasion; occasional act of kindness or malice; purpose; character; short spell, as a work; nervous shock.

turnstile, tèrn'stĭl, n. A post at some passage surmounted by horizontal arms which move as a person pushes through.

turtle, tèr'tl, n. A species of small pigeon; the sea-tortoise.

T

tutor, tū'tor, *n.* A guardian; a private instructor; a fellow of an English college who superintend the studies of undergraduates.—*vt.* To instruct.

typesetter, tīp'set-ėr, *n.* One who sets up type; a compositor; a typesetting machine.

typewriter, tīp'rīt-ėr, *n.* A machine used as a substitute for the pen, producing letters by inked types.

typhoon, tī-fön', *n.* A violent hurricane on the coasts of China and Japan.

typical, tip'ik-al, *a.* Pertaining to a type; emblematic; symbolic; representative.

typographic, typographical, tī-pograf'ik, tī-po-graf'ik-al, *a.* Pertaining to typography or printing.

typology, tī-pol'o-ji, *n.* A discourse on types; the doctrine of types in Scripture.

tyranny, ti'ran-i, *n.* Rule of a tyrant; despotic exercise of power; oppression.

U

ubiety, ū-bî'e-ti, *n.* The state of being somewhere.

ubiquity, ū-bi'kwi-ti, *n.* Existence everywhere at the same time; omnipresence.

udder, ud'ėr, *n.* The glandular organ of cows, etc., in which the milk is produced.

ugly, ug'li, *a.* Repulsive; disagreeable in appearance; hateful; ill-omened.

ukulele, ū'kü-lā'lē, *n.* A small Hawaiian guitar.

ulcer, ul'sėr, *n.* A sore that discharges pus.

ultimatum, ul-ti-mā'tum, *n.; pl.* **-ta** or **-tums.** The last offer, a final proposition which being rejected may be followed by war.

ultra, ul'tra, *prefix a.* Beyond due limit, extreme.—*n.* An ultraist.

ultramarine, ul'tra-ma-rēn", *a.* Being beyond the sea.—*n.* A beautiful and durable sky-blue.

umbrage, um'brā j, *n.* Shade; obscurity; jealousy; offense; resentment.

umbrella, um-brel'la, *n.* A portable shade which opens and folds, for sheltering the person from the sun or rain.

umlaut, um'lout, *n.* The change of a vowel in one syllable through the influence of a different vowel in the syllable immediately following.

umpire, um'pîr, *n.* A person to whose decision a dispute is referred; a judge, arbiter, or referee.

unable, un-ā'bl, *a.* Not able, not having sufficient ability; not equal for some task.

unacceptable, un-ak-sept'a-bl, *a.* Not acceptable or pleasing; unwelcome.

unadorned, un-a-dornd', *a.* Not adorned; not embellished.

unadvisable, un-ad-vîz'a-bl, *a.* Not advisable; not expedient; not prudent.

unaffected, un-af-fekt'ed, *a.* Not affected; natural; simple; sincere; not moved.

unalterable, un-äl'tėr-a-bl, *a.* Not alterable; unchangeable; immutable.

unanimous, ū-nan'i-mus, *a.* Being of one mind; agreeing in determination, formed by unanimity

unauthorized, un-a'thor-î zd, *a.* Not authorized; not warranted.

unavailable, un-a-vāl'a-bl, *a.* Not available, vain; useless.

unbroken, un-brōk'n, *a.* Not broken: not tamed' not interrupted.

uncalled, un-käld', *a.* Not called; not summoned; not invited.

uncanny, un-kan'i, *a.* Not canny mysterious; of evil and supernatural character.

uncared, un-kā rd', *a.* Not regarded; not heeded; often with *for.*

uncle, ung'kl, *n.* The brother of one's father or mother

unclean, un-klēn' *a.* Not clean; foul; dirty; morally impure, lewd.

uncomfortable, un-kum'fort-a-bl, *a.* Not comfortable; uneasy; ill at ease.

uncommon, un-kom'mon, *a.* Not common; rare; strange; remarkable.

unconditional, un-kon-di'shon-al, *a.* Not limited by conditions; absolute.

unconscious, un-kon'shus, *a.* Not conscious; not perceiving; un-aware.

unconstitutional, un-kon'sti-tū'' shon-al, *a.* Not agreeable to the constitution, against the law.

uncover, un-ku'vėr, *vt.* To divest of a cover; to disclose.—*vi.* To take off the hat.

unction, ungk'shon, *n.* Act of anointing; an unguent; religious fervor; sham devotional fervor; oiliness.

unctuous, ung'tū-us, *a.* Oily; greasy; nauseously emotional; oily; fawning.

under, un'dėr, *prep.* Below; beneath; undergoing; affected by; subject to; inferior; during the time of, included in, in accordance with.—*adv.* In a lower condition or degree.—*a.* Lower; subject; subordinate.

underclothes, underclothing, un'dėr-klōTHz, un'dėr-klōTH-ing, *n.* Clothes worn under others or next to the skin.

undercurrent un'dėr-ku-rent, *n.* A current below another; some movement or influence not apparent.

undergo, un'dėr-gō, *vt.* To bear; to experience; to suffer.

undergraduate, un-dėr-grad'ū-āt, *n.* A student who has not taken his first degree.

underground, un'dėr-ground, *a* and *adv.* Below the surface of the ground, operating in secret.

undergrowth, un'dėr-grōth, *n.* Shrubs or small trees growing among large ones.

underhand, un'dėr-hand, *a.* Working by stealth; secret; deceitful.— *adv.* In a clandestine manner.

understand, un-dėr-stand', *vt.* To comprehend; to see through; to suppose to mean, to infer; to assume; to recognize as implied although not expressed.—*vi.* To comprehend, to learn.

undertake, un'dėr-tāk, *vt.* To take in hand; to engage in; to attempt; to guarantee.—*vi.* To take upon oneself; to promise; to stand bound.

undertaker, un'dėr-tāk-ėr, *n.* One who undertakes; one who manages funerals.

underwear, un'dėr-wār, *n.* Under-clothes.

underworld, un'dėr-wėrld, *n.* The lower world; this world; the antipodes; the place of departed souls; Hades.

underwrite, un-dėr-rīt, *vt.* To write under, to subscribe one's name and become answerable for a certain amount.

undisturbed, un-dis-tėrbd', *a.* Free from disturbance; calm; tranquil; not agitated.

undivided, un-di-vīd'ed, *a.* Not divided; whole; entire.

undo, un-dö', *vt.* To reverse what has been done; annul; to loose; to take to pieces; to ruin.

undying, un-dī'ing, *a.* Not dying; imperishable.

unearned, un-ėrnd', *a.* Not merited by labor or services.—**unearned increment,** the increase in the value of property not due to any expenditure on the part of the owner.

unearth, un-ėrth', *vt.* To drive or bring from the earth; to uncover; to discover.

unequal, un-ē'kwal, *a.* Not equal inadequate; insufficient; not equable.

unequivocal, un-ē-kwiv'ō-kal, *a.* Not equivocal; not doubtful; clear; evident.

unerring un-er'ing, *a.* Not erring; incapable of error; certain.

uneven, un-ē'vn, *a.* Not even or level, rough; crooked; not fair or just; odd.

unexpected, un-eks-pekt'ed, *a.* Not expected, not looked for; sudden.

unexpired, un-eks-pīrd', *a.* Not expired; not having come to the end of its term.

unexplored, un-eks-plör'd', *a.* Not explored; not visited by any traveller.

unfading, un-fād'ing, *a.* Not fading; not liable to wither or decay; ever fresh.

unfailing, un-fāl'ing, *a.* Not liable to fail, that does not fail; certain.

unfair, un-fār', *a.* Not honest or impartial; not just; inequitable; disingenuous.

unfamiliar, un-fa-mil'i-ėr, *a.* Not familiar; not accustomed; strange.

unfasten, un-fäs'n, *vt.* To loose; to unfix.

unforgiving, un-for-giv'ing, *a.* Not forgiving, implacable.

unfortunate, un-for'tū-nāt, *a.* Not fortunate; unlucky; unhappy.—*n.* One who is unfortunate; a prostitute.

unfounded, un-found'ed, *a.* Having no real foundation; groundless: idle.

ungrateful, un-grāt'ful, *a.* Not grateful; not thankful, unpleasing, harsh.

ungrounded, un-ground'ed, *a.* Having no foundation or support; groundless.

unguarded, un-gärd'ed, *a.* Not guarded; not cautious; negligent.

unguent, un'gwent, *n.* An ointment.

unhinge, un-hinj', *vt.* To take from the hinges; to unfix; to loosen; to derange.

unholy, un-hō'li, *a.* Not holy; not sacred; unhallowed; profane; impious; wicked.

unicorn ū'ni-korn, *n.* A fabulous anima; like a horse, with a long single horn on the forehead.

unification, ū'ni-fī-kā''shon, *n.* The act of unifying or uniting into one.

uniform, ū'ni-form, *a.* Having always one and the same form equable; invariable; consistent.—*n.* A distinctive dress worn by the members of the same body.

uniformity, ū-ni-for'mi-ti, *n.* State or character of being uniform; conformity to one type; agreement; consistency.

unify, ū'ni-fi, *vt.* To form into one.

unimaginable, un-im-aj'in-a-bl, *a.* Not imaginable; inconceivable.

unimpaired, un-im-pā rd', *a.* Not impaired; not diminished; uninjured.

unimpassioned, un-im-pa'shond, *a.* Not impassioned; tranquil; not violent.

unimpeachable, un-im-pēch'a-bl, *a.* Not impeachable; blameless; irreproachable.

uninterrupted, un-in'tėr-rupt''ed, *a.* Not interrupted; unintermitted; incessant.

uninviting, un-in-vīt'ing, *a'* Not inviting; unattractive; rather repellent.

union, ū n'yon, *n.* Act of joining; combination; agreement; harmony; marriage; confederacy; a trades-union, a mixed fabric of cotton, flax, jute, silk, or wool, etc.; a certain kind of flag.

uniparous, ū-nip'a-rus, *a.* Producing one at a birth.

unique, ū-nēk', *a.* Without a like or equal, unmatched, unequalled.

unison, ū-ni-son, *n.* Accordance agreement; harmony; concord.

unit, ū'nit, *n.* A single thing or person; an individual; the number 1; a dimension or quantity assumed as a standard.

Unitarian, ū-ni-tā'ri-an, *n.* One who ascribes divinity to God only and denies the Trinity.—*a.* Pertaining to Unitarians.

unite, ū-nīt', *vt.* (uniting, united). To combine, to connect, to associate.—*vi.* To become one; to combine, to concur.

unlike, un-līk', *a.* Not like; dissimilar;

having no resemblance; diverse.

unmanageable, un-man'āj-a-bl, *a.* Not manageable; beyond control.

unmerciful, un-mėr'si-fül, *a.* Not merciful; cruel; merciless.

unmerited, un-mer'it-ed, *a.* Not deserved.

unmindful, un-mīnd'fül, *a.* Not mindful, regardless.

unnerve, un-nėrv', *vt.* To deprive of nerve, strength, or composure; to enfeeble.

unnoticed, un-nōt'ist, *a.* Not observed.

unobjectionable, un-ob-jek'shon-abl, *a.* Not liable to objection; unexceptionable.

unobservant, unobserving, un-obzėrv'ant, un-ob-zėrv'ing, *a.* Not observant.

unobtrusive, un-ob-trö'siv, *a.* Not obtrusive; not forward; modest; retiring.

unorthodox, un-ȯr'tho-doks, *a.* Not orthodox; heterodox.

unpleasant, un-ple'zant, *a.* Not pleasant.

unpolished, un-po'lisht *a.* Not polished; rude, plain.

unpopular, un-po'pū-lėr, *a.* Not popular.

unprecedented, un-pre'sē-dent-ed, *a.* Having no precedent; unexampled.

unprincipled, un-prin'si-pld, *a.* Not having settled principles; immoral.

unqualified, un-kwo'li-fīd, *a.* Not qualified, not having the requisite qualifications, not modified by conditions.

unquestionable, un-kwest'yon-abl, *a.* Not to be called in question indubitable.

unravel, un-ra'vel, *vt.* To disentangle; to disengage or separate; to solve.

unreadable, un-rēd'a-bl, *a* Incapable of being read; illegible; not worth reading.

unreal, un-rē'al, *a.* Not real, not substantial.

unreason, un-rē'zn, *n.* Want of reason; folly, absurdity.

unrequited, un-rē-kwī'ed, *a.* Not requited, not recompensed.

unreserved, un-rē-zėrvd', *a.* Not reserved or restricted; full; free; open, frank.

unrest, un-rest', *n.* Disquiet; uneasiness.

unrestrained, un-rē-strānd', *a.* Not restrained; licentious; loose.

unrighteous, un-rīt'yus, *a.* Not righteous, not just, wicked.

unripe, un-rīp', *a.* Not ripe; not mature; not fully prepared; not completed.

unsavory, un-sā'vo-ri, *a.* Not savory; insipid; unpleasing; offensive.

unscathed, un-skāTHd', *a.* Not scathed, uninjured.

unscrew, un-skrö', *vt.* To draw the screw from; to unfasten by screwing back.

unscrupulous, un-skrö'pū-lus, *a.* Having no scruples; regardless of principle.

unseasonable, un-sē'zn-a-bl, *a.* Not seasonable; ill-timed; untimely.

unsound, un-sound', *a.* Not sound; erroneous; not orthodox.

unsparing, un-spār'ing, *a.* Not sparing; profuse; severe, rigorous.

unspeakable, un-spēk'a-bl, *a.* Incapable of being spoken or uttered; unutterable.

unspoken, un-spō'kn, *a.* Not spoken.

unstable, un-stā'bl, *a.* Not stable; inconstant, irresolute, wavering.

unsteady, un-sted'i, *a.* Not steady shaking, fickle; varying.

unstop, un-stop', *vt.* To free from a stopper, as a bottle; to free from obstruction.

unstrung, un-strung', *a.* Deprived of strings; having the nerves shaken.

unsuccessful, un-suk-ses'ful, *a.* Not successful; not fortunate in the result.

unsuitable, un-sūt'a-bl, *a.* Not suitable; ill adapted; unfit.

unsung, un-sung', *a.* Not sung; not celebrated in song or poetry.

untenable, un-ten'a-bl, *a.* Not to be maintained by argument; not defensible.

unthinkable, un-thingk'a-bl, *a.* That cannot be made an object of thought.

unthinking, un-thingk'ing, *a.* Not given to think; not heedful; inconsiderate.

unthread, un-thred', *vt.* To draw or take out a thread from.

untie, un-tī', *vt.* (untying, untied). To loosen, as a knot; to undo; to unfasten.

untrue, un-trö', *a.* Not true; false.

unwieldy, un-wel'di, *n.* Movable with difficulty, unmanageable.

unwilling, un-wil'ing, *a.* Not willing; loath; disinclined; reluctant.

unwise, un-wīz', *a.* Not wise; injudicious.

unwitting, un-wit'ing, *a.* Not knowing; unconscious; unaware.

unwrap, un-rap', *vt.* To open or undo, as what is wrapped up.

unwritten, un-rit'n, *a.* Not written; blank; understood though not expressed.

up, up, *adv.* Aloft, in or to a higher position; upright; above the horizon; out of bed, in a state of sedition; from the country to the metropolis; quite; to or at an end.—*prep.* To a higher place or point on towards the interior of.

upland, up'land, *n.* Higher grounds; hillslopes.—*a.* Pertaining to uplands.

upmost, up'most, *a.* Highest; uppermost.

upper, up'ėr, *a.* Higher in place or rank.— *n.* The upper part of a shoe.

upset, up-set', *vt.* To overturn, to discompose completely.—*n.* up'set. Act of upsetting.—*a.* Fixed, determined.— **upset price,** the price at which anything is exposed to sale by auction.

upstairs, up'stärz, *a.* or *adv.* Ascending the stairs; in or pertaining to the upper part of a house.

upward, up'werd, *a.* Directed to a higher place; ascending.—*adv.* upwards.

Uranus, ū'ra-nus, *n.* The most distant of all the planets except Neptune and Pluto.

urban, ėr'ban, *a.* Of or belonging to a city or town.

urbane, ėr-bān', *a.* Courteous; polite.

urchin, ėr'chin, *n.* A hedgehog; a sea-urchin, a child or small boy.

urine, ū'rin, *n.* An animal fluid secreted by the kidneys and stored in the bladder before being discharged.

urn, ėrn, *n.* A vase swelling in the middle; a vessel for water.

usable, ūz'a-bl, *a.* That may be used.

usage, ūz'āj, *n.* Act or manner of using; treatment; practice; custom, use.

use, ūs, *n.* Act of employing anything; employment; utility; need; practice, wont.—*vt.* uz (using used). To put to use; to employ; to accustom, to treat.— *vi.* To be accustomed.

usher, ush'ėr, *n.* A door-keeper; an officer who introduces strangers etc.; a subordinate teacher.—*vt.* To give entrance to, to introduce.

utmost, ut'mōst, *a.* Being farthest out; uttermost; extreme.—*n.* The greatest power, degree, or effort.

utter, ut'ėr, *a.* Complete, total, absolute.— *vt.* To give vent to; to put into circulation; to declare; to speak.

uvula, ū'vū-la, *n.* The small fleshy body which hangs over the root of the tongue.

V

vacant, vā'kant, *a*. Empty; void; unoccupied; leisure; thoughtless; inane.

vacate, va-kāt', *vt*. (vacating, vacated;. To make vacant; to leave unoccupied; to annul.

vacuum, va'kū-um, *n*. Empty space, a void; an enclosed space void of air.— **vacuum cleaner**, *n*. An apparatus used for removing dust from carpets, etc., by means of suction.

vagabond, va'ga-bond, *a*. Wandering to and fro; pertaining to a vagrant.—*n*. A wanderer; a vagrant; a rascal.

vagrant, vā'grant, *a*. Wandering; unsettled.—*n*. A wanderer; a vagabond; a sturdy beggar; a tramp.

vain, vān, *a*. Without real value; empty, worthless, ineffectual light-minded; conceited.—**In vain**, to no purpose.

valance, valence, val'ans, val'ens, *n*. The drapery hanging round a bed, couch, etc.

value, va'lū , *n*. Worth; utility; importance; import; precise signification.—*vt*. (valuing, valued). To rate at a certain price; to estimate; to esteem, to prize; to regard.

valve, valv, *n*. A leaf of a folding door; a lid for an orifice, opening only one way and regulating the passage of fluid or air; a separate portion of the shell of a mollusk.

vandal, van'dal, *n*. One who willfully or ignorantly destroys any work of art or the like.

vane, vān, *n*. A weathercock; the broad part of a feather on either side of the shaft; blade of a windmill, etc.

vanity, va'ni-ti, *n*. Quality or state of being vain; worthlessness; vain pursuit; desire of indiscriminate admiration, conceit, a trifle.

variable, vā'ri-a-bl, *a*. That may vary or alter; changeable; fickle; unsteady.

varicose, va'ri-kōs, *a*. Exhibiting a morbid enlargement or dilation, as the veins.

variety, va-rī'e-ti, *n*. State or quality of being varied or various; diversity; a varied assortment; a sort; a kind.

various, vā'ri-us, *a*. Different, several; changeable; uncertain; diverse.

varnish, vär'nish, *n*. A clear solution of resinous matter, for coating surfaces and giving a gloss; outside show; gloss.—*vt*. To la varnish on; to gloss over.

vary, vā'ri, *vt*. (varying, varied). To change; to diversify.—*vi*. To alter; to change; to differ; to swerve; to disagree.

vascular, vas'kū-lėr, *a*. Pertaining to those vessels that have to do with conveying blood, chyle, etc.

vase, vāz, *n*. A vessel of some size and of various materials and forms, generally ornamental rather than useful.

vast, väst, *a*. Of great extent; immense; mighty; great in importance or degree.—*n*. A boundless space, immensity.

vein, vān, *n*. A blood-vessel which returns impure blood to the heart and lungs, a blood-vessel, a sap tube in leaves; a crack in a rock, filled up by substances different from the rock, a streak; disposition; mood.—*vt*. To fill or variegate with veins.

veneer, ve-nēr', *n*. A thin facing of fine wood glued on *h* less valuable sort, any similar coating; fair outward show.—*vt*. To overlay with veneer; to put a fine superficial show on.

venerate, ve'nė-rāt, *vt*. (venerating, venerated). To reverence, to revere; to regard as sacred.

Venetian, vē-nē'shi-an, *a*. Belonging to Venice, denoting a window blind made of thin slats of wood.

vengeance, venj'ans, *n*. Punishment in return for an injury; penal retribution.

vent, vent, *n*. A small opening; flue or funnel; an outlet; the anus; utterance, expression, sale market.—*vt*. To let out; to publish.

ventilate, ven'ti-lāt, *vt*. (ventilating, ventilated). To winnow to expose to the air; to supply with fresh air to let be freely discussed.

venture, ven'tūr, *n*. An undertaking which involves hazard or danger; a commercial speculation; thing put to hazard, chance.—*vi*. (venturing, ventured). To make a venture, to dare.—*vt*. To risk.

venue, ven'ū, *n*. A thrust, the place where an action is laid or the trial of a cause takes place.

verdant, vėr'dant, *a*. Green with herbage or foliage; simple and inexperienced.

verify, ve'ri-fī, *vt*. (verifying, verified). To prove to be true, to confirm, to fulfill.

vermifuge, vėr'mi-fūj, *n*. A medicine that expels intestinal worms.

vermilion, vėr-mil'yon, *n*. Cinnabar or red

V

sulfide of mercury; a beautiful red color.—*vt.* To color with vermilion.

vermin, vėr'min, *n. sing.* and *pl.* A term for all sorts of small noxious mammals or insects.

versatile, vėrs'a-til, *a.* Readily turning; inconstant; having many accomplishments.

versatility, vėrs-a-til'i-ti, *n.* Aptness to change, facility in taking up various intellectual pursuits.

verse, vėrs, *n.* A line of poetry; meter, poetry, versification, a stanza a short division of any composition.

vertebrata, vėr-te-brā'ta, *n.pl.* The highest division of animals, consisting of those which possess a backbone.

vertebrate, vėr'te-brāt, *a.* Having a backbone.—*n.* One of the vertebrata

vertical, vėr'ti-kal, *a.* Pertaining to the vertex, directly over the head perpendicular to the horizon; upright.

vertiginous, vėr-ti'jin-us, *a.* Giddy or dizzy; affected with vertigo.

vertigo, vėr-tĭ-gō or vėr'ti-gō, *n.* Dizziness or swimming of the head; giddiness.

very, ve'ri, *a.* True, real; actual.—*adv.* Truly; in a great or high degree.

vesical, ve'si-kal, *a.* Pertaining to the bladder

vesicate, ve'si kāt, *vt.* To blister.

vesicle, ve 'si-kl, *n.* A small bladder-like structure or cavity; a little sac or cyst.

vesper, ves'pėr, *n.* The evening, the evening-star; *pl.* evening worship or service.—*a.* Relating to the evening or to vespers.

vessel, ves'el, *n.* A hollow utensil for holding liquids or solids, a ship a tube or canal for blood or sap; a person.

vest, vest, *n.* Undergarment for the upper part of the body; a waistcoat.—*vt.* To clothe, to endow, to invest.—*vi.* To descend to; to devolve; to take effect, as a title or right.

vested, vest'ed, *a.* Clothed or habited; robed; well settled or established.

veterinary, ve'te-ri-na-ri, *a.* Pertaining to the art of healing the diseases of domestic animals.

veto, vē'tō, *n.* The power or right of forbidding; any authoritative prohibition or refusal.—*vt.* (vetoing vetoed). To forbid, to interdict.

via, vī'a, *prep.* By way of.

viable, vī 'a bl, *a.* Capable of living applied to a new-born child.

vicarious, vī-kā'ri-us, *a.* Pertaining to a substitute; deputed, substituted or suf-

fered for or in the place of another.

vice, vīs, *n.* A blemish; fault; moral failing; profligacy; a fault or bad trick in a horse, an iron instrument which holds fast anything worked upon, a prefix denoting position second in rank.

vicious, vi'shus, *a.* Characterized by vice; faulty; depraved; immoral; spiteful.

vicissitude, vi-sis'i-tūd, *n.* Change or alternation; one of the ups and downs of life.

victim, vik'tim, *n.* A living being sacrificed. a person or thing destroyed; a person who suffers; a gull.

victory, vik'to-ri, *n.* Conquest, a gaining of the superiority in any contest.

view, vū, *n.* A look, inspection; consideration; range of vision; power of perception; sight; scene; pictorial sketch, judgment; intention.—*vt.* To see; to survey; to consider.—*vi.* To look.

vigil, vi'jil, *n.* Act of keeping awake; a devotional watching; the eve or day preceding a church festival.

vignette, vin-yet' or vi-net', *n.* Flowers, head and tail pieces, etc. in books; a wood cut without a definite border; a small photographic portrait; a small attractive picture.

vigorous, vi'gor-us, *a.* Full of vigor; strong; lusty; powerful; energetic.

vindicate, vin'di-kat, *vt.* (vindicating, vindicated). To prove to be just or valid; to maintain the rights of; to defend to justify.

vinegar, vi'nē-gėr, *n.* Diluted and impure acetic acid, obtained from wine, beer, etc.; sourness of temper

vintage, vint'āj, *n.* The gathering of the grape crop; the crop itself the wine produced by the grapes of one season.

vintner, vint'nėr, *n.* One who deals in wine; a wine-seller; a licensed victualler.

violation, vī-ō-lā'shon, *n.* Infringement; transgression; desecration; rape.

violence, vī 'ō-lens, *n.* Quality of being violent; vehemence; outrage; injury.

violin, vī-ō-lin', *n.* A musical instrument with four strings, played with a bow, a fiddle.

virgin, vėr'jin, *n.* A woman who has had no carnal knowledge of man, a maid; a sign of the zodiac.—*a.* Chaste; maidenly, unsullied.

Virgo, vėr'gō, *n.* The Virgin in the zodiac.

virile, vi'ril or vi'ril, *a.* Pertaining to a man; masculine; manly; strong.

virility, vi-ril'i-ti, *n.* Manhood; the power

virtual

of procreation; masculine action or vigor.

virtual, ver'tū-al, *a.* Being in essence or effect, not in name or fact.

virtue, ver'tū, *n.* Moral goodness; rectitude; morality; chastity; merit; efficacy.

virtuoso, vėr-tū-ō'sō, *n.;* pl. **-osos** or **-osi.** A man skilled in the fine arts or antiquities, curiosities, etc.

virtuous, vėr'tū-us, *a.* Marked by virtue; morally good; pure or chaste.

visible, vi'zi-bl, *a.* Perceivable by the eye; apparent; open; conspicuous.

visionary, vi'zhon-a-ri, *a.* Pertain-ing to visions; imaginative; imaginary, not real.—*n.* One who is visionary; one who upholds impracticable schemes.

visit, vi'zit, *vt.* To go or come to see to view officially, to afflict.—*vi.* To practice going to see others; to make calls.—*n.* Act of visiting; a call.

vitamin, vī'ta-min, *n.* One of several substances necessary for animal nutrition, and occurring in minute quantities in natural foods; numerous types have been distinguished, and designated by the letters of the alphabet.

vivacious, vī-vā'shus or vi-, *a.* Lively; brisk; sprightly; tenacious of life.

vocal, vō'kal, *a.* Pertaining to the voice; uttered by the voice; endowed with a voice; having a vowel character.

voice, vois *n.* The sound uttered by the mouth; articulate human utterance; state of vocal organs; speech; sound emitted; right of expressing an opinion; vote; a form of verb inflection.—*vt.* (voicing, voiced). To utter or express; to declare.

void, void, *a.* Empty; devoid; ineffectual, null.—*n.* An empty space.—*vt.* To make vacant; to quit; to nullify; to emit; to evacuate from the bowels.

volley, vol'i, *n.* A discharge of a number of missile weapons, as small-arms, emission of many things at once.—*vt.* and *i.* To discharge or be discharged in a volley, to sound like a volley, to strike and return a ball (in lawn-tennis, etc.) before it touches the ground.

volt, vōlt, *n.* A sudden movement in fencing to avoid a thrust; the unit of electromotive force.

volume, vo'lūm, *n.* Something rolled up; a book; a coil; a convolution; mass or bulk; quantity or strength.

voluntary, vo'lun-ta-ri, *a.* Willing; free to act, spontaneous, regulated by the will.—*n.* A volunteer, a supporter of voluntaryism; an organ solo during a church service.

volunteer, vo-lun-tēr' *n.* A person who enters into military or other service of his own free will.—*a.* Pertaining to volunteers.—*vt.* To offer or bestow voluntarily.—*vi.* To enter into any service voluntarily.

vortex, vor'teks, *n.;* pl. **-tices** or **-texes.** A whirling motion in any fluid; a whirlpool or a whirlwind; an eddy.

votary, vō'ta-ri, *n.* One who is bound by a vow; one devoted to some particular service, state of life, etc.

vote, vōt, *n.* Act or power of expressing opinion or choice; a suffrage; thing conferred by vote; result of voting; votes collectively.—*vi.* (voting, voted). To give a vote.—*vt.* To choose or grant by vote.

votive, vō't'iv, *a.* Pertaining to a vow; promised or given, in consequence of a vow.

vowel, vou'el, n. A sound produced by opening the mouth and giving utterance to voice; the letter which represents such a sound.—*a.* Pertaining to a vowel; vocal.

vulgar, vul'gėr, *a.* Pertaining to the common people; vernacular; common; coarse.—**The vulgar,** the common people.

V

W

wad, wod, *n.* A soft mass of fibrous material used for stuffing; material for stopping the charge in a gun.—*vt.* (wadding, wadded). To furnish with a wad or wadding.

waddle, wod'l, *vi.* (waddling, waddled). To walk with a rolling gait; to toddle.

wade, wād, *vi.* (wading, waded). To walk through a substance that hinders the lower limbs, as water to move or pass with labor.—*vt.* To ford.

wafer, wā'fėr, *n.* A thin cake, as of bread; a thin disc of paste for fastening letters.—*vt.* To seal with a wafer.

wagon, waggon, wag'on, *n.* A four-wheeled vehicle for heavy loads.

waif, wāf, *n.* A stray article; a neglected, homeless wretch.

wail, wāl, *vt.* To lament; to bewail. —*vi.* To weep.—*n.* A mournful cry or sound.

wait, wāt, *vi.* To stay in expectation; to continue in patience, to attend; to serve at table.—*vt.* To await.—*n.* Act of waiting; ambush, a musician who promenades in the night about Christmas time.

waiter, wāt'ėr, *n.* One who waits; a male attendant; a small tray or salver.

waitress, wāt'res, *n.* A female waiter.

waive, wāv, *vt.* (waiving, waived). To relinquish; to forgo.

walk, wäk, *vi.* To advance by steps without running; to go about; to behave.— *vt.* To pass over or through on foot, to lead about.—*n.* A short excursion on foot; gait; an avenue, promenade, etc.; sphere; way of living; tract of ground for grazing.

wallow, wol'ō, *vi.* To tumble and roll in water or mire; to live in filth or gross vice.

walnut, wäl-nut, *n.* A valuable tree, a native of Persia; the edible nut of the tree.

walrus, wol'rus, *n.* A huge marine carnivorous mammal inhabiting the arctic seas.

waltz, wälts, *n.* A kind of dance for two persons; music for the dance.—*vi.* To dance a waltz.

wand, wond, *n.* A long flexible stick; a rod; a staff of authority; a baton.

wander, won'dėr, *vi.* To ramble here and there, to roam, to rove; to err; to be delirious.—*vt.* To traverse.

wanton, won'ton, *a.* Not kept in due restraint, unprovoked; lustful; frolicsome; rank.—*n.* A lewd person, a trifler.—*vi.* To revel unrestrainedly; to sport lasciviously.

war, wär, *n.* A contest between nations or parties carried on by force of arms, profession of arms; art of war; hostility; enmity.—*vi.* (warring, warred). To make or carry on war, to strive.

wardrobe, wärd'rōb, *n.* A piece of furniture in which wearing apparel is kept, a person's wearing apparel collectively.

warehouse, wär'hous, *n.* A storehouse for goods, a large shop.—*vt.* To deposit or secure in a warehouse.

warn, wärn, *vt.* To caution against to admonish; to advise; to inform previously.

warning, wärn'ing, *n.* Act of one who warns; caution against danger, etc.; admonition; previous notice.

warp, wärp, *vt.* and *i.* To turn or twist out of shape, to contort; to pervert; to move, as a ship, by a rope attached to something.—*n.* The threads extended lengthwise in a loom; a rope used in moving a ship; deposit of rich mud; twist of wood in drying.

warrior, wä'ri-or, *n.* A soldier; a brave or able soldier.

wart, wärt, *n.* A hard dry growth on the skin.

was, woz, *v.* The first and third person singular of the past tense of to *be*.

waste, wāst, *vt.* (wasting, wasted). To make desolate; to ravage; to wear away gradually; to squander.—*vi.* To decrease gradually.—*a.* Desolate; spoiled; refuse. —*n.* Act of wasting; prodigality; refuse matter, gradual decrease; a desert region.

wasteful, wāst'fül, *a.* Causing waste; destructive, ruinous; lavish; prodigal.

waste-pipe, wāst'pīp, *n.* A pipe for carrying off waste water, etc.

wasting, wāst'ing, *a.* Such as to waste, desolating, enfeebling.

watch, woch, *n.* A keeping awake to guard, etc.; vigilance; a guard; time during which a person is on guard or duty; a small pocket time-piece.—*vi.* To keep awake, to give heed; to act as a guard, etc.; to wait.—*vt.* To look with close attention at or on, to tend to guard.

water, wä'tėr, *n.* A transparent fluid; a fluid consisting of hydrogen and oxygen, the sea, rain, saliva; urine; color or luster of a diamond, etc.—*vt.* To wet or supply with water; to give a wavy appearance to, as silk.—*vi.* To shed liquid matter, to take in water, to gather saliva; to have a longing desire.

water-level, wä'tér-le-vel, *n.* The level at which water stands, a levelling instrument in which water is employed.

watt, wot, *n.* The practical unit of power, or rate of conveying energy, used in electricity.

wave, wāv, *vi.* and *t.* (waving waved). To sway or play loosely; to undulate, to brandish, to beckon.—*n.* A swell or ridge on moving water; anything resembling a wave, an undulation, a signal made by waving the hand, a flag, etc.

waver, wā'vér, *vi.* To wave gently: to fluctuate; to be undetermined.

wavy, wāv'i, *a.* Rising or swelling in waves; full of waves; undulating.

wax, waks, *n.* A tenacious substance excreted by bees or in the ear; any similar substance; sealing-wax.—*vt.* To smear or rub with wax.—*vi.* To increase; to grow; to become.

wax-work, waks'wérk, *n.* Work in wax; figures of persons in wax as near reality as possible.

weakness, wek'nes, *n.* The state or quality of being weak; irresolution; want of validity; a failing.

weal, wēl, *n.* Welfare, prosperity happiness; mark of a stripe; wale.

wealth, welth, *n.* Riches; affluence; opulence, abundance.

wealthy, welth'i, *a.* Possessing wealth; rich; opulent; abundant; ample.

wean, wēn, *vt.* To accustom to do without the mother's milk, to alienate; to disengage from any habit.

wear, wār, *vt.* (pret. wore, pp. worn). To carry as belonging to dress; to have on; to waste by rubbing; to destroy by degrees; to produce by rubbing; to exhibit.—*vi.* To last well or ill, to waste gradually. to make gradual progress.— *n.* Act of wearing; diminution by friction, use, time, etc., fashion.

weather, weTH'ér, *n.* The general atmospheric conditions at any particular time. —*a.* Turned towards the wind; windward.—*vt.* To affect by the weather to sail to the windward of; to bear up against and overcome.

web, web *n.* The whole piece of cloth wov'en in a loom; a large roll of paper; membrane which unites the toes of water-fowl, the threads which a spider spins; a cobweb; anything carefully contrived.

wedge, wej, *n.* A body sloping to a thin edge at one end.—*vt.* (wedging, wedged). To drive as a wedge is driven, to crowd or compress, to fasten or split with a wedge.

week, wēk, *n.* The space of seven days; space from one Sunday to another.

weep, wēp, *vi.* (pret. and pp. wept). To manifest grief, etc., by shedding tears.

weigh, wā, *vt.* To raise; to find the heaviness of; to allot or take by weight, to consider, to balance, to burthen.—*vi.* To have weight; to amount to in weight; to bear heavily.

weight, wāt, *n.* Heaviness; gravity; the amount which anything weighs, a metal standard for weighing; a heavy mass; pressure; burden; importance; moment.—*vt.* To add to the heaviness of.

well, wel, *n.* A spring; a pit sunk for water, perpendicular space in a building in which stairs or a hoist is place.—*vi.* To bubble up; to issue forth.

well, wel, *adv.* In a proper manner; rightly; commendably; considerably.—*a.* Being in health; comfortable; fortunate; convenient; proper.

west, west, *n.* The point where the sun sets, opposite to the east.—*a.* Being in or towards the west, coming from the west.—*adv.* To the west.

what, whot, *pron.* An interrogative pronoun used chiefly of things employed adjectively as equivalent to how great, remarkable, etc., substantively as equivalent to the thing (or things) which.

whelp, whelp, *n.* A puppy; a cub; a young man.—*vi.* To bring forth whelps.—*vt.* To bring forth; to originate.

when, when, *adv.* and *conj.* At what or which time; while; whereas, used substantively with *since* or *till.*

where, whār, *adv.* and *conj.* At or in what place; at the place in which; whither.

whether, wheTH'ér, *pron.* Which of two.—*conj.* or *adv.* Which of two or more, introducing alternative clauses.

which, which, *pron.* An interrogative pronoun, used adjectively or substantively, a relative pronoun the neuter of *who;* an indefinite pronoun, any one which.

while, whîl, *n.* A time, short space of time.—*conj.* During the time that; though.—*vt.* whiling, whiled). To cause to pass pleasantly usually with *away.*

whisky, whiskey, whis'ki, *n.* An ardent

W

spirit distilled generally from barley; a light one-horse chaise.

whisper, whis'pér, vi. To speak with a low sibilant voice, to converse secretly.—vt. To utter in a whisper.—n. A low soft sibilant voice; a faint utterance.

whistle, whis'l, vi. (whistling, whistled). To utter a clear shrill sound by forcing the breath through the lips; to warble; to sound shrilly.— vt. To utter or signal by whistling.—n. Sound produced by one who whistles; any similar sound; a small pipe blown with the breath; instrument sounded by steam.

white, whit, a. Being of the color of pure snow; pale; pallid; pure and unsullied.— n. The color of snow, a white pigment; white of an egg eye, etc,—vt. (whiting, whited). To make white.

who, hö, pron., possessive **whose** höz; objective **whom**, hom. A relative and interrogative pronoun always used substantively and with reference to persons.

whoever, hö-ev'er, pron. Any one without exception; any person whatever.

whole, hōl, a. Sound; healthy; healed; intact, entire.—n. An entire thing; total assemblage of parts.

wholesale, hōl'sāl, n. Sale of goods by the entire piece or in large quantities.—a. Pertaining to trade in large quantities; extensive and indiscriminate.

widen, wi d'n, vt. To make wide or wider.—vi. To grow wide or wider.

widow, wi'dō, n. A woman whose husband is dead.—vt. To bereave of a husband.

wield, wēld, vt. To manage freely in the hands; to sway; to exercise.

will, wil, v. aux. (past. would), expresses futurity in the second and third persons, and willingness, etc., or determination in the first.—vt. and i. To determine by choice, to wish, to bequeath.—n. Wish; choice; determination purpose; legal declaration of a person as to what is to be done after his death with his property; faculty by which we determine to do or not to do something, volition.

win, win, vt. (winning, won). To gain, to be victorious in; to allure to reach; to attain.—vi. To gain the victory.

wind, wind, in poetry often wind n. Air in motion, a current of air; breath; power of respiration; empty words, flatulence.—vt. wind (pret. & pp. wound, sometimes winded). To blow,

as a horn.—vt. wind (pret. & pp. winded). To follow by the scent; to render scant of wind, to let rest and recover wind.

wind, wind, vt. (pret. & pp. wound). To bend or turn; to twist; to coil.— vi. To twine or twist, to crook, to bend; to meander.

window, win'dō, n. An opening in a wall for the admission of light or air, the frame (usually fitted with glass) in this opening.

wing, wing, n. One of the anterior limbs in birds; organ of flight flight; a lateral extension; side; side division of an army, etc.—vt. To furnish with wings; to fly, to traverse by flying; to wound in the wing.

wink, wingk, vi. To shut and open the eyelids; to give a hint by the eyelids, to connive, to be willfully blind (with at)—n. Act of shutting and opening the eyelids rapidly; a twinkling; a hint given by means of the eye.

winter, win'tér, n. The cold season of the year a year: any cheerless situation.—a. Belonging to winter.—vi. To pass the winter.—vt. Ta keep or feed during winter.

wit, wit, vt. and i. (pres. tense, wot pret. wist, pres. part. witting and wotting). To know; to be aware.—**To wit**, namely; that is to say.—n. Understanding, sense; wisdom; intelligence; faculty of associating ideas cleverly and in apt language; a person possessing this acuity; cleverness.

with, wiTH, prep. Against in the company of; among; showing; marked by; immediately after through; by.—n. With or with. A withe.

witness, wit'nes, n. Testimony; attestation of a fact or event, one who knows or sees anything; one who gives evidence in a trial..—vt. To attest; to see the execution of a legal instrument, and subscribe it.—vi. To bear testimony.

wolf, wülf, n.; pl. **wolves**, wulvz. A carnivorous quadruped akin to the dog, crafty and rapacious; a cruel or cunning person.

woman, wü'man, n.; pl. **women** wi'men. The female of the human race: the female sex: an adult female.

wonder, wun'dér, n. Something very strange; a prodigy or marvel feeling excited by something strange.—vi. To be struck with wonder; to marvel; to entertain some doubt and curiosity.

wood, wüd, *n.* A large collection of growing trees; the hard or solid substance of trees; timber.—*vi.* To take in or get supplies of wood.—*vt.* To supply with wood.

word, wėrd, *n.* An articulate sound expressing an idea; a term; information, a saying, motto; order, assertion or promise; in *pl.*, talk; wrangle.—*vi.* To express in words.

work, wėrk, *n.* Effort; labor; employment; a task; achievement, a literary or artistic performance; some extensive structure, establishment where labor of some kind is carried on; result of force acting.—*vi.* (pret. and pp. worked or wrought). To put forth effort, to labor, to take effect, to tend or conduce, to seethe, to ferment.—*vt.* To bestow labor upon; to bring about, to keep at work, to influence to achieve, to fashion, to embroider; to cause to ferment.

world, wėrld *n.* The whole creation, the earth, any celestial orb; a large portion of our globe; sphere of existence, a domain or realm mankind; the public; great degree or quantity.

worm, wėrm, *n.* A small creeping animal; an intestinal parasite; *pl.* the disease caused by such parasites; something vermicular or spiral.—*vi.* To wriggle; to work gradually and secretly.—*vt.* To effect by stealthy means; *refl.* to insinuate oneself, to extract cunningly.

worry, wu'ri, *vt.* (worrying, worried). To tear with the teeth, as dogs; to harass; to annoy.—*vi.* To trouble oneself, to fret.—*n.* Trouble; care; anxiety.

worse, wėrs, *a.* Bad or ill in a greater degree, inferior, more unwell; more ill off.—**The worse,** defeat; disadvantage.—*adv.* In a manner or degree more evil or bad.

worship, wėr'ship, *n.* Dignity; honor; a title of honor; religious service, adoration; reverence.—*vt.* (worshipping, worshipped). To adore, to pay divine honors to, to idolize.—*vi.* To perform religious service.

wound, wönd, *n.* A cut or stab etc.injury, hurt or pain to the feelings damage.—*vt.* or *i.* To inflict a wound on.

wrap, rap, *vt.* (wrapping wrapped or wrapt). To fold or roll; to cover by something wound, to envelop. —*n.* An outer article of dress for warmth.

wreck, rek, *n.* Ruin; overthrow; a ruin, destruction of a vessel at sea.—*vt.* To cause to become a wreck; to ruin.

wrench, rensh, *n.* A violent twist; injury by twisting; an instrument for screwing a bolt or nut.—*vt.* To pull with a twist; to distort.

wrestle, res'l, *vi.* (wrestling, wrestled). To contend by grappling and trying to throw down to struggle.—*vt.* To contend with in wrestling.—*n.* A bout at wrestling.

wrinkle, ring'kl, *n.* A small ridge or furrow; a crease; a hint; a notion.—*vt.* and *i.* (wrinkling, wrinkled). To form into wrinkles; to contract into furrows to crease.

writ, rit, *n.* That which is written; the Scriptures; a legal document commanding a person to do some act.

write, rīt, *vt.* (writing, pret. wrote, pp. written). To form by a pen, etc.; to set down in letters or words; to cover with letters; to send in writing; to compose.—*vi.* To trace characters with a pen, etc., to be engaged in literary work, to conduct correspondence.

wrong, rong, *a* Not right; not fit; not what ought to be; erroneous.— *n.* What is not right; an injustice; injury.—*adv.* In a wrong manner.—*vt.* To do wrong to; to treat with injustice.

W

X

xanthin, xanthine, zan'thin, *n.* A yellow coloring matter.

xanthous, zan'thus, *a.* Fair-haired.

xerotes, zē'ro-tēz, *n.* A dry habit of the body.

xiphoid, zīf'oid, *a.* Shaped like a sword

x-rays, eks'rā z, or **Röntgen rays,** runt'gen, *n.* Electromagnetic waves of high frequency, which penetrate most substances, except bones, metal, etc., and enable photographs to be taken of these in the living body.

xyloid, zī'loid, *a.* Having the nature of wood; resembling wood.

xylonite, zī'lō-nīt, *n.* Celluloid.

xylophagous, zī-lof'a-gus, *a.* Wood-eating.

xylophone, zī-lo-fōn, *n.* A musical instrument in which the notes are given by pieces of wood struck with hammers

xyst, xystus, zist, zis'tus, *n.* A covered portico or open court for athletic exercises.

Y

yacht, yot, *n.* A light vessel used for racing, pleasure, etc.—*vi.* To sail in a yacht.

yard, yärd, *n.* A standard measure of 3 feet; a long beam slung crosswise to a mast and supporting a sail, piece of enclosed ground.

yard-stick, yärd'stik, *n.* A stick 3 feet in length.

yarn, yärn, *n.* Thread prepared from wool or flax for weaving; a story.

yaw, yä, *vi.* To swerve suddenly in sailing.—*n.* The sudden temporary deviation of a ship.

yawn, yän, *vi.* To have the mouth open involuntarily while a deep breath is taken; to gape.—*n.* A gaping; act of yawning, a chasm.

yea, yā, *adv.* Yes: the opposite of nay.

yean, yēn, *vi.* and *i.* To bring forth young, as a goat or sheep.

year, yēr, *n.* The period of time during which the earth makes one revolution in its orbit; twelve months; *pl.* old age; time of life.

yeast, yēst, *n.* A yellowish substance produced in alcoholic fermentation; barm.

yell, yel, *vi.* To cry out with a loud piercing noise; to scream.—*n.* A loud, piercing outcry.

yellow, yel'ō, *a.* Being of a bright golden color.—*n.* A bright golden color.

yelp, yelp, *vi.* To utter a sharp bark or cry, as a dog.—*n.* A sharp cry of a dog.

yes, yes, *adv.* Even so; expressing affirmation or consent; opposed to no.

yield, yēld, *vt.* To produce in return for labor, etc.; to afford; to grant; to give up.—*vi.* To submit; to comply; to produce.—*n.* Amount yielded; product, return.

yodel, yodle, yō'dl, *vt.* and *i.* (yodeling, yodling; yodeled, yodled). To sing like the Swiss and Tyrolese mountaineers by changing suddenly from the natural voice to the falsetto.

yoke, yōk, *n.* Gear connecting draught animals by passing across their necks, a pair of draught animals; something resembling a yoke; shoulder-piece of a garment supporting the rest; servitude, burden a bond, a tie.— *vt.* (yoking, yoked). To put a yoke on, to couple; to enslave.

young, yung, *a.* Being in the early stage of life. youthful.—*n.* The offspring of an animal.

youngster, yung'stèr, *n.* A young person.

your, yör, possessive corresponding to ye, you. Pertaining or belonging to you.

yours, yörz, *poss. pron.* That or those which belong to you. **yourself,** yor-self' —*pron.;* pl. **-selves.** You, used distinctively or reflexively.

youth, yōth, *n.* State or quality of being young; period during which one is young; a young man; young persons collectively.

youthful, yōth'ful, *a.* Young; pertaining to youth; fresh or vigorous, as in youth.

yowl, youl, *vi.* To give a long distressful or mournful cry, as a dog.—*n.* A mournful cry.

Yule, yöl, *n.* Christmas.

Z

zany, zā'ni, *n.* A buffoon or merry-andrew.

zeal, zēl, *n.* Eagerness; passionate ardour; enthusiasm.

zealot, ze'lot, *n.* One who is zealous; a fanatical partisan; a bigot.

zero, zē'rō, *n.* Number or quantity diminished to nothing: a cipher lowest point.

zest, zest, *n.* Orange or lemon peel, used to flavor liquor; relish; charm; gusto.

zigzag, zig'zag, *n.* Something in the form of straight lines with sharp turns.—*a.* Having sharp turns or bends.—*vi.* (zigzagging, zig-zagged). To move in a zigzag fashion; to form zigzags.

zinc, zingk, *n.* A metal of bluish-white color, used for roofing, to form alloys, etc.

zircon, zėr'kon, *n.* A hard lustrous mineral, one of the gems called also jargon.

zither, zithern, zith'ėr, zith'ėrn, *n.* A flat musical instrument with from twenty-nine to forty-two strings, played with the fingers.

Zodiac, zō'di-ak, *n.* An imaginary belt or zone in the heavens, within which the apparent motions of the sun, moon, and principal planets are confined, divided into twelve equal parts or signs.

zoetrope, zō'ē-trōp, *n.* An optical contrivance by which, when the instrument revolves, certain painted figures inside appear to move in a lifelike manner.

zone, zōn, *n.* A girdle or belt; one of the five great divisions of the earth, bounded by circles parallel to the equator; any well-defined belt.

zoography, zō-og'ra-fi, *n.* The description of animals.

zooid, zō'oid, *a.* Resembling or pertaining to an animal.—*n.* An organism, in some respects resembling a distinct animal.

zoolite, zō'ol-līt, *n.* An animal substance petrified or fossil.

zoology, zō-ol'o-ji, *n.* The science of the natural history of animals.

zymotic, zi-mot'ik, *a.* Pertaining to fermentation; applied to epidemic and contagious diseases, supposed to be produced by germs acting like a ferment.

XYZ

SPECIAL OFFER
Reference Library

Special: Purchase any first book at regular price of $5.95 and choose any second book for $2.95 plus $1.50 for postage and handling. *For Canadian orders add $1.00 per book. All payments must be in U.S. Dollars.*

Please send me the following books:

____ New Webster's Dictionary   ____ New Webster's Expanded Dictionary
____ New Roget's Thesaurus   ____ Webster's Spanish/English Dictionary
____ Home Medical Dictionary   ____ New Webster's Large Print Dictionary
____ New Webster's Crossword Dictionary   ____ Webster's French/English Dictionary
____ Webster's Spelling & Pronunciation   ____ Calorie Fat and Nutrition Guide

Name_____

Address _____

City_____ State_____ ZIP _____

I have enclosed $_____ for ____ books which includes all postage and handling costs. (No C.O.D.)

Send to: Paradise Press, Inc.
8551 Sunrise Blvd. #302
Plantation, FL 33322